LIFE IN TH
OF FLINTSHIRE AND DENBIGHSHIRE

Life in the
Victorian brickyards
of Flintshire and Denbighshire

by Andrew Connolly

ISBN: 0-86381-892-7

Cover design: Sian Parri

First published in 2003 by
Gwasg Carreg Gwalch, 12 Iard yr Orsaf, Llanrwst, Wales LL26 0EH
☎ 01492 642031   🖷 01492 641502
✉ books@carreg-gwalch.co.uk   Internet: www.carreg-gwalch.co.uk

Acknowledgements

I would like to thank the many local landowners who allowed me access to their property in the course of my
investigations. For their assistance in supplying material and information for compiling this book,
I would also especially like to thank the following: Flintshire Records Office (F.R.O.).
Denbighshire Records Office (D.R.O.). The Chester Chronicle. The Wrexham Leader. Wrexham Library
and Museum. Chester Library. Mold County Library. British Library Document Supply Centre.
British Newspaper Library. Buckley Library. National Library of Wales. Crewe and District Libraries.
The Buckley Society. Flexys Ltd. Dennis Ruabon Ltd. Mr William Lacey.
Mr Danny McLeod. The Ffrwd Inn, Cefn y Bedd.
Mr Julian Brown. Mr Dennis Gilpin. Nene. Mr J B Lewis. Mr Harry Leadbetter.

Contents

Preface

"The growth of the clay and terracotta industries carried on at the great works form one of those romances of industrial enterprise which is yet and ought to be written"

Those words were penned by a man who witnessed within his lifetime what no living soul today has been privilege to – an Industry of clayworks and brickworks on a scale which most people in our modern times have never really appreciated or even realised existed. Published in the Wrexham Advertiser of 25th June 1892, the sentiments of that anonymous journalist have waited over 110 years to be realised here, for no exploration of this subject has before now been attempted on this scale.

For centuries past, if not thousands of years, mankind has fashioned his comforts from the most basic materials of his natural surroundings; from mud, stone, wood and clay, and the working of the very ground into bricks has been one of civilisation's most prolific, important and continued achievements. The creation of bricks, especially in their more fanciful forms, has for generations symbolised man's desire to order his surroundings, and by the time the Victorians came to stamp their achievements upon the world, the brick industry had become a source of great wealth, employment and productivity. For the Victorian travelling throughout the districts of Flintshire and Denbighshire he would not have had to go far before he would have come across yet another brickworks, for they flourished in their many varying forms throughout the countryside as well as in the towns. In this book you will find listed nearly 130 different works which functioned as commercial brickmaking sites in an area covering from Flint in the north to Cefn Mawr in the south, and from Gwernymynydd in the west to Marchwiel in the east. Within this specific area, home to some of Britain's most prestigious clayware manufacturing companies, I have attempted to locate and catalogue every site which produced clay bricks at such works which were purposefully established to function as permanent brickworks, whether they existed as part of colliery and ironworks operations, or as independently run companies.

It would perhaps be of benefit to first outline certain points which will help in understanding some of the references contained within later chapters, and to start with, it might be of interest to know what historical sources formed the basis for this work. For the most part the main sources of information were gleaned from the following documents deposited in the Records Offices at Hawarden and Ruthin and the Document Supply Centre of the British Library:

Letters, reports and Indentures of Lease between the brick companies, their solicitors, land agents, surveyors and customers formed much of the core information.

Rates assessment books listed buildings together with their owners and occupiers from year to year.

Ordnance Survey maps and surveyors plans. The first edition OS maps appeared circa 1871, followed by an updated second edition circa 1899, and a third in 1914 and so on. The earlier tithe maps of the 1840s, which also listed site ownerships, were especially valuable in identifying the smaller country sites which did not survive the later competition from the larger works.

Trade Journals. These covered the fortunes of the brick and coal industries, and the British Clayworker and the Colliery Guardian proved particularly valuable in discovering yet more of those otherwise obscure gems of information which escaped the pages of the general newspapers.

Railway Proposal Maps were another extremely valuable source of research. The explosion in railway speculation between the 1840s and 1880s meant that hundreds of new lines were planned, many of them intentionally routed to run past brickworks and collieries, and if every line had been allowed to see the light of day the country would have ended up covered by a tangled web of metal tracks. To avoid this potential mayhem, highly detailed plans of all proposed new lines had to be submitted for parliamentary selection and approval, and from these surviving documents we can again learn much about the more obscure brickworks.

Lastly, I cannot avoid mentioning the efforts of the local newspapers over the passing years. Their dedicated recording of the changing world around them has left us with an invaluable picture of the interactive growth of industry and society throughout the economic boom years of the Industrial Revolution and beyond. The Victorian press not only catalogued the world they knew and experienced at first hand, but they did it with an eloquent and perceptive use of language which to our modern senses fires and fascinates the imagination. Of all the newspapers of old I should like to particularly commend the efforts of the editors and contributors to the now defunct Wrexham Advertiser; a newspaper which during the 19th century applied itself to analysing every aspect of life in Flintshire and Denbighshire, and to all historians of this district I cannot overstress the value and importance of its contents.

I would hope that everything I have committed to these pages is as truthful as it can be, and whilst compiling and editing the information from my many researches I held one principle firmly in mind. That was: *Trust the evidence of the past.* If our goal is to learn about the history of the times which have preceded us, then surely it is better to heed the records left from those who lived in those times, and not simply rely on believing that which some modern historians have written. It only takes one modern writer to publish a mistake for others to take it up and re use it as reliable evidence, and before long a mistake can take on the mantle of truth. Unfortunately I have come across many published articles written by authors who probably did not have access to the source materials which I studied, and have consequently, albeit unwittingly, published articles which have proven to be somewhat inaccurate. I therefore hope that this book might go a long way to realising a more realistic understanding of the subject.

To allow our forefathers the right to tell the story of the brickmaking industry for themselves I have taken the step of including direct quotations from many of the sources which I researched. It was after all they who lived and experienced life at the kilns, and who better than they to give witness to this body of evidence. To this end, you will notice that I illustrate certain points by including as corroboration an example or two from contemporary reports, but it is important to understand that I was careful never to base any historical conclusions on any single source

of reference – I only include such examples to merely negate the use of too much repetition. It took me many years to cautiously pick my way through the vast volume of evidence which are contained within the local newspapers alone, and in that time I was able to learn much about the general trends, opinions and movements which were prevalent throughout the industry.

* * *

Our district has altered much over the years since coal and brick works dotted the landscape, and you might find it valuable to get a more accurate picture of where these works were by referring to a modern Ordnance Survey map. Each site in this book is given an OS reference, and the best maps to work from are the OS Explorer Series, 1: 25 000 scale. For the benefit of accuracy I decided to use "four figure" references, such as 3097 5839, which corresponds to the position of the church in Hope village. The first set of numbers refer to the references along the map's horizontal axis, followed by those down the vertical. On an OS map you will see that each square is identified by a two figure reference number, with each square marked off into ten divisions. In the Hope example, the church lies within the 9th division of square 30 along the horizontal axis, but to more accurately pinpoint the church itself I have subdivided the 9th division into ten further, therefore resulting in the reference 3097. This four figure method allows for greater precision when describing the position of the smaller country brickworks or the small kilns found at colliery sites.

Another consideration we should examine is that of land area, as I sometimes quote areas as an indication of the size of the works. The old Imperial standard of measurement relied on what were termed *acres, roods* and *perches*, represented by the symbols a,r,p.

An acre is a square area of land, each side of which measures 69.57 yards or 63.58 metres.

Each acre was then quartered into four roods. Therefore, a rood represents a square area, each side of which measures roughly 34.7 yards or 31.79 metres.

Each rood was then subdivided into 40 perches, and each perch was a square area whose sides therefore measured a fraction over 5 metres. Every acre subsequently contained 160 perches.

The question of monetary values is also one which might cause some confusion to those younger readers who have no understanding of the old system of coinage, and as time goes by, that number of readers will inevitably increase. The modern decimal system of 100 pence to the pound is a simple one – yet perhaps to be confused by the introduction of the Euro – but the old system, as with the subject of area, was much more complicated. Until the introduction of decimalisation in 1971, the pound was divided into 20 shillings, each of which was subdivided into 12 pence. Shillings were represented by the letter "s" and pence by the letter "d", but the usual method of denoting monetary values was, for example, as follows: £2-5-6, which means 2 pounds, 5 shillings and 6 pence.

Inflation has by now given us a wholly distorted view of the difference between what the Victorian pound was worth compared with its present day value, but we should understand a little of what money was worth in the past, and for convenience I will quote the modern decimal equivalents in brackets. For instance, we know that the weekly rent on an average workman's cottage in Ruabon in the year 1876 was 2s 6d (22.5 p), whilst the manager of the Ffrwd Colliery in 1882 stated that his men earned an average daily wage of 4s 8d, which equates to a six day weekly wage of £1-8-0 (£1.40). Interestingly, a Denbighshire clergyman experimented with living on a workman's wage in 1887, and his findings show us a lot about the cost of domestic necessities at the height of the Victorian era. 5lb of bread cost 5.75d (2.4p)... six apples cost one half of a penny, which in modern decimal coinage is an incredibly small 0.2p... 12 ounces of meat cost 4.5d (1.8p)... coal to last the week cost 6d (2.5p)... 6 ounces of cheese cost 2. d (1p) and seven pints of skimmed milk cost 1.75d (0.7p).

By 1924 inflation had raised the average Buckley brickman's weekly wage to £1-16-0 (£1.80) and by 1962 the brickman's wage at Buckley's Castle Works had again increased to between £14 and £17.

* * *

Before I contemplated writing this book, my original interest in this subject was restricted simply to collecting name-stamped bricks which I intended using in some building work at home. My original forays into the field of research were intended only to find out where these brickworks were... just in case anybody asked! But it wasn't long before I found myself encroaching into a world out of time with my own; a world where people worked with horses and steam engines; where they found their working lives curtailed or ended by accidents with little hope of financial compensation, and a world where poverty and plague could strike without warning. I can remember the first time I sat at a table in the Hawarden Records Office and thought that if all this could prove of such interest to me, then perhaps it could to others also. In the end, I suppose I wrote this book for two groups of people... for us in the modern world, as an illustration of how much our lives have changed since the heydays of the Industrial Revolution, and for our Victorian ancestors, whose hard lives and proud achievements created an industry whose story most deservedly "ought to be written".

An Introduction to Brickmaking – The Geology of Clay

This book concentrates solely on the Welsh brickworks of Flintshire and Denbighshire which were situated within close proximity to Buckley and Ruabon in those respective counties. All the brickworks covered are those which manufactured goods from that ancient traditional material-clay. Although there are today, and certainly were even since late Victorian days, works making bricks, tiles and blocks from concrete, I have totally excluded them for the simple reason of economy – the clay works alone having required years of research and numbering well over 100.

The principal question must therefore be: What is Clay? In searching for a technical answer on any specialised subject, it's best to turn to those whose lives are or were devoted to such, and we can find a good answer to our question within the journals of the British Clayworker – the published collective wisdom of decades of brickmakers since late Victorian times. In February 1897 they recorded that: "In brickyard parlance, anything is a clay which, being dug out of the earth is, either in its natural condition or after being ground and tempered, sufficiently plastic to be moulded into bricks etc, and which when heated to a sufficiently high temperature, is rendered hard and more or less like stone in texture".

The majority of clays quarried in Britain are termed as *plastic*, which means that they have a consistency which gives under pressure; much like heavy mud, and the word clay itself derives from an Old English word which translates into modern English as *adhesive* or *plastic*. In the district of N.E. Wales however, most of our clays are so hard that they require serious physical effort to quarry them – as the British Clayworker said of North Wales clays, they "look more fit for being used as road metal".

In days gone by, when the clay industry was at its peak of popularity and production, Flintshire's and Denbighshire's brickworks figured as the most important amongst the works of north and mid Wales, and a careful topographical study of the contours of the Ordnance Survey maps show us why. From the geographical point where our brickworks ended, so did the rich clay lowlands, and there rose up the great stratas of another landscape – the hills and mountains of mid and western Wales, where stone and slate were king. Compare these figures of clays and brickearths mined in the North Wales counties in the heydays of 1895-6.

Denbighshire .... 180,678 tons
Flintshire 116,526
Caernarfon 21,413
Cardigan 5990
Merioneth 188

The chemical composition of clays vary considerably, and dependent on what proportions of the constituent minerals are present, the products made from them are just as numerous. Such qualities as colour, weight, hardness, brittleness and resistance to heat, acids and alkalis – all these are affected by the slightest variance in any one or more of these chemical components, so I personally think it would be futile to even make any generalisations concerning this side of the subject. Let's instead concentrate on the uses of the basic types of clay and to what degree they occurred throughout the districts.

Firstly, let's understand that the success of any brickworks depended principally on its claybed. This can be illustrated very practically by looking at the relative prosperity of the two Delph works at Acrefair. On one side of the road was the Delph Fireclay Works and on the other, within a short walking distance, was the smaller Delph Brick Works. I have examples of the two types of brick made at each, and they could not be more different – the former being a hard, heavy marl brick, dense in structure, and the latter a lighter and more fragile brick. The qualities of their respective clays was the reason why the Fireclay Works saw its centenary, and the little Brick Works came and went within twenty years!

But although such variations in workable clay strata can occur even within such a small area, it is possible to make certain broad generalisations between the geology of the Buckley and Ruabon districts themselves, and we will first consider Buckley. Here is what the great works manager John M Gibson said on the subject: *"The Buckley clays are all above the coal and appear to be entirely independent of the coal measures, and in my opinion, a distinct formation only to be seen on Buckley Mountain. The clays of the coal measures (Ruabon district) are only about two or three yards thick, but the Buckley clay is now worked at least 40 yards thick and I have proved it to be nearly twice that depth".*

Most fireclay is known to occur below the subterranean coal seams, which is more technically termed the "coal measures", but as Mr Gibson noted, Buckley had a distinct advantage over its neighbours in the availability of their clay, as it outcropped closer to the surface. This observation was also confirmed by the owner of another Buckley works, Edward Parry, who said in 1862: *"There are small fireclay works at Ruabon but it is hard to get and more expensive to work. Our fireclay is on the surface, that of Ruabon is under the coal".*

So how was the basic geological strata of the Buckley claylands formed? Under the 3 -4 ft of surface soil lay a crumbly purple shale which could be 4 -15 ft thick, and this was referred to as the **brick clay**, which was an inferior clay used for making a dark red common brick. The mineral surveyor Mr Griffiths wrote of it in 1895 saying *"The brick clay is the least valuable portion. It is good for nothing except to make bricks, and to make those it has to be mixed with some of the blue clay – these bricks are the least profitable goods manufactured at Buckley and are supposed to realise only about cost price".*

That **blue clay** was the next layer to be encountered – a purer form of clay than the upper brick clay, which could be put to a good profit in the making of tiles in particular. The blue clay was generally around 15ft in thickness and was locally referred to as "top stuff", because the tiles made from it were burnt in the upper parts of the kiln and required more heat than the common bricks burnt below.

Next down was the **fireclay** proper, which was the most profitable commodity, as specialised and very strong products were made from it, and these items were what made Buckley particularly famous.

All the Buckley brickworks excavated their clays from opencast quarries or "clayholes", and the only works which received their clay from mine workings were the ones which were developed as part of a colliery.

I should make a technical observation at this point. In the clayworker's terminology of old, a clay*hole* is an opencast quarry working, whereas a clay*pit* is a seam of underground clay worked by access via a pit shaft – much like in a colliery. Quite often though, we find the word pit being used to describe a quarry; even though the term is technically incorrect.

The Wrexham and Ruabon districts mined a clay which although having many properties similar to the Buckley fireclay, was of an particularly high purity. Their clay beds also had the top layers of rubbishy brick clay and surface soils, which was referred to as **fey**, but their most valuable natural reserve was a type of clay called **marl**, which produced an extremely hard, smooth finished surface used as best facing brick and terracotta architectural mouldings – these being one of this district's principal products. The rich cherry red tint of these various goods was mainly caused by the presence of sesquioxide of iron within the clay, and for this reason the Ruabon manufacturers did not have to experiment with chemical admixtures to try to attain that distinct colour – they just used their clay neat. The Ruabon companies were very proud of their product, and rightly so. Some of the district's marl beds produced the best red bricks in the country, and especially the works of J C Edwards at his Penybont factory. The following text is taken from his brochure of 1890:

"It is by far the best material for large and smoky towns for it is not affected by acids, and the small particles of dust and soot that blacken stone and soft faced terracottas are washed away by every shower of rain.

The quality of fuel used is an important matter, as a sulphurous coal throws off gases in the firing which combine with the moisture evaporated by the clay and cause a disfiguring scum. The Welsh coal from the Ruabon district being most free from these objectionable qualities, the Penybont Manufactory is placed at a great advantage compared with works situated in other parts of the country.

Architects generally have not hitherto been sufficiently careful in the selection of their material. So long as the modelling and colour has appeared satisfactory they have accepted a material of such a soft nature that they are of very little use in a climate such as ours. One only has to take a walk in London and examine some of the terracotta buildings erected there of late years and one will see examples of the thin veneer peeling off. The best clay for the production of brick or terracotta is that in which silica and alumina bear a proportion of 60-65 parts silica to 20-25 parts alumina with about three per cent potash and soda. The best known available beds that contain these qualities are confined to Ruabon".

Again, many of the Ruabon works received their clay from opencast workings, but there were quite a few that received their supply, or supplemented it, from pit workings.

Throughout this book you will occasionally come across specific names given to the different types of products made at these works, and the most commonly used of them will fall into the following categories.

Common brick. This term is fairly self explanatory. These are basic building bricks made with no particular need for their being absolutely perfect in form. They range from very crude hand moulded bricks on which it may be difficult to discern an absolutely straight line, to mass produced machine made examples, and they are mainly manufactured from the surface brick clay, which in some districts was often termed *boulder clay*. This basic clay is sometimes also called brick earth.

Slop brick. The cheapest form of brick, due to the amount of inexpensive additives mixed with the brick clay. This brick is recognised by the presence within it of small stones, cinders, shale shards etc, and this rough mixture would have damaged a brick moulding machine – they were therefore always hand moulded. Most famously made in the Buckley district.

Facing brick. A smooth faced brick, nearly always machine made, used to give a solid, more dignified appearance to a building.

Architectural bricks. Bricks with some form of decorative moulded surface, widely used as dado courses, usually beneath the roof line, or as some fancy work around doors and windows. A lot of architectural bricks were specially designed in a brick company's drawing office to suit the requirements of individual customers, and were produced to construct elaborate chimneys, ornate porticos, or to create sculptured features on the fascia of more important buildings.

Refractory goods. These are special products made from fireclay and used as furnace linings, insulating materials and the like, and were produced in a multitude of odd and bizarre shapes to suit specialised industrial applications.

Firebricks. Bricks made from fireclay and used for any purpose requiring strength of construction or heat resisting quality.

Rustic brick. A facing brick which has had its surface "roughed up" to give it a more textured appearance. It was developed in the late Victorian period to suggest the characteristics of the earlier hand made bricks from the country brickyards – hence the term "rustic".

Before we leave this chapter, I should mention something about the clay quarries themselves. It was the development of brickworks and the opening out of large clayholes that gave rise in the early Victorian era to the discovery of most of our earliest dinosaur fossil finds – not in the Welsh districts, but in the S.E. of England. The spirit of that age was one of new discoveries in every field of endeavour, and the gentlefolk of the newly burgeoning educated middle classes took a great interest in the development of the new sciences, and especially geology. The following text gives a typical description of one of the many field trips which were taken to industrial sites in order to view the mineral excavations which were beginning to expose windows into the past. The ironworks mentioned was most likely the Sydallt Iron Works at OS 312 557, and the firebrick maker would probably have been a contract brickmaker employed there:

Wrexham Advertiser 14th November, 1874 – Last Saturday Mr Mackintosh accompanied about twenty young ladies from the Wynnstay Place School to Cefnybedd. From the station the party walked to where the new line of railway crosses the Rossett turnpike road. The exposure of a bed of coal on both sides of the railway cutting was first examined and further on the distinctive character of the lower brown boulder clay was pointed out. A few hundred yards on Mr Mackintosh gave a short address on the striking evidence of violent pressure exhibited on the series of beds of coal, sandstone, shale and fire clay which were exposed in the railway cutting. Near the resuscitated ironworks the young ladies discovered an extensive loft with boarded floor, on which they practised various physical exercises with evident delight, but this episode was not very long in being brought to a close by the appearance at the door of the astonished countenance of a firebrick maker, who however, behaved with the most becoming respect.

The Development of the Brickmaking Industry

"What are the Chief Industries of Wales?
1 – The agricultural is the first and foremost in this as it is in most other countries.
2 – The mining industry undoubtedly comes next and this we must sub divide into several branches... a – coal mining,
b – metalliferous mines such as lead, copper, iron. c – clay mines including the fireclays of the coal measures and the Permian clays or marls, now so important as regards the terracotta industry.
3 – The quarrying industry... a – the slate and slab quarries of North Wales. b – the valuable limestone quarries. c – granite.
Amongst the most important is probably the terracotta industry of Denbighshire, and the manufacturing of sanitary ware – now so much in demand – depend on the fireclays. Although comparatively a small industry, yet there is none more important in the kingdom. Fireclay is of little value in its raw state, yet how indispensable it is for the manufacture of vessels that will withstand the most intense heat".

The above report from the Wrexham Advertiser of 19th August, 1899 establishes the position of clay manufacturing within the structure of the Victorian industrial scene in our district. In point of fact, we owe more as an advanced industrial nation to the manufacture of clay products than we might initially realise; clay products representing much more than simple bricks used to throw up walls and houses. The brickworks of N.E. Wales were in their days, along with others within these Isles, a formidable catalyst to the advancement of British trade and social improvement during the Victorian era, and as we proceed through this book these facts will hopefully become apparent.

Brick technology goes back thousands of years, although the materials used and methods of production in those ancient times could be, almost literally, worlds apart from those used in nineteenth-century Britain. The earliest usage of clay bricks seems to have originated in the Middle East with the simplest method of mixing clay mud and chopped straw (used as a binder to prevent cracking whilst drying) and allowing the bricks to bake in the hot sun. The more proficient method of burning bricks in kilns could also be found in antiquity, and even glazed bricks and enamelled tiles have been found in the ruins of the Palace of King Sargon of Assyria. And ancient bricks need not necessarily have been of poor quality, as this following text suggests, delivered as part of a radio lecture in 1942 by Dennis Griffiths, the then manager of Buckley's Lane End brickworks:

"The earliest known burnt bricks are those still to be found on the sites of the ancient cities of Babylonia. The walls of Babylon running 14 miles in each direction were so thick that a chariot and four horses could be driven along them passing their 250 towers. A Royal brickmaker, King Nebuchadnezzar was probably the first one to burn clay to make bricks strong. Hard dried clay bricks had been made there thousands of years before. King Nebuchadnezzar did the work well, for just ten years ago some of the bricks made in his time were being re-used. The art of brick-making spread eastwards through Persia and North India to China, where many millions were used in building the Great Wall of China about 20 BC".

Although this book will concentrate solely on the development of brickmaking in N.E. Wales, it's generally true that the basic trends in the growth of the industry were much the same across the entire British Isles.

So where do we start? Any careful examination of the earliest buildings of our district will show that, once upon a time, stone was the building material of choice, and the reason was one of pure logistics – stone being the material most readily available on site. No doubt wood and wattle had their place even earlier, but such buildings were never destined to survive. The art of brickmaking was first introduced into Britain by the Romans, and their nearest known brickworks to our district was established at modern day Holt, where they made use of the surface boulder clay easily found on the alluvial plains. But once the Roman Empire had fallen into decay, their technologies became forgotten, and not only did the use of brick disappear, but their methods of manufacturing pottery and glassware were also lost for centuries to come.

The use of brick seems to have resurfaced some time around the mid-16th century during what historians refer to as the "great rebuilding" – a time when a new and wealthy class of gentry and merchantmen began to stamp their mark on the landscape, and in their choice of building materials they most probably sought to emulate the Dutch, who were renowned throughout Europe as masters of commerce and good architectural taste. Dutch architects had long used fine pressed bricks to achieve stunning results, and it is believed that the earliest houses to be built of good strong bricks in North Wales were Bachegraig and Plas Clough near Denbigh, built by Sir Richard Clough, who had for many years been a merchant in Holland. In the 1560s he had thousands of Dutch bricks shipped over to the nearest port at Rhuddlan and then transported to Denbigh by road, but when it was realised that not enough had been ordered, it is believed that he might have brought over brickmakers from Holland to manufacture the shortfall from local clays. Brick was becoming a symbol of social status, as its manufacture could require more time, effort and expense to produce it, and to have a house built even partly from it was, during this period, a way of flaunting your wealth and prestige.

As time went by, the use of brick became much more commonplace and much less of a status symbol, and the presence of easily accessible surface clays in many parts of Denbighshire in particular, meant that brick could be more readily utilised as a cheaper alternative to stone; brick having the added advantage that it could also be manufactured on the building site, negating the necessity of paying the expensive haulage costs of transporting stone from distant quarries. The account books of Erddig Hall at Wrexham remain as a testament to brick's burgeoning popularity, as the following excerpts testify:

"Account book of Richard Jones, agent of Erddig Hall:
1721: 27 loads of coals went to ye kiln of brick at ye house.
April 1721: kiln of bricks at ye house. 2 kilns out of which 74,250 bricks counted.
13th February, 1722: paid the brick makers more in part for Riseing Clay at Coed y Gline, £1.
14th February, 1722: paid Mr James Birch £12 with £3 paid him before, in all £15 toward making 600,000 bricks".

All over Britain the ever more popular material became so plentifully used that Parliament finally decided that much needed revenue could be collected on it, and in 1784 the first of several Brick Taxes was imposed, levying a duty of 2s 6d on every thousand bricks made. Ten years later the tax was increased to four shillings to help raise money for Britain's war with France, so the brickmakers compensated by making their bricks bigger, until a new Act of 1803 got around this by imposing a massive duty of ten shillings on the manufacture of every thousand bricks measuring over 150 cubic inches each, and five shillings on those under that size. The Act was reinforced in 1839, making it compulsory for all makers to keep a pattern mould of their bricks, which had to be stamped as approved by an inspecting Excise Officer; failure to produce this pattern to any Inspector resulting in a fine of £20.

These financial restrictions naturally resulted in builders trying to minimise their use of solid brickwork, and many walls hidden behind plastered fascia during this period were constructed by slapping thick courses of mortar between the layers of brickwork and using small stones and rubble in place of the odd brick – a practice which today would be nothing short of jerry-building, but which was all too common back in Georgian times. Due to these restrictive taxes, the brick industry now found itself in an extremely repressed state with no potential to expand, until a great social upheaval changed the fortunes of the brickyards for at least the next fifty years. Britain found itself in the throws of the new Industrial Revolution, and the opportunities for expanding trade and profit were beginning to grip the country. Britain's manufacturing industries suddenly went into overdrive, resulting in the country's commercial undertakings beginning to dominate the world's markets. The captains of British industry were crying out for new factories, warehouses and dwellings for the increasing numbers of workers flocking into the towns, and the rapidly expanding railway network, the new wonder of the age, also found itself undertaking massive new civil engineering projects – tunnels, bridges, viaducts and stations by the hundreds. The building industry needed the restrictive shackles of the Brick Tax removing, and in 1850 the tax was repealed. The brick industry was free of restraints, and the boom time had begun.

In our particular district of Flintshire and Denbighshire this new commercial boom time was most readily noticed in the expansion of the colliery and brick trades, and we must investigate the important relationship between the two in order to understand why the brickworks of this region developed as successfully as they did.

Wrexham Advertiser 1856 – Deep down in the bowels of the earth many hundred feet from the light of day, yet all round us, and not more than a few hours ride from any portion of these British Isles, exists a race of men unknown; almost unrecognised in the land; yet are these men the bulwarks of England's greatness.

The roller-coaster of industrial expansion had placed a demand on the coal industry as never before, and the 1850s especially saw new pits being sunk at an alarming rate, particularly in the Buckley and Mold districts. "Every new enterprise is an augmentation to the trade of the town. The tradesmen heartily rejoice at every fresh hole dug and hope that his Majesty King Coal will welcome them all" said the Chronicle of 6th August, 1853, commenting on the growth of coal-mining in Mold.

Of course, quite a lot of the numerous new colliery speculations quickly came to nothing, but Britain's industrial lead on the world still meant that in the year 1856 our country had produced 31.5 million tons of coal compared to France's 4.15 million and Prussia and Austria's combined 4.2 million.

Wrexham Advertiser 22nd March, 1856 – Local mining speculation in the Mold district has almost become a mania. The new collieries in the course of operation are as follows – Glan yr Afon, still combating with water and accidents, Mold Town Hall, erecting engine and sinking pit with a view to prove the extensive bed of Main Coal supposed to exist in the Vicar's Meadow, Rock Colliery Soughton sinking a pit to discover coal under the thick Black Brook sandstone, and another party from near Wrexham is making a series of borings in the flat plain between the river Alyn and Mold station. There are others "looming in the distance" but the above-mentioned are in actual operation.

What few brickworks existed at that time had always relied on the collieries for their survival, as no coal meant no bricks. The demand for stronger, more load – bearing bricks was fast growing, as well as the demand for the refractory firebricks for the linings of the hundreds of boilers in the new factories and for furnaces in ironworks, and these new type of bricks required a kiln which would burn much hotter than had previously been required. Coal was the only fuel of the age able to produce enough intense heat to do the job and, on average, every ton of raw clay required five to twelve tons of coal to perform the burning process, dependent on what type of clay it was. As coal was therefore of paramount importance to the brickmaking industry, the early brick manufacturers nearly always ensured their supplies by taking shares in local collieries, and many of the earlier collieries were co-owned by the proprietors of the small brick companies of those days.

But as the brickworks needed the collieries, so the collieries themselves relied heavily on a supply of bricks, for once the existence of good and workable coal seams had been proven, the first task in opening out a mine was to sink a shaft down to the seam. Wynnstay's main pit, for example, was 5.18 metres in diameter and dropped to a depth of 274 metres, and the shaft had to be bricked up to avoid collapsing in on itself. Every colliery's pit shafts had to be bricked up, and apart from the inevitable steam engine and pumps to keep the water at bay, bricks were therefore a colliery's number one requirement, and for this reason almost all the collieries of the early to mid-Victorian period had their own small brickworks established on site, utilising the clay which "underlay" the coal measures to make their own bricks. In time, some of the collieries even found that their brick production became a more profitable venture than their sales of coal, and even the British Architect journal in 1878 remarked that "where worked alone a colliery will not pay, a valuable source of income may be found in the clays that are thrown on the rubbish heap".

As the demand for coal grew, even old defunct collieries were reopened. "The old coal banks of our forefathers need not frighten anyone, for as sure as they exist, equally so is the certainty of immense treasure lying within easy access of present engineering skill" noted a commentator in 1867. To illustrate the close connections between the brick and coal industries, we can read what Mr Davies, the weighbridge operator at Vauxhall Colliery at Ruabon, said of the closure of the smaller collieries in the 1860s. His implication was that, in many cases, the clay industry had expanded from an earlier colliery industry: "It is a most remarkable thing that when the collieries did stop, people turned their attention to clay and what is known as Ruabon marl was discovered and the brickworks were commenced, and therefore in all probability, if the collieries were working the people would never have troubled themselves about the clay". Although his remarks concerned the Ruabon district, they were in the most part true of all the districts.

As the burgeoning colliery industry began to invest in brick production, the manufacturers of brickmaking machinery soon realised that they had as good a sales opportunity for their products in the collieries as they did with the independent brickyards themselves, and the technical journals of the mining profession are witness to this. The Colliery Guardian – the encyclopaedia of the industry – was during Victorian times littered with advertisements for drying sheds, kilns, brick-cutting tables, pugging mills and moulding machines. Schofields Brick Machine Co, for instance, advised their colliery readership that "the economical method of making bricks from the refuse taken from the pits during the process of coal getting, which instead of storing at the pit mouth and making acres of valuable land useless, is at once made into bricks at a very small cost to the advantage of all colliery owners", and the Dutton Co rather proudly said of their hand operated brick presses that "only a small amount of power is required, as a boy 14 years of age can work them with ease".

Wrexham Advertiser 31st May 1873 – No less than four new collieries have been recently started near Mold, and it is becoming a serious question how to get labour to work them, all the men available in the district being already engaged. The colliery nearest the town on the north side is named "Hard Struggle" from the difficulty experienced in obtaining water to get up steam. Another to the east side is named "Slap Bang" from the fact that coal has been found near the surface. To the south the "Linger and Die" company are doing their best to reduce the price of coal and to enhance that of labour. While to the south east the "Strip and at it" company are showing the world how to make the most of it. We hear of numberless other ventures, but these are the principal.

Strange and affectionate nicknames for pits were not restricted to our district alone. I have come across the Do Well pit at Chesterfield, and in the Durham area there were the Pity Me, Sorrowful, Stand Alone and Cold Comfort.

As the speculation in mining expanded, by 1858 Government statistics showed that Flintshire had 40 working mines and Denbighshire 39. At its height Denbighshire had no less than 83 mines working, and even as late as 1901 Denbighshire still had 38 operational pits to Flintshire's 26.

By the onset of the 1860s mineral speculation had taken off at a serious pace, and the number of brickworks within the districts began to grow, initially more so in Buckley. Records of coal mining in the town go back to the 12th century, although clay working was probably not established quite as early as that. The Buckley pottery industry emerged first, and examples of the famous Buckley black glazed pottery have been unearthed in archaeological excavations at Yorktown and Jamestown in the USA from sites dating back to 1690. By the early days of Victoria's reign, the census figures of 1851 showed just how much the trade of brickmaking had overtaken the much more ancient craft of pottery making – the number of households whose heads were colliers were shown to have numbered 123, whilst 75 were engaged in farming, 85 in the brickworks and only 15 in the potteries. To fund this boom in mineral exploration, gentlemen of wealth and substance found themselves easily tempted to increase their wealth by investing in the burgeoning industries. It's not surprising that the majority of works throughout Wales were during that period founded and financed by wealthy gentlemen from England; many of them having previously made their money through mining their English homelands. The native Welsh had until then been mainly tenant farmers and, excepting a very few, had not the funds to capitalise on their own country's mineral wealth. During those days, if a land agent or mining surveyor had a promising hole in the ground anywhere around Mold or Buckley, he would have been sure of finding more than one investor itching to throw his money into it. The following story illustrates this principle perfectly, albeit in an allegorical way, with the clay speculator rather humorously named Capt. Stratum – obviously a play on the concept of mineral strata! Our storytellers are Bob Sparkles and Joe Juniper (Victorian reporters loved pseudonyms), who took a trip on the newly opened Wrexham, Mold & Connah's Quay Railway from Wrexham to Buckley:

Wrexham Advertiser 2nd June, 1866 – The Booking Clerk, a dapper little man of very agreeable manners and obliging disposition, said the Company had not begun to book for Connah's Quay, but he should be very happy to stamp them a ticket for Buckley, where they might spend a very lively day amongst the Buckley bricks, which were admitted before a committee of the House of Commons to be the very finest bricks in the world. Our heroes at once took a first class return for Buckley. On reaching the Buckley Station our heroes were fortunate enough to meet Capt. Stratum, who was just starting a limited liability company for working a bed of virgin clay, supposed owing to a very peculiar fault to pass right through the globe from Buckley to Tasmania. Sparkles at once eyed the Captain, and by a masonic sign attracted his attention, and the fraternising which followed was most cordial. The Captain at once volunteered to show our mutual friends the various beds of clay already laid bare, some partially worked it was true, but what had been consumed he assured his new friends were not the one hundred millionth part of what was left behind. He at once proceeded to quote from the highest authority in England, the Right Honourable William Ewart Gladstone, Chancellor of the Exchequer. The Chancellor had stated that 100,000 tons of earthenware goods could be made out of a single acre of Buckley clay. The Captain stated the Buckley trade was an old trade, but it had never until within the last few years been worked out on modern principles. Sparkles said he should take a hundred shares in the new company that Capt. Stratum was engaged in promoting. Juniper declined. He said he never had anything to do with trade – there was something vulgar about it. The Captain then conducted his new friends through the extensive works now in operation, including the works of Messrs Hancock, Messrs Davison, Messrs Meakin and others, which had the effect of greatly enhancing the Buckley bricks in the estimation of Sparkles. Our friends returned to Wrexham and resolved to have frequent excursions on the railway until they had exhausted all that was to be seen of the beauties, the curiosities and the mineral wealth of the district.

It might be interesting and useful to explore a few other usages which the products of the growing brick industry were put to. As I touched on previously, heat resistant firebricks were of paramount importance in lining the furnaces which powered the boilers of the Industrial Revolution, producing the steam without which nothing would have been possible. Consequently it could be argued that without the firebrick furnace linings there would have been no giant factories, no railway engines, no ships etc etc. The effects of thousands of degrees of heat upon cast iron and steel fireboxes would have been catastrophic without a refractory material to insulate the metal and avoid the build-up of destructive hot spots – naked heat alone on bare metal would have led to warping, cracking and even melting. Blast furnaces in steelworks also required this refractory brick insulation. For instance, when the 2ft 7in of brickwork was eroded by the constant flow of molten iron on Shotton Steelwork's No. 1 furnace, it led to an explosion on 27th July, 1956 which killed two men. In much the same way, if you were to investigate the construction of stone cottages and houses you will most always find that the fireplaces and flues are made of brick-stone in close contact with flames would crack and splinter!

Brick was also used as an insulation jacket for industrial boilers to help distribute the heat evenly over the boiler's surface and prevent heat loss, and I have come across many reports of boilers exploding due to damaged brick jackets.

By far though, one of the most valuable and profitable outputs from a Victorian brickworks were the glazed pipes used in implementing the strident new improvements in public sanitation:

> *The British Architect, 1878 – Owing to the birth and growth of the science of sanitation and the great sewage and drainage works which have resulted from increased desire for cleanliness and health as well as from the great impetus given to the building trades, the growth of the manufacture of the clays into all manner of useful materials and appliances has been most marked within the last quarter of a century.*

The greatest scourge of the new industrial towns and cities was that of disease, caused by the insanitary practice of jamming hundreds of people into cramped housing conditions without adequate drainage or effective means of disposing of waste, and such was the growth in improvements in this area that sewer pipes became one of the principal sources of a brickworks revenue. Thousands of land drainage pipes also poured out of the brickworks – another very important and lucrative product line, which was greatly needed in the agricultural sector. Even the brickworks clay itself was sold to the Local Boards (councils) and this was used as a covering for the stinking human refuse which was carted from communal cesspits to farms or early sewage processing works.

These then were the principal reasons for the expansion of the brickworks in our district... the presence of clay and coal, the opening of numerous collieries, the new sanitation works and the demand for bricks to supply the new buildings of the Industrial Revolution. Now we can look at what these brickworks might have looked like, and there were to my mind basically three types of works which it would have been possible to come across throughout the great days of Victorian brickmaking.

SMALL COUNTRY BRICKYARDS

The country brickyard, of which there were many to be found in isolated positions, existed because of one principal factor, and that was the terrible condition of Victorian roads. In a later chapter I will address the subject of road and rail transportation in more detail, but from the outset it must be understood that up to the end of the 19th century (and this period encompassed the rise of *all* the brickworks) the roads of our land were nothing short of appalling. Nowadays a few large factories can send out massive loads of bricks from one side of the country to another in a single day, but the notion in Victorian days of transporting large quantities of heavy goods along miles of what were then dirt roads by horse and cart, was not only impractical but injurious to cost effectiveness, and this is the overriding reason as to why there were so many small country brickyards dotted throughout the land.

Most of these small yards were *Summer Yards* using the techniques of *clamp burning*, and this will be described in the chapter on Manufacturing

Processes, but as to their outward appearance, most of them were little more than an earthen yard with a shed for a steam engine and perhaps a brick machine, a small chimney and an area of open cast clay holes and a kiln or two. From these small yards the requirements of local builders could be supplied for a few miles around, and in most cases they were sited in areas which then certainly, and even today in some cases, seem to be in the middle of nowhere.

As well as these small independently owned rural works, we must not overlook the little brickyards which belonged to the estates of landowners and farmers, and in the chapter covering the brickyard sites themselves we will come across some of these. The farming community had been making bricks long before most of the independent commercial brickworks had been established, and in as far back as 1845 I have found that the Royal Agricultural Society of England had included exhibits of clay machinery at its exhibitions, awarding prizes that year to the firm of Thomas Scragg for their "machine for making draining tiles and pipes" and Henry Clayton for his "hand machine for the manufacture of pipes, tiles and bricks". Agricultural shows all over Britain regularly exhibited such machinery for farm usage well into the 1890s.

CONTRACT BRICKMAKING BY JOURNEYMEN

As the march of time and technology moves ever onwards it changes aspects of our social landscape to the point at which what was once a commonplace sight eventually becomes the subject of history books. Even up to the late 1950s the sight of horses drawing milk floats and tradesmen pushing barrows was commonplace in some districts, and as a child of those days I can remember the travelling knife – grinder, who pushed his little treadle operated cart from house to house, sharpening people's kitchen knives and garden implements. But what I think we might today find most amazing – if we were to ever come across it – would be the sight of the journeyman brickmaker with his boy assistants, making bricks along the roadside and tending a smouldering kiln.

The journeymen were very common in days gone by. They were travelling craftsmen who would go from town to town and job to job, not unlike a present day jobbing builder, although the true journeyman of old had to take lodgings away from his home in whatever town he could find work in. The professions covered by these people were many and varied – tailors, shoemakers, well sinkers, saddlers, coopers, basket makers etc etc.

Yet again, because of the difficulty of transporting bricks over long distances, it was often found to be much more convenient and less expensive to employ a " contract journeyman brickmaker " to make the bricks on the building site itself, if clay was to be easily had, which in our district it usually was. When land for building purposes was offered for sale, the advertisements for such would very often mention the presence of clay on site as an added advantage to the purchaser, as these three very typical examples of Victorian advertisements illustrate:

Wrexham Advertiser 1st April 1852 – Building land at Rhosddu for sale, in lots to suit purchasers. Bricks will be made on part of the ground for a limited time for the convenience of building.
Wrexham Advertiser 8th March 1873 – On sale. Several valuable sites abutting on good roads and in every respect suitable for building purposes. Excellent clay abounds on the estate and the proprietor is disposed to treat liberally either with a brick manufacturer or with those desirous of making their own bricks.
Wrexham Advertiser 11th November, 1876 – To be sold. Several plots of building land close to the Wheatsheaf Pub, Gwersyllt, having good frontages to the road. Under these lots there is a splendid bed of clay of great thickness, and parties desirous to build might make their own bricks upon their lots for building or for sale.

Bricks made in this fashion were burnt in simple clamp kilns, that is, temporary kilns which were deconstructed after the bricks were burnt through. This next ad is from a builder requesting tenders to be submitted from contract brickmakers:

Chester Chronicle 1859 – Estimates are at

once desired for the making and burning of 600,000 common field bricks, to be used near Padeswood station. The bricks to be burnt in clamps and turned out sound and good. Coals and water near the place of making.

The making of bricks on the building site was a practice which was commonly taken advantage of by the closely bound local communities of those days, and it was not uncommon for them to get together and assist with building projects which had a communal purpose, such as a school or chapel. Helping with the brickmaking and building would also have had the benefit of greatly reducing the building costs amongst a poor populace, especially in the more rural districts, as we see next.

Wrexham Advertiser 25th April, 1863 – The Primitive Methodists belonging to the Mill Lane Chapel intend to alter and enlarge the same during the summer. On Monday they commenced active operations for making bricks. From the number of ready hands and willing hearts there is no doubt but that the work will be speedily accomplished.

The journeymen makers who travelled the land were sometimes quite well equipped for the job; using horse drawn portable steam engines to power their brick machines, and they often employed local lads to assist in their work, which sometimes, due to an unfamiliarity with the machinery, could result in serious injury. This next story illustrates such an occurrence:

Wrexham Advertiser 24th June, 1865 – A serious accident took place at the brickfield of the proposed British Schools near Holywell, whereby a young man named Richard Dennis lost his right hand. In order to make the reader more acquainted with the circumstances, we might remark that owing to the large quantity of limestone which is in the clay used for the making of the bricks, it was found necessary to obtain a small engine which works two large iron rollers between which the clay is passed, thereby crushing the stones that may be

therein. It would appear that Dennis was engaged to feed the rollers with clay, and the rollers having become clogged with large stones, he put in his hand to withdraw the same without having first ordered the engine to be stopped. We feel it is our duty to state that there is no evidence of any blame whatsoever to Mr Hawthorn the Brick Contractor.

Many of the working classes in far off days found it a necessity to have more than one occupation to enable them to make ends meet, and in truth, that is a situation which some folk find themselves in even today. However, it was much more often the case during Victorian times, and census records show us very many examples of this. In the Ruabon of 1861 we can find Samuel Roberts who was a railway plate layer and grocer, and John Jones, a coal miner and victualer; two examples from a list which is as extensive as it is varied. The reason for this state of affairs was that the labouring classes were very often employed on a day to day basis on short time contract work, and could not always be assured of regular employment, and for the contract brickmaker this could very easily prove his way of life, particularly as his specialised line of work was usually only possible during the drier months of the year; the same also being true for the workers at the smaller country brickyards. What follows next is part of the proceedings at a court case in Mold, reported in the Wrexham Advertiser of 17th December, 1870. John Lloyd, a builder, had asked Mr Janion Jones, a "druggist and part time brickmaker", to supply some sample bricks for the new jail at Mold, but Jones had gone ahead and made the full consignment and was attempting to claim the 19 shillings for their making. Incidentally – this took place in the winter months, when Jones was unable to burn his bricks in a clamp kiln, and take note of how he had to send his newly made bricks to one of the larger patent kilns at a Buckley brickworks to enable them to be fired.

His Honour – Tell me what he said to you.
Jones – He told me to prepare a quantity of bricks as a pattern for the walls of the new jail.
His Honour – Tell me what he said, man.

Jones – I am doing so, Sir. He told me to prepare the brick.

His Honour – Tell me in his own words, if you can tell a straightforward story, which I seem to doubt.

Jones – He told me to prepare the bricks.

His Honour (to Mr Allen) – Will you try and get it out of him?

Mr Allen – Just tell His Honour what he said in his own words.

Jones – I can only say that he asked me to supply him with the bricks. I made about three hundredweight of them and had to send the clay to Buckley to be burnt. I had also to pay for the cartage of the clay there, and also the cartage of the bricks back. I am sure he ordered the bricks from me and promised payment.

* The builder Lloyd then gave evidence denying he ordered the full consignment and said that the brickmaker promised to supply samples only. His principal complaint was that Jones had sent him not good hard bricks, but the cheaper kind of slop brick (made from poor clay mixed with aggregate), to which Jones replied:

Jones – No It was not. It required to be burnt very hard.

His Honour – It was a slop brick after all, and a slop brick is a slop brick. Everyone knows that! (laughter in court)

Jones – But it had to be burnt very hard.

His Honour – What do you charge per thousand for slop bricks?

Jones – Well, you can get some for 22 shillings and others for 28 shillings.

His Honour – Yes, and for £1 per thousand if you like, or less than that. (laughter)

* Jones admitted to further questions that he intended to have taken the contract for the supply of bricks, had those which he sent in been selected.

His Honour – You intended to make a nice sum of money out of the County no doubt. Was Mr Jones carrying on brickmaking at this time?

Lloyd – Yes, Sir.

His Honour – And I suppose he was anxious to get business.

Lloyd – I suppose so, Sir.

His Honour – I think this is the most absurd claim I ever met with, and I find in favour of Mr Lloyd.

Brickmaking on the building site was not only an activity confined to the labours of the individual working for himself, as large civil engineering contractors also employed on-site brickmakers. In 1840, after the completion of a section of railway workings at Guilden Sutton near Chester, the contracting firm sold off the surplus 200,000 field bricks which had been made at the construction site, and advertised that "the quality of the bricks may be seen in the bridges on the railway".

Incidentally, that's the second time we have now come across the term *field bricks* – a perfect description of the contract maker's work – quite literally, bricks made in a field!

It seems to be an unusual peculiarity that whenever a large contracting company had completed their work, they quite often auctioned off all their plant and machinery! Why I cannot imagine, but for instance, when the Mold Railway was completed in 1850, the contractor Peto & Betts sold all their used tools and brickmaker's benches, and likewise, on the completion of the Chester Workhouse in 1878 the contractors sold off their two brickmaking machines together with miscellaneous other machinery. I have even found examples of larger contractors selling off steam engines and railway locomotives!

In conclusion, it must be said that the profession of the journeyman contract brickmaker, working from site to site, is one which amongst all the classes of brickworker has by today been almost totally forgotten , and I hope that I may have helped to correct that situation. Of all the brickmen of old, despite the hard lives they led, their work must surely have been the most interesting, and like the travelling troubedours of earlier times, perhaps the most romantic.

LARGE BRICKWORKS

The larger brickworks are probably the only ones which people today imagine ever existed! The reason why they attained their size and lasted for as long as they did is a simple one – they were sited on areas of valuable clay resources. Its no accident that the largest and most enduring brickworks were concentrated into two distinct districts – Buckley with its vast beds of fireclay, and south Wrexham and Ruabon on the valuable red marl deposits.

The small rural and agricultural brickyards, together with the little brickyards of the earlier smaller collieries, had existed for a few decades before the majority of the big brickworks were established on their larger, more industrialised scale, and it was around the 1860s and 70s that most of these larger works were built to supply the growth of Britain's new industrial age. In the scramble to build these larger works, Buckley had the narrow lead over Denbighshire, mainly because Buckley had for many years been the centre of a thriving pottery industry, and its entrepreneurs more easily expanded into brick production; the earliest of the big Buckley brickmasters, Jonathan Catherall and William

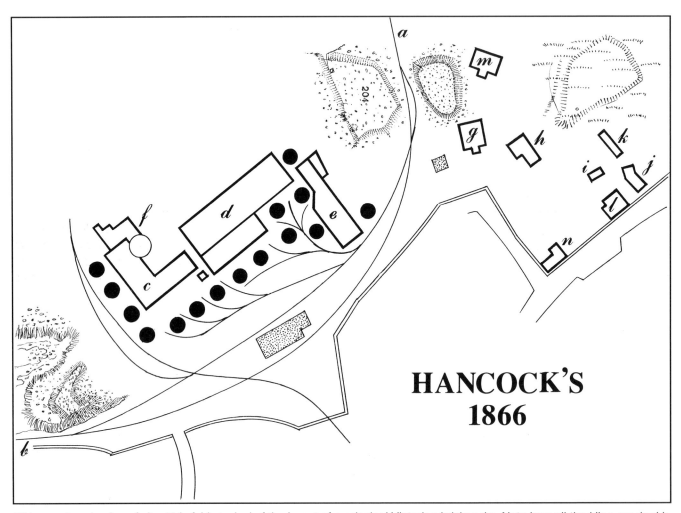

HANCOCK'S 1866

This exact scale plan of site 48 is fairly typical of the layout of a principal Victorian brickworks. Note how all the kilns, marked in black, are serviced by tramways. At a the tramway runs northwards via a tunnel under Knowle Hill to the interchange sidings on the main line of the Buckley Railway, whilst at b it connects to the Ashtons Works at site 45. c, d and e are marked on the original plan as drying sheds, where the brickmakers would have also worked at the moulding tables. The works engine house is at f. The site was run from the office at g next to the stables at h with the smithy at j. The important woodworking and modelling shops were the joiners shop at i and the sawpit at k.
Cottages are marked at l, m and n. The shaded plots are ruined buildings, perhaps part of the earlier works before the 1852 modernisation.

Hancock, originally having been pottery manufacturers, and they both had impressively sized brickworks by the very early 19th century.

Concerning the layout of these larger works, I will cover that on the chapter concerning Manufacturing Processes.

For now though, it is important that we should understand just what it took to initially set up an industrial concern during those days.

The organisational structure of a Victorian brick company was much more than simply workman – foreman – manager – owner. At the head of all life was the landlord, and in the majority of cases, he would have been a titled gentleman, whose wealth was founded on the rents and royalties accrued from his tenants. In Victorian days hardly anyone owned the house he lived in, or the land on which his factory was built, or the farm whose land he tilled, and the landowners of N. E. Wales profited very nicely from the brickworks and collieries sited there. In the 1840s the Chronicle made an interesting reference to Baronet Sir John Hanmer by naming him "The Lord of the Black Diamonds" – a reference to the value of the many collieries on his lands around Flint and Bagillt, and when discussing how important the tenants were to the landowners, the same newspaper in 1841 said "Sir Philip Egerton's, Sir Stephen Glynne's and Mr Cornwall Leigh's tenants are considered only as so many bricks in the mansion of each gentleman".

Once a brick or colliery company had gained the landowner's permission to establish a works on his land, a surface rent or "Dead Rent " was agreed upon. This annual sum covered only the acreage of land taken and was required to be paid whether the works was producing profitably or not. A payment was then agreed covering the amount of mineral to be worked from the ground itself – so many pence per ton – and this was called the "Royalty ". In the case of a brickworks, a separate Royalty was also levied on the number of bricks made from the clay, and yet another Dead Rent was charged on each kiln to be constructed. If a company were to build a railway or tramway running over any other lands, a Royalty per ton of goods transported upon it was also required. There was even the situation where a company might be paying Dead Rent to one owner of the surface land, and Royalties to a separate owner of the underground minerals – a not altogether unusual state of affairs. In time however, some of the larger companies became wealthy enough to buy outright the freehold of their works' land, releasing themselves entirely from any further payments.

All such transactions were brokered through the landowner's mineral agent, whose duty it was to ensure that all agreements were honoured. To this end, the agent would travel constantly from factory to factory, checking the companies' books and gaining access to the workings; taking the measurements of clay and coal seams, and seeing that everything tallied.

* * *

Within this chapter on the Industry's development we shall now focus on a few aspects of industrial life which affected the day to day functioning of a brickworks.

THE USE OF EXPLOSIVES

The use of some form of blasting explosive was a great time saver to the "clay getters" at the works where the clay was of a particularly hard rock-like nature. The earliest form of explosive was simple blasting powder which was ignited by a long burning fuse wire. It used to be the practice that the workmen who used explosives would be expected to account for it themselves, and thusly they would usually end up taking it home with them at the end of each working day.

Wrexham Advertiser 16th May 1874 – Some time ago I called the attention of the Mold Local Board to the necessity of preventing or of prohibiting the very dangerous practice prevailing amongst colliers and others of carrying casks of powder without any protection whatever through the public streets, and keep the same in their houses. I am informed that it is quite a common thing for persons when conveying these casks to their houses, placing the cask on the hearth or some other convenient place, until they leave. The consequence of such practice is now well known by the explosion which took place last Sunday at Gladstone Terrace, and I am told that when the explosion took place there were two casks in an adjoining cottage, kept in the bedroom. A medical man of this town had occasion to go to a house in the course of his business, and as the sitting accommodation was rather scarce, the worthy gentlemen was obliged with one of these identical casks filled to the brim, of course little dreaming of the dangerous matter upon which he was seated.

This laxity shown towards any safety procedures meant that the Victorian newspapers not uncommonly found themselves reporting on accidents resulting from this state of affairs, and it was often children playing around industrial sites and finding carelessly discarded detonators and fuses who were the unfortunate victims. From 1st January, 1908 an Act of Parliament made it illegal for any person to take home or keep at home explosives of any kind, and companies using explosives were required to build locked stores at their works and apply for an Explosives Licence.

As blasting powder became superseded by stronger substances, Dynamite became the favoured explosive, but there were many other concoctions on the market – Ammonite, Bellite, Tonite, Fortis, Securite, Roburite and Westphanite being just some.

The greatest "showman" of explosives technology was not a brickmaster, but Mr Lester of the Minera Limestone Quarry, and to ignore a mention of this man's exploits would be a shameful oversight. His preference for doing things in a big way had made him a nationwide legend in his own lifetime within the mineral professions, and the announcement that he was to rock the district with another gigantic blast would bring both rich and poor alike flocking to his quarry.

Wrexham Advertiser 10th October, 1874 – The inhabitants of Wrexham must not be alarmed if about 3 o'clock on Wednesday next they hear in the distance a report resembling the discharge of ordnance, and feel some slight vibration of terra firma. It will not proceed from an earthquake, neither will it be the consequence of an explosion on a canal monkey-barge. The cause will be a great blast at Mr Lester's lime works at Minera, by which it is estimated that Messrs Williams and Kyrke, mining engineers, will be displacing 20,186 tons. This will be the largest blast ever known in the district, and to witness it, most of the leading engineers and scientific men of this part of the country will be present. The charge will consist of 2000 lbs of Messrs Curtis and Harvey's new extra-strong mining powder. There will be other explosions in the quarry and lead mine, which are to be followed by luncheon at the works.

To effect that blast, a 4ft diameter tunnel was hewn 20 yds into the rock hillside and a chamber 8ft by 4ft constructed at its end. This was crammed with the explosive and a connecting fuse wire; the tunnel finally being plugged up with sand and clay. On that occasion thousands of onlookers scaled the surrounding hillsides and climbed into trees to view the outcome, and a marquee was erected in which Mr Lester could entertain his more important guests, one of whom was the future Prime Minister, Mr W. E. Gladstone. So numerous were the great and the good attending that particular demonstration that Mr Lester requested a special train to be laid on for them from Wrexham to Minera, but the railway company, on learning of the number of important notaries who were to crowd onto the one train, refused to supply it for fear of any accident which might occur. This led to a scene worthy of a comic opera, with everybody hiring whatever form of transport they could, the newspaper later reporting that "the visitors were conveyed from Wrexham in omnibuses, brakes, phaetons, drags and dog-carts".

In those days before radio and television, such visual spectacles were the entertainment of the day, and many hundreds of people would travel far to witness anything unusual. The night spectacle of the blast furnaces at Ffrwd near Brymbo were also a big draw, being visited by specially organised excursions, and when the Rhossdu Colliery flooded in 1872 the Chronicle reported that "the colliery has been visited by a large number of people for the purpose of hearing the loud noise caused by the rush of water into the workings".

Throughout this book you will also come across evidence of what a great attraction the clayhole drowning fatalities were to the local populations.
The more modern workings of Minera quarry closed in the mid-1990s, but Mr Lester's original workings are still to be seen, now overgrown by pleasant woodlands, centred at OS 258 519.

Wrexham Advertiser 16th May, 1884 – It is well known to our local readers that Mr Lester adopts a system of big blasting at his works in lieu of the ordinary custom of firing a large number of small charges. For many years Mr Lester has adhered to this plan. Not only is it more profitable to the proprietor, but far more attractive to the onlookers who usually crowd the neighbouring hills to witness the tremendous effects.

TRESPASS AND ACCESS

One of the more noticeable differences between modern industries today and the works of yesteryear would be on the subject of security. In the early days of the brickworks, hardly any works, large or small, had any form of restrictive fencing; access to such a potentially dangerous environment being completely open, and the best way I can illustrate this fact is to let the evidence of those times speak for itself:

Wrexham Advertiser 6th September, 1862 – On Saturday night a fatal accident occurred to an old man named Robert Price, 84 years of age, who met with his death by falling into the clay pit of Messrs Catherall. The depth of the pit where the poor man fell is upwards of 12 yards. About ten minutes to nine he started home and the night being very dark he missed his way. He was discovered the following morning by James Davies, whose wife lost her life in the same way some two years ago. It is quite time that something should be done, the place being extremely dangerous, to protect the lives of people who have to pass that way at night.

Wrexham Advertiser 8th June, 1889 – On Tuesday an inquest was held at the Queen Inn,

Cefn Mawr, on the body of John Howell Davies, aged five years. The deceased was sent with his brother's dinner to the Trefynant Brickworks on Friday last. He was brought back by his brother, having been injured, but died the following day from concussion. Richard Evans, a labourer at the works, stated that the deceased fell from the staging leading to the room in which his brother was engaged. The staging was an incline leading from the yard to the first floor of a two-storey building. The staging was about 4 ft wide and at the spot where the deceased fell it was 9ft 4in from the ground. At the side from which he fell there was a hand rail 2ft 6in high. The coroner suggested that the deceased was too young to go to the works and that such young people ought to be prevented from going there. The jury returned a verdict of accidental death and the foreman added: We wish to say that we consider children so young should not be sent with dinners to the works and that a notice should be put up that children are not allowed to go up the staging. The coroner thought that a better suggestion would be that all children sent to the works with dinners should take them to a certain place and leave them there.

Wrexham Advertiser 2nd March, 1907 – During the early mornings of last week a stranger visited the workmen's cabins of the brickyards in the Ruabon neighbourhood and took their food.

Wrexham Advertiser 4th June, 1910 – Under tragic circumstances the death of Edward Jones, a well-known resident of Connah's Quay, formed the subject of a coroner's inquest. Deceased was 70 years of age and was discovered lying in a heated brick kiln where he had gone to sleep. Whilst sleeping he sustained considerable blistering on his back, and when removed from the kiln he died after exhibiting signs of agony. The medical testimony was that the death was due to heart failure caused by the oppressive heat of the kiln.

Most of the trespassing at the brickworks was

confined around the clayhole pools and many deaths took place in those waters; mostly accidental, but also from suicides. The pools were a great draw to both children and adults, who treated them principally as bathing facilities – the working masses having no other means by which to wash themselves thoroughly in those mostly poor and squalid districts. The clayhole trucks were also an attractive lure to playful youngsters; more than a few receiving crushing injuries from them over the years.

Chester Chronicle 19th April, 1890 – Two young boys were hurt on Tuesday at Ashton's Brickworks. The first had his leg very badly cut. It appears that they were in company with other boys playing in the dinner hour with the clay-hole wagons, when one of these wagons overpowered them down an incline. It is a very common thing in all the brickworks for young persons to congregate together and play in dangerous places and with dangerous tools. When will the workmen come to think it is their duty to stop them?

Government had attempted to render these places safer by passing the Quarry Fencing Act of July 1887, which stipulated that all open quarry excavations, including clayholes, should be fenced off if they were within 50 yards of a public right of way. Although well intentioned, in most cases I should imagine that this law was not implemented. Fines for the infringement of such laws were piteously inadequate in those days, and most companies would have saved much from paying the fines rather than spending more on putting up fences in the first place.

As the clayholes attracted the playful and the dirty, so the brickworks buildings themselves were a mecca for another class of society, and one which was none too small at that. The "tramping fraternity" had always existed since before the brickyards were established, but the men of the open road soon came to see them as a much welcomed blessing – an easily accessible collection of sheds and huts and heat – the kilns themselves being the greatest draw. From my investigations, it seems very much the case that

the tramps favoured the works which were situated in the countryside near to towns, but not too close to the towns themselves, as this would have led to more chance of being discovered by a patrolling policeman; vagrancy in Victorian days being punishable by imprisonment and possible hard labour. The works which seemed most regularly to suffer from this activity were Parrys and Castle near Buckley, E M Jones near Wrexham and the Wilderness Works near Gresford. Had the tramps caused no trouble, no doubt they would have been better tollerated, but their disregard for other people's property usually proved costly to the brick companies, and the early years of the 20th century were a particularly problematic era. "They pull down doors, apparently to sleep on, and walk on the soft bricks. If this happens in the summer season, I don't know what will happen in the winter, and above all they are very dirty in their habits" explained Mr G A Parry of Parrys Brickworks in June 1907. Its not hard to imagine what he meant by the term " dirty habits", and in 1924 a certain Wrexham brickworks manager explained that he had great difficulty in persuading his workers to go into the sheds on dark mornings because of their dislike of what they might end up finding there!

Wrexham Advertiser 3rd March 1906 – Buckley Courthouse. The tramp problem still remains unsolved at Buckley and the brickworks of Messrs Parry and Son appear to be the rendezvous where the genus most do congregate.

"Are these Parry's lodgers?" queried the chairman amid much laughter as four typical specimens were led in. "Yes sir", replied Sergeant Davies. "These are four out of thirty we found there last night". The pilgrims were well to the fore when the opportunity of pitching a plausible tale arrived, but the Bench were not standing on ceremony, and "cheap lodgings for fourteen days" was the announcement made by the chairman.

Once they had been evicted from the works in the mornings, explained the Chester Courant of 1906, "they then proceed to the workmen's houses and frighten the women after the men have gone to work". Even as late as in 1955 there was still a problem in some districts; one Buckley councillor explaining *"These people are attracted here by these brickyards and it is high time the question was looked into. Such people seem to make Buckley their winter quarters, attracted by the warmth of the brickyards. The chairman recollected that it was nothing compared to what it was thirty years ago. There used to be hundreds of them".*

Further stories about the tramp problem are included in the chapters on the brickworks themselves.

THE BRICKYARDS IN WARTIME

The 20th century wars endured by Britain had serious repercussions on the country's manufacturing base, and the brick trade of our district was no exception. Even going back to the Napoleonic Wars we can find evidence of this – Jonathan Catherall at Buckley having found it necessary in 1797 to lay off ten of his clay getters in consequence of his bills not being paid by over taxed, cash-strapped customers.

If his modestly sized works of those early days found the restrictions of wartime a burden, the larger works of the modern age, more reliant on the need for a steady trade, found the going much harder. Let's first consider the 1914-18 conflict.

In August 1914, two months after the onset of the war, the collieries and brickworks, the district's principal wealth producing industries, were all operating normally. The call to arms at that point had only been on a voluntary basis, and conscription had not yet been implemented; the employers having promised to keep open the jobs of those volunteers who had left until they returned from abroad. The building trade was still unaffected and confidence in a short end to the war was high. Building projects continued as normal, but when problems did arise, they came from an unexpected quarter. It soon became apparent that the shipping trade was falling off rapidly, with vessels becoming "very scarce in the Dee", and without the ships necessary to supply the important export market, the brickworks at

Buckley soon began operating on short time, and by Christmas that year both Parrys and Hancocks had closed down their production, the stock yards having become glutted with unsold bricks.

Wrexham Advertiser 12th December, 1914 – At Wrexham County Police Court, George Shute appeared on a charge of being an alien enemy and failing to report himself. The defendant was a labourer and night watchman employed at the Llay Hall Brickyard and lived in a hut on the premises. Defendant produced a letter which he said had been written for his mother by his old school master. He was certainly English bred and born. The Chairman: It is a great pity you did not have some papers with you. Defendant: In going about the country I have been apt to lose them. Probably it is due to the way I have been doing my job that I have been suspected wrongly. I would have been in lodgings if they had not provided a cabin for me.

By early 1915, with the cost-of-living beginning to rise and with more and more men answering the call to arms, the works in the Cefn and Rhos district also began to experience difficulties. British workers began applying for increases in their wages and in May the Buckley brickmen asked for a 20 per cent rise, but settled for a special War Bonus of between 5-15 per cent, dependent on their type of work. The brickyards were also having to contend with the crippling increase in fuel prices; the cost of coal having doubled from 9 shillings per ton before the war to 18 shillings. Transportation difficulties then hit the Denbighshire yards, not this time from a lack of ships, but a lack of railway wagons "due to the great demands which the Government is making on the railway companies for delivering of stores to the troops".

The accumulative problems led the Wrexham Advertiser on 3rd July 1915 to note "the brick trade of the district is undergoing very acute depression and it appears to be more marked week after week, and the management experiences great difficulty in keeping the men working". But by a strange twist of fate, the war effort itself eventually became the saviour of the industry. As the country geared up to increase output to supply the war machine, the Buckley yards by September were all engaged in government contracts, although down in Ruabon, the yards were still crying out for work, and their desperate workforce was leaving in droves either to join the Army or to seek employment in the large brickworks of Lancashire. But it was not long however before the demands of wartime production brought the stricken Ruabon yards some respite, and eventually, as in all other areas of manufacturing, the Government brought the brickyards under the control of the Ministry of Munitions. Government now controlled to what usage it deemed any factory should be put to, and as some yards were left to continue with brick production, yet others were turned over to different functions. For instance, the Vron Works at Coedpoeth had its plant converted to the production of much needed agricultural fertiliser, whilst Davies Brothers at Abenbury became a dynamite stores. Some of the yards however did close.

From mid-1916 onwards, as conscription to the army depleted the country's workforce, the newspapers on a regular basis highlighted Industry's attempts to hold onto its dwindling source of labour. Tribunals were set up to grant war exemptions to workers who were deemed invaluable in keeping the factories running, and the brickyards featured regularly at these hearings.

Wrexham Advertiser 21st October 1916 – The Ruabon Brick & Terracotta Co applied for the exemption of Herbert Richards, bricklayer, 33; Frank Hampson, kiln setter, 33; John Crump, boiler stoker, 32; John Barrett, timekeeper, 40; Edward Jones, engine driver, 34 and Isaac Jones, loading superintendent, 35. The firm was just in the same position now as when the men were previously exempted. They were very busy making bricks for munitions works, and if their men were taken, other firms would have to make the bricks, which would be unfair to the company and the neighbourhood. A lot of their business was also export and it was thought that to "keep the home fires burning" until the boys came home was necessary. Barratt and Isaac Jones were granted conditional exemption and the remaining men a further four months each.

It's interesting to note that during that era women were virtually excluded from brickyard work. The 1911 census figures show that whereas 691 men worked in the brick factories in Flintshire (not including the clay quarriers) there were no women at all, and in Denbighshire there were three women, probably in the offices, to the 1,094 men. During wartime however, the steadily increasing drain on the male workforce meant that women had to be taken on to fill the vacant jobs, and we are lucky to have the evidence of Mrs Annie Owens to corroborate this fact. Annie celebrated her 103rd birthday in 2003, and remembers how she, along with many of her friends, joined other young women in taking on every aspect of keeping the Buckley brickworks in production. "We did all the work that the boys did before they left to fight. We made the bricks and my hands used to bleed from the work", she said. One might imagine that this change in the social balance would have attracted much interest from the press, but apart from an advertisement in the County Herald of Aug 1919 for "four strong young women wanted at once for brickyard work. Ruby Brickworks", there were no other documented reports to commemorate the part which women played in brickyard life during the First War. Whatever the reason for this was, Annie had a vivid memory that all the women were immediately sacked as soon as the men returned to the town.

But as those who were lucky to have survived returned, it was found that mass unemployment was all they could look forward to. The Ministry still held control over the country's production base and did not immediately release the brickyards back to private enterprise. In the Wrexham district the brick companies and the local councils held a conference in July 1919 to determine the core problems facing the industry, and they were identified as follows:

1 – Government still held control over all building projects. Of 1,450 proposed projects, only 75 had been approved throughout the entire country, and by the end of May only seven schemes had been started. It was resolved that private enterprise

would have to be given free rein over housing schemes.

2 – There was an acute shortage of railway wagons. What orders were obtained were often cancelled, simply because the brick companies could not move their products out. J C Edwards Co reported that their works were rapidly coming to a standstill for want of wagons, and that 450 men and boys were in imminent danger of being laid off. Ten trucks per day were required for each of the works at Trefynant and Penybont.

3 – Unstable coal prices and difficulty in obtaining it made brick production very insecure, and Dennis Co complained that no priority was being given to the brickworks to ensure a proper supply.

The redevelopment of the once prestigious industry proved a slow and arduous one, and many of the smaller works saw the hardships of the 1920s as marking their epitaphs. Government proved unwilling or unable to help, leading one Wrexham councillor to later recall "When it was a question of producing shells, works were seen converted, but on the question of bricks we were stuck".

The Second World War also caused repercussions which seriously decimated the brick trade yet further. As in the First War the initial effects were minor, and in 1940 the feared threat of German invasion and air raid prompted government to initiate a great building programme to set in place the airfields, pill box guns and shelters required. This meant that the brickyards were on full-time, but were hindered by lack of manpower – many of the workers having already been called up – so government responded by releasing all the brickmen from the Forces so that they could return to work until the demand for bricks had been met.

Incidentally, the Second War caused one social change which was not implemented in the first – the need for total night time blackout, and this led to the occasional accident which had last been common back in the dark Victorian times. Just after the blackout was imposed in 1939 a man fell into the Standard Work's clayhole and was killed, and the coroner noted "I am disposed to think that this is one of the numerous fatalities which I fear may take place owing to the lighting restrictions". And

the brickworks presented a knotty problem for the Air Raid Wardens, as to how to cope with the night glow sometimes emitting from the kilns, but the public's fears were allayed as our propaganda machine swung into action. " A complete success" was the verdict of the newspapers on Connah's Quay's blackout trials in May 1939, despite the fact that the Minute Books of the Urban District Council reported a serious transgression from the kilns of John Prince's brickworks.

As the war progressed, the need for bricks naturally declined in favour of armaments production etc, resulting in the now un-needed brickworkers being sent to war, and we can see this reflected in the government reports on manpower levels in industry. In 1939 Denbighshire's brickyards employed 1,558 men and 40 women, which by 1945 had plummeted to 566 men and 47 women; those ratios of men to women seeming to imply that the women were again taking a more active role in actual brickyard production.

After the war ended, the same difficulties became apparent as had done 26 years earlier. Castle Firebrick Co evaluated two reasons for the difficulties experienced in re-establishing production. In their own words:

"1 – Failure of the Government for the release of labour from the Forces. 2 – Delay by the Board of Trade in de-requisitioning premises used for storage purposes".

The Ministry of Works had during wartime reduced the number of functional brickworks within Great Britain from a pre-war figure of approximately 1,200 to 393 left open by December 1944. By the end of the war these mothballed works had had their operating efficiency seriously compromised by a long term lack of maintenance; a state of affairs made even worse by serious manpower shortages. By this point in the 20th century it had become a fact that brickyard wages had fallen pathetically short of rates of pay in other areas of industry, and the demobbed soldiers saw no future in returning to the brickyards. The Ministry of Works did give financial help to some yards under the Essential Works Order scheme, and Ruabon

Brick & Terracotta Co was one such to benefit from this help, but recuperation continued sluggishly. The Wrexham area required 80,000 bricks per week by 1946, but the local works could produce only just short of 30,000. The local brick trade had been shockingly crippled. In the following year the government granted special coal concessions to the country's brickworks in an attempt to speed up recovery, but even by 1959 the works in both Buckley and Ruabon districts were still unable to supply even the local demand. Castle Firebrick Co, a strong and powerful company compared to most of its competitors, reported "We have been rationing bricks for the past six months. We try to let all our customers have some supplies. The biggest shortage is of facing bricks and we are quoting a three months delivery date".

Manufacturing Processes

A new beginner may think that anybody can make and burn bricks and has only to live next door to a brickmaker to learn, but it is not very long before he becomes of a different opinion. Brickmaking is a science and requires considerable experience, and the longer a man is in the business, the more he finds he can learn.

A Peterborough brickmaker, 1892.

In this chapter I will endeavour to describe the sequence of processes which followed the clay from the quarry to the finished product, and in general, these procedures were fairly standardised practices throughout the various brickworks – some slight variations sometimes arising, dependent on the type of goods being made. It should be borne in mind that throughout most of its history brickmaking was a much more labour intensive occupation than it is today, and the "hands on" approach of yesteryear has to a great degree now disappeared.

Before we look at the practices of the larger, more mechanised works which were becoming common from the 1860s onwards, we should not ignore the labours of the earlier brickmakers , whose ways of working had been followed in the simple country brickyards and by contract brickmakers for decades. Some of their working ways had been almost unchanged since the days of antiquity, and their methods managed to survive certainly until the First World War.

These simple brickyards were properly called *Summer Yards,* because not having any large drying sheds needed to dry the *green* (unburnt) bricks, they had to concentrate their work into the dryer, warmer months. Failure to do this would have meant that the bricks might not have burnt properly, having been too moist, as happened in 1767 when Philip Yorke acquired the Erddig Estate and decided to rebuild King's Mill. On that occasion his brickmaker, Edward Fabian, found that only 5,000 of his 54,000 new bricks proved fit for use "which was owing to the wet season when they were made".

The first operation was to *get* the clay, which simply means digging it out of the ground, and this was done in the autumn or winter before the summer's brickmaking. The clay was then left to *weather*. For instance, in December 1844 the Birkenhead Dock Committee contracted a London firm of brickmakers to manufacture 45 million bricks for the construction of new warehouses, and the Chester Chronicle noted that "the land on the borders of Wallasey Pool are now alive with sturdy workmen employed in preparing clay for brickmaking during the ensuing summer". This weathering process was the best way to prepare a hard clay for later usage. It would be laid out on the ground and allowed to be rained upon. During the frosts of winter, the water present in the clay would freeze, and this would disintegrate the clay particles, making it more *plastic*, thereby rendering it much easier for the brickmaker to work, saving much on time and labour. The clay might also have been turned over with a fork during the spring to help break it up.

When the brickmakers eventually came to start work, the next stage was to grind the weathered clay into an easily workable state, devoid of any lumps, and if portable machinery was to hand, this was done in a roller mill or a horizontal grinding pan; the machinery powered by a steam engine or perhaps a horse. *Pugging* was then done – this process being the actual mixing of the clay with water into a workable paste. Again, this may have been done in a steam powered *pugging mill,* or perhaps it was done in a circular trough constructed in the ground and worked by a horse which walked constantly around a central axis pivot, onto which was attached long mixing spikes; churning up the clay and water until it reached the desired consistency. One of the most common methods used, certainly in the early days, was that of employing *tread boys* – bare footed youngsters who would tread the mixture in a pit in the ground. I think it is somewhat uncertain as to how long this particular practice survived in our district. With so many mechanised plants in the large brickyards which proliferated throughout N E Wales, it seems unlikely whether the use of tread boys would have proved economical, although it may be certainly possible that they might have been employed in the smaller country yards. However, the British Clayworker in as late as 1924 mentions the continued use of tread boys in English brickyards, recording that one English brickmaker talking on this subject, "said he did not know of a brickfield in Portsmouth where a pugmill was used".

Once the clay was in a suitably *plastic* state and ready to be moulded into bricks, it was sent to the brickmakers themselves.

Even in the larger brickworks many hand moulders were employed in the production of basic common bricks, well into the late 1930s in some cases. This hand moulding process was undoubtedly the most arduous of all brickyard tasks; each brickmaker being paid for the number of bricks he could turn out, the average each day being 3,500-4,000. There is a fascinating description of this procedure in the later chapter dealing with the employment of children.

A brick-moulder would always work with two or more boy assistants, one of whom would be responsible for continually *throwing on* lumps of clay onto the maker's moulding table. The maker would slap enough clay into a wooden mould and turn out a brick onto the table; the duty of the other boy, the *carrier off,* to speedily take them to be laid out in a row. In the larger works these *green* bricks would be placed directly onto the floor of a drying shed, but in the outdoor yards they were then taken directly by boy *brick runners* to be stacked for drying in the open air. This type of drying method was called *hacking*, and was a skilled art in itself. A *hack* is a row of stacked green bricks which was protected from any sudden fall of rain by having a covering of straw, slates or special wooden hack-covers placed on top; the sides being protected by mats or planks. The bricks were hacked into long rows about 2 ft wide and between six to eight courses of bricks high – any higher and the lower courses would have been crushed by the weight. I have seen photographs of hacks in large English brickyards which were hundreds of feet long and lined in separate parallel rows, enough space left between to get a single wheeled brick-barrow down. Once the soft bricks had dried a little harder, the hack would then be taken down and the bricks re-hacked, leaving spaces between them to allow the wind to blow freely through, thereby achieving a more thorough drying. This process was called *scintling*. A good brickmaker would also have taken great care to have the rows aligned in consideration of the wind direction, as this varies from district to district, and the more vulnerable lengthwise sides of the hacks had to be protected from any direct onslaught of rain.

Bad weather was the curse of the summer yard, and this next report, taken from the British Clayworker of the turn of the century, recounts the accumulative problems of the nation's brickmakers during a particularly wet season:

Although a great many manufacturers of clay goods now conduct their operations the whole year round under cover, millions of bricks are dried in open hacks. This is especially the case with hand made bricks. Such a season as we have just passed through is about the worst on record, and has been as bad as possible from the brickmaker's point of view. He has needed all the resources of straw and wooden hack covers, and yet with all his precautions he has probably had many a fallen hack, thousands of rain-washed goods and has been compelled to crowd his bricks into kiln in a greener state than he has done for years. From bricks with their arrises gone and their ends spattered; from the longer time taken drying, there has been an increased consumption of coal and the kilns have been longer about. For all this the clayworker has to thank the rain. But the worst disaster is when the lower tiers get so sodden that they can no longer support the weight of the tiers resting upon them, and the whole hack collapses.

The final stage of production was the burning of the bricks in kilns. The larger works, which were designed for year round production of a generally better class of brick used *patent kilns* – permanent constructions filled and emptied time and time again. But the small summer yards, and the journeymen contract makers, used *clamp kilns*, which were built and used only once and good only for basic common bricks. As this once all too commonly seen phenomenon was last practised many decades ago, I feel I should describe it for you. It was, after all, the most important procedure undertaken by more brickmakers than there were individual brickyards themselves. Put very basically, the building of a clamp involved the following procedures –

• Prepare a rectangular area of ground with a flat base, gently sloping upwards on the edges. Cover with a layer of sand and ash to insulate the above clamp from rising ground moisture.

• Layer the green bricks over this area and continue building upwards with more layers until a large block of green bricks has been built, sloping the sides of the clamp gently inwards as you build it up. This wider base and narrower top prevents the clamp from falling over once the heat begins expanding the structure.

• As you build the lower courses, leave little tunnels about 26 inches apart, running through the width of the clamp at its base. These are the *firing channels* and will be filled with combustible material to start the initial burning process.

• Between the courses of bricks place a layer of a slow burning fuel – thicker layers at the base, reducing to thinner layers towards the middle of the clamp.

• Finish off by enclosing the whole structure with a casing of old bricks to insulate the entire clamp, and complete it by daubing the outside with mud, turf or clay to prevent seepage of hot gases. The clamp kiln is now ready to be fired by igniting the fuel in the firing channels.

As more and more brickworks turned over to using the more efficient patent kilns, the clamp method began to become less popular, and in 1893 the British Clayworker journal was rather surprised when it realised that this older method was still in use as much as it was. "It must be a matter of astonishment to many readers to find so many enquiries as to methods used in clamping" the magazine remarked, and the information it subsequently published is the basis for this author's text; the authenticity of the information having come directly from a generation of brickmakers long gone!

The most easily built and functional size of clamp was apparently a block 16 bricks wide, 25 courses high, and as long as you liked, provided enough firing channels were included to ensure a good burn throughout, but in the massive London brickyards these clamps could be huge, and I have seen photographs of them, unfortunately too poor to reproduce here, in which they were as big as bungalows, rising to easily twice the height of a man.

In some yards they were built, as The Clayworker put it *"like an Egyptian pyramid, as if it had to stand for all time, and it is no uncommon thing to crowd a million bricks into one clamp for burning"*. The continental yards in Germany and Holland used to build them even bigger – over 20ft high at times!

The question of the fuel used is quite an interesting one. I am truly not sure what was used in our district, but the traditional fuel of Wales was known to be coal dust and slack – a slow burning, smouldering fuel ideal for the clamp process, and dependent on the number of bricks within, a clamp could take from three weeks to two months to burn through. In the S E of England they used a fuel called breeze, which was an amalgam of road sweepings (twigs, horse dung, dust) mixed with household refuse and cinders, and apparently this burnt very well. What this concoction must have smelt like presents a mystery for us to ponder over, but perhaps the following remark might spice our imagination. A contemporary observer noted that *"the most nauseating fumes often arise from the stacks of bricks made and burnt in this manner and tend to make the immediate neighbourhood of these clamps anything but a desirable place"*.

There is a wonderful story from the British Clayworker of December 1898 of a London brickmaker who travelled to Wales and observed the Welsh makers using coal dust in their clamps. When he arrived back at his yard he thought he would try this method himself, but failed to calculate that coal burns a lot more fiercely than breeze. He packed his kilns with as much coal dust as he normally did with his usual fuel, and set light to it. The whole thing became a raging inferno and at night it "illuminated the country for miles around".

As more and more larger, more productive yards were established, and transportation of goods by road became easier, the availability of stronger factory-made bricks began to supersede the need for clamp making, and by 1908 the older methods were "almost obsolete at the present day".

* * *

Now we shall investigate the larger yards. The mechanised brickworks of the Industrial Age had their own ways of working, presenting the workers with new and increased dangers to their safety, and the following descriptions will sometimes highlight the many everyday risks which the factory brickmaker encountered. I have included such reports, not purely for any sensationalistic reasons, but because they teach us much about the hands-on duties of the brickyard workers of times gone by.

CLAYHOLE PRACTICES

The larger brickworks naturally had larger clayholes, the reason for this being quite logical. As the works were developed to turn out an ever more increasing quantity of goods, so the production lines themselves had to be similarly improved by the installation of larger and faster clay processing machinery, which in turn resulted in the demand for an increased clay supply from the *clay getters* – the quarrymen who not only stood at the clay face, but at the head of the whole production line. Up until the 1930s and the introduction of mechanical diggers, it is probably true to say that this job had always been "hands on"; the men using picks and shovels alone, and in essence, clayhole work was composed of two principal actions – the removal of the clay from the quarry face, and its transportation to the factory. The clayholes of these larger brickworks were imposing sights, and working them could at times be no easy task. Consider this observation of a clay getter at the Kings Mills Works at Abenbury, Wrexham in 1933: "He was engaged in heavy work consisting of timbering and clay trimming etc, and he was required during his work to climb to the top of a clayhole by means of a rope up a distance of 40 ft to clear and trim the sides of the clay pit". As the face of the clayhole was extended ever outwards, the top soil and upper layers of poor clay, known in brickyard parlance as fey, first had to be removed, and at the large Hafod works of Messrs Dennis, these layers alone were 20-30 ft deep. Even this initial process could have its dangers, as happened here:

Rhos Herald 24th August, 1895 – On Monday last a serious accident happened to Mr J.A.Pruett, who was contracted with the Ruabon Brick & Terracotta Co to remove some surface soil. He was busily engaged on the work when a large quantity of soil fell on him. Besides being severely crushed he sustained injuries to one of his hip joints.

The clay of our district, because of its rock-like consistency, was dislodged from the quarry face in one of two ways; either by manually *working down* the vertical quarry face, or by blasting. The first method is fairly self explanatory and was the safest way of working – starting at the top of the quarry face and working down to the base by means of ropes and ladders, the men hacking out lumps of clay as they went. This method had one disadvantage however, in that it was a laborious and time consuming practice showing only modest productivity. The second method was favoured by the clay men, as the yield was greatly increased, and as all the men in the brickworks were paid on piecework, this was naturally to their advantage. But blasting, of course, held its own dangers. Firstly, there might be the incidence of *miss shot,* where a charge of blasting material might not go off, only to explode when the *fireman* later returned to investigate the malfunction. Or there could be the possibility of a freak accident, as happened to John Iball at Buckley's Knowle Lane brickworks in October 1881, when a spark from the newly ignited fuse wire leapt into the open tin in which he kept his powder, causing an explosion which left him badly burnt. Another cause of clayhole accident however, was the result of the practice of *holeing*. This was the tunnelling of a hole into the base of the clay face, into which a blasting charge would be placed to bring the entire face down. This hole could be quite a large affair – a tunnel in all but name, and the removal of such a volume of material could cause the fractious, crumbly rock above to give way all too easily. Shoring up the hole with pit props was the advised way to proceed, but following the maxim "time costs money", this was all too often ignored, and the following report on the inquest into the death of 21 year old Charles Ridgeway at H R Bowers Ruabon works perfectly highlights the various reasons why this treacherous procedure was often resorted to:

Wrexham Advertiser 28th March, 1884 – John Thomas Baker, foreman at the works, stated that the deceased and another man were " holeing" under a piece of clay 20 ft in height, preparing for a fall. This was done in order to make the clay easier to get. The witness was responsible for the proper working of the clay bank, and it was his duty to see that everything was free from danger. He left the works at 12 o'clock and returned shortly after 2 o'clock. During his absence the deceased and another man had holed under the clay, which he did not consider a proper way of working.

Coroner: Did they work according to your instructions?

Witness: No Sir. I told them emphatically to work it straight down the face. The clay can be got without working in the way they did. They were working to make it easier for themselves. They are paid by piecework. There was no occasion to hole under the clay.

Government Inspector: Is it the custom in this part of the country to work clay in that way by undermining it?

Witness: They do it sometimes.

Government Inspector: Is it a very dangerous way of working?

Witness: If I had been present, I should have stopped them working in that way. I should think two or three tons fell down.

Edward Tudor, the man who was working with the deceased, went on to say that they could not keep up with supplying the factory machinery without holeing under the clay – they could not get the clay quick enough.

Coroner: And so kill yourselves! You have no business to work under the clay like that, you ought to work it from the top.

Tudor: By undermining the clay two men can do as much work as six would do if working it straight down.

Government Inspector: This method of getting clay is a constant source of danger. Two men were killed in Liverpool last year in exactly the same way.

Clay face working was always fraught with danger. Despite the risks of purposeful holeing, a clay face, if weakened by natural fault lines or cracked by the action of heavy frost, could just as easily collapse of its own accord, and in truth, most of the clayhole accidents occurred in this way.

Flintshire News 21st December, 1911 – Whilst following his employment in the clayhole of the lower brickyard owned by the Buckley Brick & Tile Co, Enoch Shone aged 69 was instantaneously killed by a large piece of rock which fell from the top. The body was so badly mutilated that it had to be conveyed home in a coffin without removing his working apparel.

Once the clay was won, or *got*, it was pickaxed into pieces and shovelled into tram trucks which were then hauled to the factory. If the incline permitted, horses would do this work, but where the clayhole was too deep, the tramway was operated by a winch from a steam engine at the top of the clayhole or in the factory itself.

Wrexham Advertiser 29th January, 1887 – At the brickworks of Mr Bowers an alarming accident which happily ended without any serious results occurred to a young man named Edwin Edwards. As he was engaged with the machine which is used for winding the trams from the claypit and was in the act of throwing dust on the drum to enable the brake to work, his clothes caught in the machinery and he was carried upwards to about six feet, when a rafter arrested his progress and he was held there for a little time. While in this position the greater part of his clothes including his shirt were stripped off by the revolving wheels, which was a fortunate thing for him, as it relieved him from further peril and enabled him to reach terra firma in safety.

The simple single line tramroads were in some of the more prestigious works replaced by an endless rope system, whereby the trucks would slowly and relentlessly go to and fro, making a loop turn at each end. Dennis Ruabon and Ruabon Brick & Terracotta definitely used this system; the latter works also making use of a tramway which ran in a tunnel beneath the main Wrexham to Ruabon road. By this time electricity had replaced steam power, but it was the diesel lorry, able to drive to wherever it was immediately required, which eventually rendered the tram system obsolete in most works.

An important aspect of clayhole work was the draining of water which would accumulate from rainfall or exposed water courses and flood the workings. In 1954 for instance, Hafod Works used two pumps, each removing 600 gallons a minute to clear the hole when necessary, and during one particularly bad spell of rain, they had to call in the fire brigade to keep on top of it. Back in November 1890 production at Buckley's Brookhill Works was completely halted when their manually operated pump failed to cope with the rising waters during torrential storms, resulting in their having to purchase a steam pump in order to clear the clayhole and resume production.

Its worth mentioning that it was not always a requirement that you had to actually be in the clayhole workings to be put in danger from their practices! The following inclusions will illustrate this:

Letter from Gwysanney Estate to Castle Brickworks, 8th April, 1907 – I am informed by Mr Catherall that in blasting in your clayhole, a stone fell within a few feet of a man at Ewloe Barn Farm. This is a serious matter for anyone living in the house or working on the farm and calls for your attention.

Chester Chronicle 6th September, 1958 – On 14th August there was a heavy explosion which scattered rock over a considerable distance. Pieces of rock were blown 70 yards on that occasion and a boy was hit with a small piece, but not hurt. He had been told by people connected with Lane End Brickworks there had been what they called a "blow out". They had instances of lumps of rock going right through the roof of houses near the clayhole. Mr Gray said he had found a piece of rock the size of a man's fist embedded in a lawn. When women heard blasting they ran into their houses wondering if rock was going to land in their gardens.

MACHINERY

The most advantageously laid out brickworks were those which followed the manufacturing procedure based on the "gravity feed" principal. As clay machinery progressively improved, the individual grinding, rolling, pugging and brick moulding machines of the mid-19th century developed by the 1890s into faster and more efficient units with each function placed one above the other. This meant that the inconvenience caused by manually moving clay from one machine to another could be dispensed with by having it automatically drop down through one giant interlocked machine. To this end, the feed inclines from the clayholes would in the best of factories lead up to the highest floor of the brickworks, with the new green bricks emerging at ground level to be taken to the drying sheds. In our district however, there were many brickworks which although fairly mechanised had never managed to accumulate the level of financial investment required to achieve this apex of efficiency, and I am sure this was true of many works around Britain generally.

In the great days of the brickworks, brick

A Colliery Guardian advertisement for a wire cut brick machine illustrates the coal industry's interest in the field of brickmaking. Pugged clay is fed from an upper storey of the brickshed, to be extruded onto the two wire cutting tables at the front of the machine.

manufacturing machinery was notoriously dangerous to work with, and a glance at some of the illustrations of machines in this book will show you why. Their designers constructed them with the principle of functional usage clearly to the fore, and this explains why all the main moving parts were so blatantly exposed. Clay is a very sticky, adhesive material, and the machine operators would have been frequently required to clear away blockages. It would have meant much lost production time had the operators needed to remove heavy protective guards to constantly get to any problem areas, and in truth, as the workmen were paid for the amounts they produced, they themselves often argued against fitting restrictive guard devices, in favour of maintaining speedy production. The Factories Act insisted on guards being in place, but from the number of recorded legal actions brought against the brick companies, it's obvious that in most cases this requirement was ignored to a great extent.

There were four basic types of machine in a brickworks – clay rollers, clay grinding pans, pugging mills and the brick moulding presses. The function of

One of the many dangerous Victorian brickyard machines -- a combined clay crusher and stone separator.

the rollers was to crush the lumps of clay into small enough pieces for the grinding pans to handle; the pans themselves usually being constructed in the form of a large circular trough with a sieve base, not unlike a huge garden soil sieve, in which rollers would rotate around a central axis, grinding the clay into powder. The clay in earlier days was fed into the pan by being shovelled in, a process which was later done by mechanical "creep conveyors", and the resultant finely ground clay would fall through the sieve to be then taken to the pug mill, where water was added to transform it into a plastic mixture ready for the brick press itself.

Before we go any further, we should be aware of the fact that even though the basic steps of clay preparation were generally the same throughout the brick industry, the differences in machine design and individual working requirements were quite extensive, the reason for this being that the composition and behaviour of the clays from district to district was so varied that no one clay would behave like any other. For this reason it was all too easy for a brick company to waste much of its funds in purchasing the wrong type of machinery for their particular type of clay. An English brickworks manager in 1893 wrote "I have seen in scores of brickyards one or more machines out of use that have been purchased and found unsuitable, although it might be one of the most useful in any other locality where a different material was used". In our own district, the New North Leeswood Colliery in 1894 was sued by Whitehead & Co of Leeds, who had supplied the colliery with a new brick press which had not been paid for, owing to it not coming up to expectations; the colliery themselves actually being to blame because they could not get the clay mix to the right consistency for the machine to work properly.

To complicate matters even further, there were any number of materials which could be mixed with any number of clays; each experimental variation threatening to thwart the expectations of the unwary and inexperienced manufacturer. Shale and mining spoil from collieries and ironworks were a common admixture used in the making of cheap bricks, and in the north-western districts of Wales, slate dust was mixed with the clay. It was even the local practice in Cornish brickworks to make bricks from river mud mixed with their china clay.

But of all the machines in a brick factory, the brick presses themselves were the most dangerous to work with. Even though the catalogue of accidents with grinding pans and pug mills were relentlessly steady throughout the Victorian era, they were dwarfed when compared against those occasioned by the many types of presses to be found, be they manually or steam operated. Consider the following statement by Mr Bignold, the Inspector of Factories, made in October 1876:

"My attention has been drawn to the increase of accidents of a serious character to boys aged from 14 to 20 employed at the Spencer's Patent Steam Press, now generally used in the manufacture of bricks, tiles and sanitary pipes. The catalogue of hand mutilations in the Ruabon district tells its own tale. The question pressing on my mind is whether some means cannot be contrived to prevent such accidents. With very few exceptions these mutilations have occurred to

boys employed at the same process. Two boys are required to feed the machine with clay, for which purpose they sometimes use a small shovel, sometimes their hands. Men working below the boys and out of their sight, apply the pressure which brings down the piston with great rapidity through the clay; too often in its descent it lacerates or amputates their fingers or hands. I watched one of the pipe presses at work, and so rapidly is the process, that at each descent the feeding boys are exposed to danger, whether they use their hands or the shovel, they can scarcely get the fragments of clay into the required position without their hands being brought within the range of the descending piston".

Dr William Jones of the Ruabon Hospital collated the following table of brick press injuries upon which Mr Bignold had based his concerns, and to put the whole picture into perspective, it's worth realising that the following accidents occured in the brickworks of the Ruabon and Rhos area alone!

A typical free-standing belt driven mechanical brick press.

Date	Patient	Age	Nature of Injury	Works
12 -5-1870	Robert Davies	16	Laceration of hand	Trefynant
7-10-1870	Thomas Griffiths	14	Amputation of right hand	Delph
4-11-1870	Ellis Evans	40	Amputation of three fingers	Ponkey
26-1-1871	Robert Roberts	20	Amputation of three fingers	Tatham
18-3-1871	John Jones	38	Hand crushed	Ponkey
4-7-1871	John George	14	Hand amputated	Plaskynaston
23-11-1871	Robert Roberts	16	Amputation of two fingers	Trefynant
8-1-1872	Edward Jones	18	Amputation of three fingers	Delph
9-1-1872	Thomas Hughes	14	Amputation of thumb and finger	Acrefair
4-9-1872	Edward Brown	16	Laceration of right hand	Tatham
13-10-1872	Wiliam Rogers	15	Amputation of finger	Tatham
4-12-1872	Thomas Davies	15	Laceration of right hand	Plasmadoc
31-1-1874	Wiliam Jones	15	Amputation of index finger	Penybont
18-5-1874	Samuel Roberts	14	Amputation of left thumb	Acrefair
24-6-1874	J Williams	14	Laceration of left hand	Ponkey
25-11-1874	Adam Griffiths	14	Amputation of arm	Delph
13-4-1875	Henry Peake	14	Amputation of right hand	Trefynant
24-6-1875	John Rowland	20	Amputation of thumb and finger	Tatham
15-7-1875	Joseph Bailey	14	Amputation of finger	Trefynant
20-7-1875	R J Prichard	15	Amputation of finger	Ponkey

A brick press requires very great pressure to turn out a good brick of solid mass, and most of the bricks in the Buckley and Ruabon districts, excepting common bricks, were made by this process; the nature of the heavy marls and fireclays requiring such powerful machines to achieve the desired consistency of the finished product. It is easy to spot a pressed brick – they almost always have a recessed face on both sides which acts as a mortar key, and the old terminology for this feature was a *frog*. It is also the frog which has the brickworks name, if any, stamped into it.

At each downward stroke of the press, the brick was formed in the machine's *die*, which to prevent the clay from sticking to it was sometimes lined with a material called "fustian", and sometimes even by moleskin. The die could also be lubricated by an injection of oil or steam. Even this simple process itself could be done in different ways; even manually, as appeared to be the case in 1900, when a boy at Hafod Works had his hand amputated when it slipped under the die press due to his having put too much oil on the brick. The Government Inspector recorded 17 press accidents for 1899 in Ruabon district alone, which led to the Inspector attempting to persuade the manufacturers to fit guard devices, but all to no avail, as the works responded that they felt the guards themselves could cause hands to get trapped.

As I previously mentioned, there were so many different types of machines performing the actions of brickmaking in so many subtly varying ways, that to attempt to describe any of these machines in too finite and detailed a way would be inevitably misleading. The manufacture for example of facing bricks, silica bricks, wire cut bricks, drainage pipes and tiles involved completely different types of machines and operating procedures.

Other mechanical processes also contributed to the noise and clamour experienced in the larger works; many of these factories making good use of noisy bucket or belt elevators, and even platform lifts which raised clay tubs between floors. Even here, danger could lurk in the most unexpected way. At Wrexham's Abenbury Brickworks a workman was killed when he descended an elevator shaft into a large clay dust hopper to clear clogged machinery; another employee unwittingly restarting the elevator, causing him to fall into the bottom of the hopper where he was suffocated in the dust. And it wasn't just in Victorian times that such bizarre tragedies occurred – that accident happened in 1965.

BRICK SHEDS

After leaving the machine rooms, the next destination for our newly made brick, tile or pipe was the drying shed – more commonly called the *brickshed*, as this is where the moist green bricks were laid out to dry before going into the kilns. These large sheds were what principally gave the bigger works their advantage over the outdoor brickyards, in that drying could continue here all year round. The most commonly followed Victorian practice was to lay the bricks on planks on the floor, but as technology progressed, the bricks were sometimes stacked on pallets and placed into racks, making better use of vertical space. Most importantly, the state of the art in Victorian brickshed technology were the underground heating flues, which utilised the waste heat from the furnaces or boilers to speed up the drying time.

It was these large sheds which occasionally saw many alternative uses, as you will read in the chapters cataloguing the individual works themselves. They saw use as Sunday chapels, entertainment venues at times of celebration, but probably most regularly as makeshift dormitories for itinerant tramps. And it was not uncommon for works proprietors to very often make use of their work spaces, principally because large public halls very often didn't exist in many rural or industrial communities, and the workmen attending such events could number into the hundreds. Even Mr W H Darby, the wealthy owner of Brymbo Ironworks, had to use his works in July 1854 as the venue for his wedding reception. As the Chronicle reported: "A large yard formerly used for smelting was cleared out and prepared for the entertainment of the invited guests", and those guests numbered over 3,000!

KILNS

All permanently constructed kilns were generally termed *patent kilns*; that is to say, kilns which were designed and patented with the clear intention of attesting to perform their task better than anybody else's design. This desire to patent and protect a designer's invention was widespread in the 19th century – one might almost call it an obsession – and patents on kiln designs, as well as for clay working machinery, ran literally into the hundreds. The reason for so many kiln patents being taken out was due to the many number of functions a kiln had to perform, as the quality of a finished brick could be dramatically altered by the slightest variation in kiln design. Any designer was naturally anxious to secure the technological advantage over his competitors, and it's not surprising therefore that most of the patent holders were themselves brickworks managers or manufacturers.

Without going into any unnecessary technical detail, which considering the immensity of the subject I would be unable to supply, we should be content to understand which types of kiln were predominant in our district. The most commonly found kiln throughout our district was the *round kiln* – a brick built kiln with a gently domed roof; examples of which can be seen illustrated within. The kiln's circumference was strengthened by iron straps; there to protect the structure as it expanded with the heat, and the base of the kiln also had thick buttress walls for the same purpose. The kiln generally had one or two doorways through which the bricks were loaded and unloaded, and when ready to be fired, these would be bricked up to form a sealed interior, leaving a small viewing hole to enable the kilnman to monitor the temperature within. Ringing the kiln were a number of furnace grates; there having to be so many in order to raise enough heat within. The firing of a kiln was a very specialised and responsible job which required constant attention throughout the burning process, particularly in the days of coal firing. In later years automatic oil or gas burners were fitted, but in the earlier days kiln men had to be employed in shifts round the clock to ensure against any ruinous temperature fluctuations. The following story from the British Clayworker of May 1893 is the account of a brickmaker recollecting the days of his apprenticeship in an English brickworks in the 1870s:

"The following year I made much overtime by sitting up with the kilns at night. This work brought me additional wages which induced me to persevere. My duty did not always end in attending to the fires of one 40 hole kiln, but often I would have two and

A local kiln designer's British Clayworker advertisement of 1894.

sometimes three kilns in different stages of burning to attend to. I was told it was necessary to have plenty of work to keep me from falling asleep. On one occasion I was to have my supper at 10 o'clock and there would be ten minutes for the purpose of taking forty winks – I was to be sure and not sleep beyond that time. I obeyed my master's injunction as far as going to sleep was concerned, but I omitted to wake at the right time, and it was not till he roused me at 4am that I realised that I had been to sleep at all. My fears grew apace as I looked round and saw the fires out and the holes which should have been at a white heat, black and cold. The damage done was irreparable; always afterwards I took the precaution to up-end a brick and sit on it, and if I chanced to nod, my equilibrium was immediately upset."

Before the kilnman set about his task, the kilns were loaded with unburnt green bricks by the *kiln setter*. The whole success of the burning process relied heavily on the skill of the setter in stacking the bricks in a way which would realise the most efficient burn, as this process depended on the optimum flow of the hot gases throughout the kiln – the burn time itself being dependent on the size of kiln, the fuel used and the nature of the clay from which the bricks were made.

Rhos Herald 20th September, 1930 – Silica Brick Production at Pant Works. For nine days and nights the bricks lie in the heated kilns where they have been packed in rows by experts. The kiln packer has to be a very wary person, for where a kiln has been carelessly packed the bricks are all spoilt. During the whole time the bricks are being burnt, stokers make the rounds of the kilns at frequent intervals firing the hungry fireholes.

Apart from the round kilns, kilns might be square, oblong or *beehive*, a small round design with a high domed roof which were particularly prevalent in the Ruabon district, but the state of the art in kiln technology was undoubtedly the *continuous kiln*, and many examples of these abounded throughout the district. The first of this type was patented in 1859 by the German manufacturer Hoffman, and many which were thereafter built followed his basic design – the Hoffmann Kiln becoming almost a byword for any type of continuous model. The Hoffmann design, although much more expensive to initially build, was purposefully created to save on fuel costs, dispensing with much of the fuel needed to bring an individual kiln up to operational temperature, and avoiding the wastage of stored heat when an individual kiln was left to go cold during the *drawing out* process (the removal of the finished product).

A continuous kiln is in effect many little kilns, each called *chambers*, joined together in a continuous ring, but the whole construction was invariably oblong in outward appearance as opposed to circular. The furnaces of each chamber were placed in the centre of the kiln, thus allowing for the least amount of heat loss, and they were fuelled via vertical shutes on the kiln roof. Put simply, the firing of each chamber was done in a continuous circulatory fashion – if for instance chamber No 8 was being fired, chamber No 7 would be in the process of being filled whilst chamber No 9 would be cooling down and chamber No 10 would be being emptied. The heat radiated

from the adjacent chambers meant that the whole kiln never went cold, therefore maximising fuel efficiency. Of course, despite the Hoffman's advantages, a brickworks would have had to have been big enough and productive enough to have justified installing such a large kiln in the first place, especially as they had so many chambers within them; 16 and even 24 not being uncommon. But due to the method of firing the chambers from above, this design of kiln apparently did not suit everyone's tastes. Albert Hall, a foreman burner of many years' experience at an English works, wrote in 1895: "The bricks are completely smothered in coal and ashes from one end of the kiln to the other. In the end of the chambers the bricks are taken out in twos and threes completely welded together by the coals being poured down amongst them and combustion taking place therein. Sometimes the mess resembles a rockery".

Apart from the finished products themselves, kilns produced much else besides:

Heat. As the urban areas began spreding outwards during the Victorian era, the landscape witnessed a proliferation of clamp kilns being sited around the outskirts of the towns and encroaching onto what was once farmland. Earlier in the century, the rapid growth of London had prompted the political cartoonist George Cruikshank to publish in 1829 a print entitled the March of Bricks and Mortar, which starkly caught the mood of this rapid expansionism. Cruikskank portrayed chimney pots and wheelbarrows marching into the fields from rows of scaffolded newly erected terraced houses, with pyramidical clamp kilns spewing fourth hundreds of bricks, like grapeshot from a cannon. Running from the scene is a tree, shouting "I must leave the field", whilst a hay stack flees and cries "Confound these hot bricks. They'll fire all my hay ricks". The heat which radiated from these kilns could at times be immense. At Crewe County Court in July 1894 a farmer sued a brickmaker whose kilns were 21 yards from his field. What type of kilns they were is not recorded, but the damage they inflicted was; a supporting witness testifying that a channel of grass 50-60 yards in length had been "nicely burnt" by the heat carried on the prevailing wind. Getting too close to a kiln could certainly be an unexpectedly risky business. In 1862 a 15 year-old girl was attempting to roast potatoes on the roof of a kiln at Wickham in Kent when she spontaneously caught fire and was incinerated, and a similar accident befell a boy tramp in January 1895 at Halkyn St Brickworks in Flint – "he was warming himself when his clothes caught fire, and but for timely aid he would have been burnt to death".

Fumes. The cocktail of noxious fumes which a kiln's internal chemical reactions produced was another altogether invisible danger, and all the more unexpected, being disguised within the more harmless smoke. In 1859 at a brickyard in Shepherd's Bush, London, two vagrant girls were suffocated by such fumes as they slept on the warm roof of a kiln, and a combination of both fumes and heat put paid to another tramp at a Leeds pottery in 1849. The report of the tragedy read "It is supposed that he had gone to the kiln, fallen asleep upon it, and had been suffocated by the smoke. The deceased's head was completely burnt off, his skull was reduced to a cinder and his right arm was burnt to the socket".

In our own district in 1858 a search for a missing boy at Saltney was sadly concluded when he was found lying unconscious next to a brick kiln, the smoke from which was blowing down and enshrouding him. He died later, and experiments on the smoke proved that uneven burning of the coal within had given off poisonous gases.

Cinders. These were a valuable by-product of brick burning, and the works themselves used their hot ashes to keep the boilers warm when the furnaces were being cleared out, and I have also come across evidence of Ruabon Council having in the 1930s purchased spent ashes from the Ruabon Brick & Terracotta Co to lay as surfacing in playgrounds. The amount of waste ashes produced from a large works was prolific, and they were thrown onto large cinder banks; there to be plundered by the poor local populace who used them as a source of heating at home, especially during times when coal prices were high. Poverty caused by strikes in the local industries often forced families into taking such drastic action. The head of Acrefair School wrote in his diary on 7th May 1897 of how such a difficult time affected attendance at his classes: "Many boys are kept at home to pick coal. Owing to the lock out at Wynnstay and Plaskynaston Collieries many boys are irregular, as poverty compels them to go cinder gathering".

Cinder gathering was in truth quite a common practice, and the following report is typical of many suchlike to be found within the pages of the Victorian press:

Wrexham Advertiser 22nd September, 1900 – An old woman named Elizabeth Wright, aged 80, was shockingly burnt on Thursday at the Pant Works. It appears that the old lady went to pick ashes which had been thrown by the kilnmen down a bank. Joseph Ellis said he took a barrow full of hot ashes to the mount and tipped it over. When he had gone on his way back to the kilns he was called by some children, who stated that the woman was ablaze. Her body has been terribly burnt and even the hair of her head has been burnt away. Sarah Jones said the old woman had slipped into the hole where the ashes had been thrown and her apron took fire. Moses Williams, labourer, and two women at the works took the deceased home. They had a lot of trouble in keeping away these people from the bank. The coroner said "Now coal is so dear it is rather hard lines if they are to be stopped altogether, although strictly speaking they are trespassing".

Smoke. An ever-present nuisance which our Victorian town – dwelling ancestors had to endure was the high level of smoke pollution. *"To smoke or not to smoke. Whether in a commercial community like ours it is not better to see some clouds puffed forth from the various stacks of chimneys, than to see them smokeless".* That comment from 1888 highlighted the opinion on the one hand that the more smoke came from the factory chimneys, the more jobs it represented for the community. Unlike many areas, the Buckley district had its smoke problems much earlier than most, resulting from its earlier established pottery and brick works, and the brickmaster Jonathan Catherall II wrote in a letter dated 1813 that "I built a new house twelve years back to be out of the smoke". It's hard today to imagine how dense and black the smoke of Victorian urban industry must have been, but most reports on the subject seem to confirm that it was indeed something which we never witness in our society today:

Wrexham Advertiser 13th February, 1869 – The Wrexham Surveyor said he had had complaints of a nuisance from the smoke of a pipe works situate in the Walks. Mr Owen who had sheep in the adjoining field said he was ashamed of taking them to the fair, they were so black. Mr Jones said he had sold some of them and they were as black as if they had been in a chimney.

Wrexham Advertiser 17th October, 1903 – The annual inter colliery shooting competition for the silver challenge cup which was instituted in 1895 took place on the Ffrwd range on Monday. The teams are composed of eight men drawn from each colliery,viz Wrexham & Acton – Brynmally – Ffrwd – Westminster – Llay Hall and Gatewen. The atmospheric conditions were all that could be desired, save a slight breeze that blew across the range in the morning, but during the afternoon

frequent volumes of smoke from the Ffrwd Works partially obscured the target and thus placed at a disadvantage several of the contestants.

That second report concerned the Ffrwd Works, nestled in the countryside, whereas the first made reference to one of Wrexham's many clay smoking – pipe manufactories. Another notorious Wrexham pipe works was situated near the Willow Bridge, and had only an iron cylinder for a chimney, placed so low as to be only as high as the surrounding eaves of the adjacent houses, blowing "clouds of smoke across the road and almost suffocating passers by and tending to make horses snort and start". As for the brickworks themselves, they were known to be amongst the principal contributors to air pollution, by virtue not only of there having been so many of them, but of the fact that their numerous kilns were kept constantly in fire day and night. A temporary respite in the smoke emissions polluting Ruabon occurred during the serious coal strike of March 1912, which brought the entire Ruabon area brickworks to a standstill, causing one visitor to the district to make

The once smoky chimneys of Buckley stand dormant in the mid-1960s. From the high ground at Brookhill Brickworks are the distant works chimneys of a : Standard, b : Etna, c: Old Ewloe, d : Drury, e : Lane End , f : Mount, g : Knowle Hill. Photo: FRO.

the point of commenting how different things looked..."everything was quiet, and there was an absence of the black smoke usually associated with the brick and terracotta works". Even as late as 1961 Trevor Brickworks was producing clouds of smoke which obscured visibility on the adjacent road, so much so that some drivers unacquainted with the area believed it to have been patchy fog. By the 1970s however, government legislation had outlawed dark smoke emissions, and what brickworks had managed to survive into that decade had been long since converted to oil and gas firing; the sight of clouds of black fumes sweeping across our landscapes being one which today we can only leave to our imagination.

Other Aspects of Brickworks Life

To help in mentally collating an impression of what the working environment of a big brickyard might look like, it would be useful to know just what sort of mechanical plant might be found around the site, and we can learn much from Inventory Lists. This first list was drawn up for a bankruptcy sale at Davies Brothers Works in Wrexham in 1909 and illustrates what could be seen around the brickyard:

> 1 railway locomotive… Railway tracks… Traction engine and four trailers
> 2 tip wagons… Donkey pump… Sand washing machine… Winches
> Portable steam engine.…
> 3 cranes… Hand pumps… Blacksmith tools
> Brick barrows… Chains… 20 quarry hammers… Various lamps

The everyday maintenance of a state-of-the-art brick factory required a stores stock, the contents of which we could never simply guess at, even if we gave it much imaginative thought. But the following inventory of Davison's Old Ewloe Works at Buckley in 1957 shows us just how varied the material requirements of brick manufacturing could be:

Raw Materials Stock
Potash – 8 barrels
Black dust – 7 ton 19 cwt
Felspar – 12 cwt
Silico fluoride – 16 cwt
White Rock – 565 ton
Benzite – 76 ton
Aloxite – 70 ton 3 cwt
Bauxite
Hancocks blue bricks – 8264

Main Stores
Diesel oil – 30 gallons
Chevron oil – 40 gallons
Shell oil – 30 gallons
Engine oil – 20 gallons
Yellow grease – half drum
Gear oil – 40 gallons
White sand – 10 tons

Red sand – 18 tons
Washed sand – 2 tons
Gravel – 4 tons
Coke – 4 tons
Paint

Fitters and Mould Shop Stores
Yellow pine – 12 sq ft, two inches thick
Parana pine – 100 sq ft, one inch thick
Strober wood – 60 ft
Plain glass – 120 sq ft
Wired glass – 24 sq ft
Round nails -14.75 cwt
Oval nails – 10 cwt
Washers – 28 lbs
Assorted screws – 28 gross.

We can see from the above that they stocked much in the way of chemical minerals, used as additives in the mixtures of the different grades of clay products, and all those nails and various timbers would have been used for the construction of the special moulds for customised refractory block production. Davison's also had other stores for electrical parts and machine spares, but one thing they didn't have in 1957 however, was a stock of ferns! An odd thing to have at a brickworks, you might think, but ferns and heathers were extensively used in earlier times as material for packing the more fragile tiles into carriage crates. According to the evidence of the solicitor Hugh Jones in 1894, the farmers on Ruabon Mountain allowed the locals to cut the ferns, as this exposed the better grazing beneath, and the harvesters then sold the crop to the brickworks. And over in Buckley the Brookhill Works in 1916 were advertising for quotations for supplying them with "heather for packing clay goods".

* * *

THE USE OF HORSES.
"One of the most interesting sights that I witnessed during my stay in North Wales was a decent into the Ruabon Colliery. A Davy Lamp was given to each and we entered the cages which were protected on all sides by iron bars and at the top by

an umbrella of the same metal, and were soon at the bottom of the shaft 350 yards from the top. Here we were transferred into small coal carts drawn by a horse on a tramway; clean straw taking the place of carriage cushions. The strict instructions given to us were to keep our hands inside the carts and to bend our heads slightly, as we had to go a thousand yards into a subterraneous coal passage only large enough to enable the horse to pass through. At the end of this carbonic tunnel we came to the spot where the colliers, looking like a band of Christy Minstrels, were pickaxing and digging the coal. After visiting the furnaces, stabling and all the "lions" of this dark region, we again entered the cage and were soon on terra firma again. The horses appeared to be in good working condition, though their coats would not be clean enough for the eye of day".

That account was penned by Lord William Lennox in 1867 and gives a nice insight into the use of horses in the coal pits. The pit he visited was the Brandie Colliery, which in its earlier years was known as Ruabon Colliery, and which did later have its own brickworks. As many of the collieries were connected with their own brickmaking works, and in Ruabon district quite a few of the brickworks mined their clay from underground workings, I feel not unjustified in using such reports to illustrate the subject of the employment of horses within the brick industry. I know for certain, from talking to its former manager, that donkeys were worked within the extensive drift mines of the Garth Brickworks, and the Garth was not alone in this practice.

Throughout most of the industry's history, horses had played a primary role in a whole range of activities; their most important function being the motive power required to haul the heavy clay trucks from clayhole to factory and from the kilns to the railway sidings.

Wrexham Advertiser 13th May 1893 – On Thursday morning a horse was killed at Messrs Monk & Newell's brickworks. The animal was drawing some wagons in the siding, when it came in contact with an iron bar which pierced its breast. The boy in charge of the horse was injured and attended to by Dr Roberts.

As I touched on previously, a lot of the machinery in the earlier brickworks was made to be powered by horse as well as by steam, and the small agricultural and country brickyards naturally favoured horsepower. Even the larger works made use of horses until steam power became more of a necessity in the more competitive years of the 1870s onwards. The horses could operate a variety of machines by being hitched to a horse mill, whereby the animal would walk around a vertical axle which was connected to the machinery by gears and belts, and we know from advertisements in the press that this sort of arrangement was used in our own district. In September 1861 for instance, Rhos Brickyard was disposing of "a horse mill for grinding clay with rollers attached", and in 1872 E M Jones Wrexham Brickworks was selling for £30 their " clay mill geared for horse or steam". It's no coincidence that sale documents for almost any brickworks well into the 20th century often included the presence of stables on site, and there could be many horses stabled at the larger works, such as at Hancocks in Buckley, where we know that in 1858 they had a haystack at the works which contained 70 tons of hay, and I can't imagine what else such an amount would be used for other than to feed animals.

In general, horses seemed to have been a lot safer to work with than their mechanical alternatives, but if they had one fault it was that they could at times be unpredictable, especially if they became frightened by unexpected noises. They could also at times be a little "nippy". There is a long catalogue of fingers having been lost to hungry horses, the most prestigious victim perhaps being Mr Alletson, the manager of Castle Brickworks, who in 1902 had half a finger bitten off by his own horse as he tried to pat its muzzle.

As to the number of animals used underground, we must naturally accept that the coal mines – which often raised clay – used many more than the brickworks ever did. During the extended colliery strike of 1882, 68 horses and 20 donkeys at the Hafod Pit were brought up and given a holiday from their subterranean world, but by the turn of the century pit horses had gradually begun to be replaced by rope hauled systems.

Wrexham Advertiser 25th February, 1911 – Hugh Roberts and Robert Hughes, pit boys, were summoned for riding their ponies down the mine.

A horse pulls a clay tram from the Smelt Pit into Caello Brickworks on 22nd March 1962. Photo: Mike Lloyd .

The Coal Mines Regulations Act forbad the riding of any animal below ground. The defendants could not plead that they did not know they were doing wrong, for notices had been posted up on account of the dangerous practice. Also a colliers ' meeting was held only a few months ago with the object of impressing upon boys that they should not ride down the pit. The Inspector of Ponies at Hafod Colliery said on the date in question he met them in the back return airway riding their ponies in the direction of the stables. They were travelling at a very sharp pace. Mr John Jones, manager of No 1 Colliery, said he had a great deal of trouble with drivers riding on their ponies. The drivers ran a risk of striking their heads against the roof and it was a source of danger to miners travelling to and from their work. The drivers tried to race one another. He had received complaints from the men. Each defendant was fined five shillings and costs.

By 1901 Vauxhall Colliery, the third biggest in Ruabon, had only 12 horses left compared to 40 three years previously, but despite this movement there were, according to animal rights groups, 12,000 horses and ponies still in use in Britain's mines by as late as 1957. As for the brickworks, horses were a rare sight by this date, although they were still pulling the clay trams at Penybont Works in 1936, and the same was true at Caello Works near Brymbo as late as during the 1960s.

* * *

THE INFLUENCE OF THE WEATHER.

The severities of our British weather could cause serious problems to the brickworks of old, and I have already discussed how bad rains could flood clayholes or ruin the productivity of the outdoor Summer Yards. But in some cases even the big works could be prone to the extremes of the climate, being brought at times to a complete standstill. The best way to illustrate this is to simply quote direct reports, so we will first look at the problems caused by bad frosts. This condition had a twofold effect, the first being to render the clay too hard to work from the quarries; the resultant cessation of supply causing total factory shutdown. The second effect was a knock on from the first, as resulting unemployment was inevitable to a workforce who were paid for what they produced.

Chester Chronicle 3rd March 1855 – Great distress has been occasioned to the brickmakers at Buckley by the stoppage of the brickworks from the long continuance and great severity of the frost.

Numbers of families having been in a state of extreme destitution, the Reverend Mr Wilkinson and others have done much to aid them. Admiral Dundas having been made acquainted with the stoppage kindly sent £5, a seasonal and welcome donation. Such acts of charity cannot be too highly commended and do much to promote a kindly feeling between the rich and poor.

Wrexham Advertiser 29th January, 1881 – Owing to the continued severity of the weather nearly all the whole of the brickworks and quarries together with the men in the building trades have had to suspend work, and it is estimated that some 1,500 men are now idle, many of whom are in great distress. Some of the works have been standing a fortnight.

Chester Chronicle 14th January, 1893 – The long continuance of the frost is becoming very serious in the Buckley district. Some of the brickworks have been at a complete standstill since the holidays, and the others are only able to carry on their operations at a slow rate, and that with difficulty. Men are seen daily wandering about in large groups and while this weather continues they are hopeless of finding employment.

One condition which could prove beneficial to the brickyards was the occurrence of severe storms – if the works managed to escape having their chimneys felled! The loss of roof tiles and the damage caused to housing would result in an immediate demand for a brickyard's products, and as the Rhos Herald noted in 1927: "The recent gale has cleared the brickyards of stock that has been on the yards for years" – and they didn't mean that it had all blown away!

Apart from rain and frost, drought was the third major climatic factor affecting brick production. One thing a brickworks must have is a constant supply of water, and a drought caused by unusual summer temperatures could also cause total works stoppage. In the following report, note the term *playing*; a commonly used word in olden times to describe workers having nothing to do.

Wrexham Advertiser 8th September, 1906 – The inhabitants of Cefn and district are complaining of the scarcity of water. For some weeks there is a good deal of "playing" at the Australia Brickworks on account of the insufficiency of water. We are sorry to learn that a number of workmen employed at Trefynant Brickworks have received notice to leave on account of the same thing. Work in certain departments at Hafod Brickworks was suspended on Tuesday owing to the curtailment of water supply, but work was resumed on Wednesday after the laying of a few additional pipes to a fresh supply.

Rhos Herald 27th July, 1929 – The Pant Silica Brickworks are experiencing a rather trying time owing to the drought. Their usual supply of water, the bricked in pool, has now been dry for some time. In order to keep going the company have commenced to import water by train. The first consignment of 2,000 gallons was brought in huge tanks by railway.

Brickyard work was hard under the best of conditions, but during the summer months it could be quite uncomfortable. There are reports of coal stokers fainting at the kilns, and for the hand brickmoulders, paid on piecework and with every reason not to slack off, it could also be quite arduous. A brick machine manufacturer, eager to exploit the outdoor worker's predicament in order to promote his product, advertised in 1862 that "The employment of moulders is one which seems injurious to the men themselves. It is at the expense of severe bodily exhaustion; it being a common occurrence in hot weather for men to be carried off the field insensible".

To end on, I am sure we are all aware of the perennial debate as to whether the summers of our youth actually were better or not, and I couldn't help but be struck by the consequent irony of this following remark made over a century ago:

Wrexham Advertiser 14th July, 1883 – There is a prospect this year of one of those good old fashioned summers – something more than the three hot days and a thunderstorm which have been our melancholy experience for so many years past.

Some things never change!

THE AVAILABILITY OF WATER

To understand the relationship between the populace and its surrounding industries, we could do no better than to examine the question of the availability of water supplies to the largely populated areas which grew up around the brickworks and collieries. The brick industry in particular relied for its very existence on water, and every large works did its best to ensure a plentiful supply. But as the growth of wealthy industries transformed the landscape to suit its own needs, the water which was once easily available to all became almost a luxury for the inhabitants of the towns now surrounded by factories:

Wrexham Advertiser 25th July, 1868 – You have helped us in the Rhos out of many difficulties, and I am selfish enough to ask you to assist us to get plenty of good water. At present we are very short, the whole of the stream from the Vrondeg, which used to come to the south end of the town and through the Pant and supply us, is and has been for some time wholly impounded, and we that used with our forefathers to have plenty to use, have now to go without or pay for it. Time was when pits had plenty of water for their own use, but now we see a change. The Rhos seems drained by coal workings and now the water is conducted by pipes to the engines, and from us. If we try to help ourselves, we must go on trespass and run the risk of prosecution.

Before the coal and clay industry either diverted or destroyed the purity of underground water courses, from which most of the districts ' wells received their supply, the farming communities of earlier times had little to fear from industrial interference, but once the new industries had gained their formidable foothold, the sources of clean water fast became scarce, and it would serve us well to understand just what severities the people of the industrial districts had to endure in their quest for clean water. The following two reports are typical of many such found throughout the 1860s and 70s:

Wrexham Advertiser 23rd May & 1st August, 1874 – Being desirous to see for myself what is the actual state of affairs, I visited the neighbourhood of Prenbrigog and Buckley Square. Before arriving from Mold I had to pass through a populous village named Mynydd Isa, and in which the houses are built with some little regard for order. In going through I saw three women with tins of water on their head, and being curious to know where they got it from, I stopped until they came up. They told me that they had to go a quarter of a mile for it to a well situated in a dingle, and most difficult of access. The water they told me was excellent and they only used it for drinking and culinary purposes, there being a pool near which was the receptacle of surface water and of water pumped out of a small coal pit close by. Prenbrigog commands one of the finest views in Flintshire, but it has a natural effect in its deficiency of water, and there is only one well for the whole neighbourhood, and that on Wednesday was dry. The well in question is situated on the Mynydd Isa side, and the gutter bringing the refuse such as soapsuds, passes it, and I have no hesitation in saying that the well is polluted and rendered dangerous by this drain. On Wednesday the liquid manure coming from the houses had dried before reaching the well, but about halfway between it and the houses there was an accumulation of green half liquid matter three or four inches deep and two or three foot wide. After a shower of rain this would be washed right into the well. I called at one of these houses and I was told that if they wanted any water out of the well they must get up very early in the morning. There was a draw well near the Wellington about 400 yards further on, but the water was not good, and to get good water when their own well was dry, they had to go to Smith's Farm. "How far is that?" asked I. "Well, it's a good quarter hours walk there and back" was the reply. There are about 150 houses containing at least 700 inhabitants depending on that well alone. Below, there was a cart coming up from Smith's well loaded with water, and a lot of women were looking on, one of them crying out "Oh dear, look at that, Smith's well will be dry again!" Buckley at the present moment is far behind any place within 100 miles distance in respect to water supply, and almost any other sanitary arrangements. Why, it is a mere nothing, and will surprise the uninitiated how things are managed in

Buckley. There are one or two small springs where the poor women and children are waiting hours together and ladling it up in saucers as it springs, and in scores of cases after waiting four to six hours, return home without.

Wrexham Advertiser 30th November, 1872 – Visit by the Inspector of Nuisances to Brymbo. Many of the inhabitants have to travel a long way to certain wells for their water supply. I also saw water taken by some of the inhabitants for culinary and domestic purposes from the common outlet of all the filth of the district. I have inspected 403 houses inhabited by 1,580 persons. Out of the above number I have to report that ten houses are totally unfit for human habitation, and I further have to report that 23 privies discharged their excrement into the streams from which water is obtained.

In light of the above, many families resorted to drinking water which forever carried the threat of being contaminated, a factor which was directly contributory to the cause of so much of the sickness witnessed in the second half of the 19th century. All the industrial towns suffered this problem. In 1863 one fifth of all deaths in Rhos were attributed to the diseases caused by bad sanitation, such as scarlet fever, typhus and dysentery, and a number of families were known in that year to have fled the town in fear of their lives. Indeed, any hot summer regularly brought with it the fear of yet another outbreak of plague. The absence of proper sewers, drains, and the water needed to flush away the accumulated filth of cesspools was a problem not only confined to the crowded towns of Buckley and Rhos alone – it was universal throughout the entire country.

There were two alternatives to risking collecting polluted water supplies. The first was to collect water from the brickworks clayholes, which more often than not would have contained large pools of accumulated rainwater. The second option was not always available, and that was to have been lucky enough to live in a town supplied with water pumps, paid for through the rates. There was also the limited option of being directly connected to the supplies provided by the newly burgeoning Water Companies, but for most workmen's houses to have been supplied by what mains water pipes existed would have been unheard of – that was an expensive luxury reserved for the wealthier middle classes. The water companies began to emerge around the 1860s, and received their supplies from catchment tanks, and later from large reservoirs, situated in the upland hills. The Mold Waterworks Company was one of the first to be established in our district, but the early operations of this company left a lot to be desired. In 1859 the water in its catchment tank was reported to be covered in green vegetation, no filtration was used, and live grubs were seen to emerge from household taps. These early water companies might also prove partial as to whom they supplied – some of their most valued subscribers were many of the local industries, desirous of ensuring a constant and regular supply, and being much more able to pay for it. The Cefn Parish Council noted that during the earlier years of the Cefn, Acrefair & Rhosymedre Water Co all the supply to their domestic customers would be cut off between 9 am to 5 pm on the days when the New British Iron Co needed to fill their capacious water reservoir.

If water for cooking and drinking was in short supply, that needed for bathing purposes could never have been realised in a working man's home, leading those needing a wash to seek other alternatives:

Wrexham Advertiser 7th August, 1875 – Sir, an annual visitor in your last impression complains of the practice of bathing in the Alyn by the youths of Mold. No doubt there is indecency in some cases, but in a town where there are no public baths, it is really very hard to deprive the youngsters of the luxury of a fresh clean bath. May I suggest that a certain length of the river at certain hours be set apart for bathing.

Wrexham Advertiser September 1908 – Mr Robert Parry, brickworks manager, summoned nine boys for bathing in the Rhos Works reservoir. The reservoir supplied water to some cottages and was also used by the workmen employed at Mr J C Edwards' works for drinking purposes. The boys had been repeatedly warned and notices had been put up. There was fencing around the reservoir, but it had been pulled down. The practice might result in very serious consequences to the workmen. Sergeant Edwards said that a piece of soap was found in the water, and each defendant was fined six shillings and sixpence.

The instances of clayhole bathing were many and universal throughout the district, and led to the occasional accidental drownings; the sides of most claypools having been deceptively steep and slippery. The lack of domestic bathrooms eventually gave rise to the establishment of public bath houses, but these were mostly absent from our own districts until well into the 20th century. Public toilets were also sadly lacking. As late as in 1911, the authorities reported that within the heavily populated stretch from Sandycroft through Queensferry, Shotton and Flint there was not one public toilet. "Shop doors and every nook and corner from one end of the district to the other reek with affluvia" complained the Flintshire News, and this public health menace was rife throughout Flintshire and Denbighshire as a whole. For the average Victorian the only receptacle for any toilet waste was the local cesspit, and the following report from the Ruabon district strongly hints that for those folk who had not the privacy of a walled backyard, the street itself ended up serving as a lavatory:

Wrexham Advertiser 20th July, 1860 – We have frequently witnessed and have repeatedly conversed with those who have had their olfactory, as well as their other organs , offended by the hideous and odoriferous sights which present themselves at every turn in this densely populated locality. The liquid refuse of every house is left to find its own level, while other nuisances of a more repulsive character are deposited on the highways and byways; no one objecting or interfering any more than they would in the backwoods of America. The public roads are everywhere used for private purposes, and all those who are without a backyard, and they are not a few, do not scruple to appropriate to various domestic purposes the thoroughfare opposite their front door.

Although that report was from as early as 1860, conditions in the slums changed but little for the next twenty years or so.

Some of the more outlying districts had to contend with water shortages for a considerable number of years. Leeswood was particularly badly off, due most likely to the interference to well supplies caused by the intensive mining of the district, and perhaps it was for this reason that Mr Darbyshire, the proprietor of the Coed Talon Colliery, employed a man during the summer months of the 1890s to do nothing else but cart water from his colliery to the Leeswood village at no charge to the inhabitants. Perhaps this was as well – Leeswood Parish Council in 1895 reported that the only wells in the village were, when full, also being used to drown unwanted cats and dogs! And the scarcity of readily available water was not exclusively a Victorian phenomenon. Bangor is y Coed was without mains water until 1952, and until 1956 the village of Padeswood received its only clean water in barrels delivered on the train from Mold. By as late as 1964 government statistics showed that amongst the households in Flintshire, 10,000 had no plumbed baths, 6,000 had no inside toilets, 8,000 had no hot water systems and 2,000 still had no mains water at all.

As a footnote to this subject, we should not forget the importance which beer played in the Victorian workplace. With the absence of readily available clean water in the heavily industrialised areas, beers had naturally become the drink of necessity, as work down the pits, in the bricksheds, and in the kiln yards was gruelling and hot:

Wrexham Advertiser 1st August, 1874 – Buckley is said to be a drunken place. This under the circumstances cannot be surprised at. What are men to do who work in the hot kilns and sheds? Thirst must be assuaged and beer or porter is the most easily obtained. These drinks are quickly swallowed and again on their part create a great thirst. I have often heard it said that in Buckley there is more beer than water, which I am sorry to say is the case, as there are about 28 beer houses, but very few spring wells.

The brewing companies recognised the need for their products as much as their customers required the fluid to keep them going, and the brewers accordingly produced a wide range of beers to accommodate every sector of society, as this 1874 advertisement for the Wrexham Brewery Co shows:

"Household Pale Ale for family use. This is a delicious beer very carefully brewed for the consumption of private families. One shilling per gallon.

The celebrated strong ale "The Royal Wrexham". This pale rich flavoured malty ale is especially celebrated for its nourishing qualities. 54 gallons for £6.

Cheaper beers can be obtained for farm purposes etc".

The presence of industry was in many instances the main reason why many public houses were established where they were, hence such names as the The Railway, Rollers Arms, Miners Arms etc etc. The old Derwen Inn on the Wrexham Road out of Mold once used to be an isolated public house surrounded by fields (hence its name, which means The Oak) but it was still within easy reach of the nearby Broncoed and Oak Pits collieries. It's interesting that when Patrick Kinnair was applying for the renewal of the Derwen's licence in 1868, his primary justification for its continuance was that he was the nearest public house to the collieries, and that they had previously needed to purchase brandy from him in cases of medical emergencies.

Beer may have had its practical uses, but to the brickworks proprietors its usage could also represent a costly burden. In as early as 1841 a survey was made at an English brickworks, where it was noted that the highest total make of bricks turned out by a teetotal maker was 890,000, whereas the best total which could be achieved by a man refreshing himself with ale was only 830,000. And on the subject of "boozy burners", a Glasgow proprietor complained "I have had tons of good coal wasted and thousands of bricks spoilt by men who have spent a lifetime at the kiln, but who get awfully thirsty at times". But of course, the brewers, as they always have, saw things differently, as witnessed by this 1928 advertisement aimed at farm owners and promoting the apparent benefits of Whitchurch Ales:

"He's human – like all of us – been at it since early morn – turning and tossing the hay, raking or loading – and it's a scorching day! A good man's worth encouragement. See his eyes sparkle when there's a drink on the job. Notice how much better the work gets done. Here are beverages which bring a smile to dry and drooping lips, fresh vigour to aching arms and greater progress towards the last load".

Pay and Employment Conditions

THE CONTRACT SYSTEM

Throughout the Victorian period the economy of the country was forever swaying between prosperity and slump; the inevitable result of industry being glutted by too many producers within the same manufacturing sector. This frequently required the Masters (employers) having to impose a fluctuating scale of workers' pay to offset any losses they realised on reducing the competitive market price of their goods; a state of affairs which was universal throughout the entire manufacturing sector. This trend also led to workmen being employed on a renewable contract basis, as an employer never knew when he might find it necessary to downsize his workforce.

The method of employing brickyard workers was structured on a kind of tiered system, and the managers of the larger works, with some very few exceptions, never knew exactly who was working for them at any one time. They employed supervisors whose duty it was to take on the required number of men , and the workers themselves would then be responsible for employing whatever assistants they themselves would require. This is not to imply that skilled brickmen would not work at a particular brickworks for any good length of time – indeed, skilled men were to be valued, and could hold onto their positions for years on end. However, the vast army of general labourers which populated many industrial sites went where the work presented itself and stayed for as long as it lasted. We can see a good illustration of this in the following selections from the diary of Buckley worker Joseph Ellis, writing in the year 1890, during which time he worked at four different factories in six months, as well as tending his own farm field during his off days:

27th March, 1890 – Unloaded some timber at Aston Hall before breakfast and then went to Aston to the bricks.

2nd April… At Ewloe siding before breakfast. Loaded a truck of bricks at Aston.

20th August… Filled and emptied a wagon of ashes. Then made a hole and bricked it for the boilers at Aston Hall.

2nd December… Emptied some sand in engine shed. Loaded wagon of timbers and old bricks at brickworks.

29th December… Not working. Went to Hawarden to see opening of fountain. Band and boy soldiers was there.

13th January, 1891. On the bank emptying clay and loaded a wagon of cannel. Got the sack because I would not work half a day at night.

26th January… Started to work at Elm Colliery filling coal.

13th March… Went to New Mount to see them grinding. Two brickmakers started there. I cleaned and repaired camshaft of lathe.

20th March… Cleaning turnips and digging in garden. Went to Sandycroft Brickworks, got work to start on Monday.

23rd March… Started to work at Sandycroft mucking about cutting a trench through ashes to put fire out at face of colliery chimney.

24th March… Working at same place till about 10 o'clock, then three of us drawed a kiln of brick.

30th March… Wheeling to the kilns before breakfast, then wheeled ashes out from boilers, then working in trench.

6th May… Shifting sawmill from brickyard mortar mill to engine that pulls wagons up. Levelled countershaft and bench, two of us. Me and Watkin had two nice little pigs from Mold for eleven shillings a piece.

29th May… Emptied a wagon of slack, two of us. Then carrying rails on the bank and laying road down to clayhole, making joints on engine that pulls up getting wagons in and out.

22nd July… Repairing road at bottom length of siding, helping to cut some timber. At kilns drawing all afternoon. Weeding potatoes in field.

27th July… Cut hole 5 ft 6 inches deep between rails at top of siding for a frame for pulley before breakfast. Cleaning mouths of two kilns. Filling slack out of wagon. Turning some hay in field.

11th August… Wheeling ashes out from brickwork boilers. Getting wagons in and out of clayhole and pulling them up with engine. Greasing hauling rope.

All the men of the brickworks were paid on the principle of piecework, getting paid so much for each unit of product, be it per ton of clay or thousand of bricks made, carted or burnt, and they would usually enter into a verbal contract with the supervisor over the terms. The employee would then take on his own assistants, usually boys, and pay them directly from his own money; the boys never dealing with the company itself. From a contemporary report, the system as worked at Buckley's Davison's Works in 1882 was described thus: "He was engaged as a weekly workman, his wages regulated by the number of bricks he made at 3 shillings 1 1/2 pence per thousand; he to pay his own boy labour".

Likewise, the following is evidence spoken by Evan Jones who took on a contract to supervise the making of all the terracotta goods for Ruabon Brick & Terracotta Co in 1893. He said "I had no occasion to keep books as I received money from the company and took it down and paid the men. I had about five per cent of the money for myself. I had to run certain risks for this. If anything was broken by the men, I had the expense of replacing it, and if anything was wrongly made, I had the expense of putting it right".

This responsibility of accounting for their own affairs whilst working under the restrictions of an immovable contract price could cause grave problems if a batch of product had to be scrapped. This next account was the result of such a problem, caused when the brickburner Joseph Wyatt found his bricks under complaint from the contracting company Monk & Newell of Ruabon. His grievance was that he had been supplied a poor batch of clay by Thomas Edwards, the foreman of the clay getters, and their subsequent argument landed them in court:

Wrexham Advertiser 20th April, 1901 – Wyatt was charged by Edwards with assaulting him on 14th March and divers other dates. There had been complaints about the quality of work turned out by Wyatt. Edwards had to superintend the getting of the clay and Wyatt had attributed the bad quality of the bricks to the poor nature of the clay. Edwards in accordance with instructions went to see the kiln the defendant was then drawing. Wyatt accused him of sending him rubbish and called him a liar twice. He also put his fist into his face and threatened to smash it. Edwards stepped back and Wyatt jumped down from an elevation on which he had been standing and said "We'll go into the road". He got hold of Edwards by the collar and afterwards by the arm and endeavoured to get him into the road; his son being on the other side threatening to knock his head off.

So we see that the brickmen were entirely responsible for their own affairs, and this was true whether they worked at the small country yards or the larger brickworks – a fact of working life borne out in this local commentary made in 1860, when the few brickworks which existed at that time were mostly still but small:

"Is it not a fact that they employ men and pay them by task or piecework. Not a ton of iron is made or a ton of coal raised except on this principle. In the clay works or potteries you will find all the men so arranged that they work to their own benefit on the principle of piecework. And more, that it is supervised, for there is not an ironmaster, coal owner, pot or brick manufacturer but what employs his Paid Surveyor to look after his piecework men".

This contract system died out between the two world wars, as the rapidly growing union movement managed to negotiate more secure employment conditions, but by a strange twist of fate, we find today that some sectors of industry are moving back to short term and part time employment.

ABSENTEEISM

It was regarded in Victorian days as a serious offence for a workman to absent himself from his work or to leave entirely at a moment's notice, as this would have caused a break in the chain of the manufacturing process which could effect the working output of others who relied on him. If for instance a clay getter failed to report for work this would have reduced the amount of clay reaching the machine operators, which in turn would have decreased their production capacity and inevitably their pay. But absenteeism inevitably became more widespread as the pace of industry became ever more gruelling, and the ironworks and especially the collieries suffered similarly. In 1898 Mr E S Clarke, the proprietor of the Llay Hall Works, stated that up to a quarter of his colliers absented themselves for one or two days a week, and in an industry where work was arduous and uncomfortable, it must have been tempting for the men to take the odd day off. The law however was structured to come down hard on absentees, and in an effort to deter others from doing likewise the magistrates could impose heavy sentences, which they frequently did. For instance, in 1866 when an employee of the New British Iron Co left the company's employ only four days after giving in his statutory 28 days' notice, he was taken before the local magistrates and received a 14 days' jail sentence, and reports of such harsh sentences were very commonplace around this period.

Another way for a company to deter employees from not working their full notice was to threaten the withholding of any pay owed if they left early, and a similar practice in the earlier decades of the 19th century was to purposefully withhold a small percentage of a workman's regular wages, which would be given back when his contract term had been fulfilled. This percentage was referred to as "pence money", and its retention was a way, to all intents and purposes, of blackmailing a worker into not leaving his employment before completion of his job contract. This practice was common in England, and although I have not found actual evidence of it being used in North Wales, it's more than likely that it was.

Harsh court sentences were certainly not uncommon throughout the 19th century, but despite the resolve of both management and magistrates to crush absenteeism with heavy fines and jail sentences, they seemed not to have had much effect. By 1906 Hancocks Co were so greatly troubled by men not turning up for work that the company threatened the complete closure of the brickworks in an effort to persuade the men to be more diligent in their responsibilities. How well they succeeded is not recorded.

THE TRUCK SYSTEM

"The Truck System goes on at Rhos or the neighbourhood. A very small portion of the wages

due to the operatives is paid in money. They receive tickets which they must take to the shop. The price of provisions in these shops is much higher than in Wrexham. Ten pence is paid for bacon instead of eight pence and 4 lb of flour are sold for one shilling when 6 lb are sold for the

A one penny workers payment token issued by the Flint Lead Works in 1813. The works lay close to the quayside at Flint and the masts on the right may be those of a ship at dock. Photo: National Libraries and Museums of Wales.

same sum within five miles. The magistrates have offered to put down the practice, but the workmen will not come forward with evidence knowing that if they were to do so they would lose their employment".

This system was endemic throughout the first half of the 19th century and efforts to abolish it were forever being attempted by philanthropic social reformers all over the British Isles. The above text was part of the evidence given by a Wrexham shopkeeper to the Government Commissioners in 1847 and highlights the injustices of the system. The system operated by employers paying their workmen, either wholly or in the most part, with tokens or tickets which could be exchanged for goods in shops and alehouses owned by the companies themselves. This meant that a workman had no means of buying goods at cheaper prices elsewhere, and in effect it resulted, as we see above, in the workmen being literally robbed of the spending power of their wages. The company "truck shops" or "tommy shops" were highly organised affairs, with meat, dairy produce and vegetables being supplied from the company's own farms and market gardens.

Of course, I am not implying that *all* manufacturing industry operated this system, and I have found no direct evidence of any independent brick companies having paid wages in anything other than legal tender, but some of the larger collieries and ironworks of our district definitely did, and the brickmen who worked for them would have been similarly affected. The greatest exponent of this system in N E Wales was probably the New British Iron Co at Acrefair – a massive ironworks complex which also controlled the Green Pits Colliery at Ruabon.

This desire of a company to benefit from monopolising the spending power of money was quite a widespread phenomenon. Over at Flint the lead works once minted its own pennies, locally called Pris y Fflint which "passed in these parts regular as the current coin of the realm" throughout early Victorian days. You may know that the early banks used to issue their own banknotes, but what is less commonly known is that some local shops also did the same, ensuring that a purchaser who used that shop would have to return there in order to spend the money they received as change. An example of such money was discovered in 1868 during excavation work in Mold High Street, when six copper coins were unearthed bearing the stamping "Edward Williams – Grocer in Movld".

The Anti-Truck Association was the principal body which campaigned to abolish the injustices of this system of wage payment, and in 1850 they reported that amongst the collieries of the Ruabon area only one quarter of the workmen's wages were being paid in legal coinage. Parliament eventually acted to smash the system by law, and the Coinage Act of April 1870 made it illegal to transact any contract in anything other than legal government tender, but before this Act was passed, the Truck System had already begun to die out here and there, as this next report witnessed. It records the triumph of the Rhos colliers who had won their wage battle through the courts, led by their chief campaigner Mr Davies:

Wrexham Advertiser 17th April, 1869 – The Truck Case. The first news of the result of the case arrived here about 6 o'clock pm, and was by no means credited. About half past six confirmatory intelligence was received and soon spread like wild fire. About 7 o'clock the first load of witnesses for the defence arrived with ribbons and colours flying, and from this hour to 9 o'clock the streets and public houses were thronged with people. Ale was given away at many places, and persons generally accounted very sober, indulged in some cases rather freely. As the defendants kept arriving they were heartily welcomed and when Mr Davies arrived, his vehicle was stopped at the end of the village, his horse taken out, and the trap drawn by men up and through the Rhos.

WEEKLY PAY

With the truck system abolished, the next grievance to burden the workers was the length of time between wage payments. For the *day workers* – the general labourers taken on at a daily rate – this was of no concern, but for the workers employed on a regular full time basis, they found the usual system of monthly paydays difficult to budget.

All the major collieries, brickworks and ironworks paid monthly wages, sometimes allowing a small fortnightly "subsistence" payment to help ease their workers' intermediate financial burdens. The following anonymous plea sent to the Wrexham Advertiser of 5th February, 1876 was published to explain the working man's predicament of constantly living with monthly debts:

"Allow me to call the attention of my fellow workmen to the necessity of having our wages paid weekly as I am sure we should be benefited by it very much. We could spend our money by buying our goods at the cheapest places, and I feel quite confident that the tradesmen would reduce the price of their goods so as to get ready money which would pay them much better than giving such long and heavy credit. I should like the workmen of the New British Iron Co to try and get their wages paid weekly, as I am given to understand that the Plaskynaston Co intend paying their men's wages weekly. I also hope that weekly payments will be carried out at the brickworks, oil works, iron works and all the other collieries".

As time dragged on, very little was done to actually help improve the situation, but some of the masters eventually saw reason; Mr Bowers of the Penbedw Brickworks instigating weekly payments in June 1889. "It gives you greater independence and a chance to pay for your goods as you obtain them" he explained to his men. The majority of the masters, however, continued to hold out. On Monday 6th July, 1891 the North Wales Coalowners Association met with delegates from the workforces at the Queen's Hotel in Chester to thrash out the problem; the masters being represented principally by Mr Dennis of Hafod Colliery and Brickworks and Mr E S Clarke of the Llay Hall Colliery and Brickworks, but finding themselves unable to accede to the men's requests, they issued the following statement:

"We wish to point out that when the work is contract work, weekly pays are not the rule even in the trades you mention, while in metallifferous mines, iron and steel works, slate quarries and brickworks in this district, weekly pays do not obtain. In every case it would cause considerable extra expense, and in the face of a lessening demand for coal and falling prices, we are naturally anxious to avoid any additional cost. We should be very glad to see the credit system done away with, but we believe that weekly pays would not have this happy result".

But the tides of change were gathering pace. By November 1891 the Brynkinallt Colliery at Chirk began paying weekly, and by March the following year the North Wales Miners Federation had successfully negotiated universal weekly payments across the whole of the district's collieries, and as many of the colliery companies also operated a significant number of the area's brickworks, it wasn't long before the independently owned brickworks followed suit.

As to the matter of paid holidays, this would have been a laughable concept during the 19th century. Holidays in that era were confined to a few days each year, and were usually in the form of day trips organised by the companies themselves. In a very few cases some of the works proprietors gave a small sum of spending money to each employee, but this was rare, and it was not until the 20th century that holiday periods were extended, but they were still taken at the expense of the workers. On 25th June, 1938 the Wrexham Leader could announce that "We are officially informed that the 250 employees of the Hafod Brickworks are to receive holidays with pay this summer", and a week later they followed up with the information that the Llay Hall Brickworks "have decided to grant their workmen a week's holiday with pay". Roberts & Maginnis Brickworks followed suit in August, but these allowances were still purely at the discretion of the employers, and it was not until after World War Two that the government made it a legal requirement for employers to give holidays with pay.

PAY RATES
As I explained at the start of the chapter, the scale of pay in the brickworks and collieries was constantly in a state of flux, leading to a continuous battle between the men and the companies as to by how much each could benefit. "The question for us to consider is not how much we ought to get, but how much we can get" explained a Mold miner in 1871.

The highest paid men in a brickworks were probably the brickmoulders. In 1929 such a man at

Pant Works earned a rate of up to three shillings and eleven pence per thousand bricks, and with a man expecting to produce up to 4,000 machine made bricks per day, that represented a weekly wage of £4 -12-0 maximum. In 1946 the average Hafod brickworker earned about the same, with the moulders getting an extra five shillings. Back in 1875 a hand brickmoulder at Brookhill Works in Buckley was expected to easily turn out 1,500 bricks in an eight hour day, which represented a daily wage of six shillings, out of which he had to pay a total of one shilling and six pence to his boys. Compared to him a works carpenter or smith was earning around 24 shillings per week, an engine man 23 shillings, and a general labourer 17 shillings.

But with pay rates regularly fluctuating by 5, 10 or even 20 per cent there was never a secured guaranteed income with which to budget a family's expenses. In the Buckley district in particular, this financial insecurity led to frequent industrial unrest, although there seem to have been very few strikes reported in the press for the Denbighshire brickworks during the torrid days of Victoria's reign. The brickworkers of Buckley however had one distinct difference within the structure of their brickworks in the form of the Buckley Firebrick Manufacturers Association; a society of works proprietors, which was in effect a cartel of all the major Buckley manufacturers, who resolved at their first meeting in May 1870 "that the firms form themselves into an Association for the purpose of fixing prices and other matters connected with the trade". Let's examine what implications this had amongst the workers:

If a brick company in any of the other regions decided to impose reductions in the rates of pay, what could the workers do? They had one of two options – either to enter into discussions with the management, or to go on strike. But if they did strike, they would have found themselves fighting a lone battle, as there was effectively no strong Brickmakers Union to back them up, and in time, poverty and desperation would have overcome them. In Buckley however, the Manufacturers' Association, formed for the purpose of preventing a disadvantageous competitiveness between the various local companies, took decisions which were mandatory throughout their membership. When they decided to reduce pay, the move was implemented right throughout every major Buckley works, which had the effect of giving every Buckley brickworker a common cause for grievance. In effect, the Association had unwittingly created a rod for their own backs, and when the Buckley workers came out on strike, they could bring any number of the town's brickworks to a standstill – giving themselves a solid position from which to bargain, and causing greater losses to the companies themselves. We will look at the social effects of strike action later on.

Now that we have seen something of the brickyard worker's conditions, what was it like for their comrades in the offices?

The following inclusion is a contract of employment made between the clerk Edwin Peers and Davison's Co of Buckley in June 1880. We can see how even these white collar workers were employed on a periodical contract basis, but Edwin did receive some very nice perks which would have compensated him for earning what was less than a skilled brickmoulder, although he still got much more than most of the manual workers, and the free rates and fuel which he received would themselves have been worth a small fortune. Notice also how obsessive the company was in protecting its business interests:

1– The said Edwin Peers will well, truly, faithfully and diligently serve the said principals for the term of one year, and thenceforward from year to year in the capacity of clerk and book keeper.

2– He will devote the whole of his time, will and energies to the said business and readily, cheerfully and faithfully do and perform the careful commands of the said principals, and will be civil and obliging to their customers, and will do his utmost to promote the interests of the said business and to retain and improve the connections and custom thereof, and will keep any secrets of the principals which shall come to his knowledge.

3– He will not absent himself from their service.

4– Not within 10 years after termination of engagement in any capacity... be concerned in trade of a Buckley firebrick and tile manufacturer, nor elicit their custom for others.

5– For breach pay £500, without the principals losing right to any one above agreement.

6– They will pay Edwin Peers a salary of £78 per annum in monthly payments. And in consideration of the said Edwin Peers residing in the cottage situated on the works at Ewloe Barn, they agree to give him the use of some land attached for a garden, rent free, and will keep it in good repair and pay all rates and taxes in connection with it, and provide coal free.

7– Employment may be terminated one month from the day made in writing.

In 1872 William Arthur Davison, the nephew of the work's owner, was taken on as the manager, and he would most certainly also have had free lodgings on top of his £100 annual salary, which after five years was increased to £300 plus commission. It's not surprising that he held onto his position until 1894!

Rates of pay in the brickyards had always fallen short of those paid in the sister industry of coal mining, and this factor eventually had quite devastating results on the brick industry. It was the 1940s and 50s which really highlighted the brickyards plight over pay conditions, and this post war observation as to why the brick companies found difficulty in recruiting the necessary workforce was typical of the mood of the day within the brickyards:

Wrexham Leader 11th January, 1946 – Sir, As a branch secretary of the T & G W U at the Hafod Brick & Tile Works I may say that Alderman Cross hit the nail on the head. Men returning from military service will not go back to the brickyards. I have in front of me the wages agreement during the war for the clay industry, and all that time we were in government work, government were paying anything from £7 to £8 per week. This was the brickmaker's wage to the end of 1944. That is the bottleneck – not labour and fuel.

Since government had scrapped the higher wartime pay rates which they had imposed upon the clay industry to ensure production, the basic rate of pay had slipped to one shilling and three pence per hour plus a post war bonus of two and a quarter pence, which represented around £4-7-0 basic pay, which I have calculated as based on a six-day week of 10 hours per day – a far cry from the rates received during wartime. Even bricklayers in the building sector were earning more than skilled brickmakers, and reluctance to take brickyard work after the war was understandably strong. In response to this problem, the government, becoming aware of the need to push forward with rebuilding programmes, assisted the industry by enforcing a £6-1-5 weekly wage in May 1946. It didn't seem to have much of a result!

In the 1950s the employment and career services in Buckley were reporting that only one to two per cent of school leavers showed any interest in brickyard jobs, and desperate for labour the brick companies responded by importing brickworkers from abroad, particularly from Ireland and Italy. Italian prisoners of war had already been working in the Buckley yards during the war, and by the end of 1951 there were 72 foreigners working in the Buckley brickworks. In 1957 Castle Works made 49 workers redundant, and of those, 27 were Italian and 2 Polish, and by July 1961 the diarist George Lewis was recording that around 50 of Buckley's brickworkers were Italians. This high level of foreign labour spurred the local T & G W U into calling for a halt to the continued importation of foreign labour on the grounds that it increased unemployment amongst the indigenous Buckley community, but with so much inherent local disillusionment at the prospect of becoming brickmen, the union's efforts inevitably fell on stony ground.

Over in Denbighshire the brickyards had similar post war problems, but in their case it came mainly from the new hi-tech industries which were flooding into the district. Wrexham itself was establishing a massive new industrial estate, and the huge factories being built were offering wage rates which the brickyards could never compete with. Garth Brickworks continually ran advertisements for all sectors of brickyard work from January to June 1947 and again from August to December, which suggests their great difficulty in attracting new workers, and their old manager Mr Lacey told me that it was entirely due to the much more attractive terms offered by the newer, cleaner and better paid industries.

CHILDREN IN THE BRICKYARDS

"There are 2,825 brickyards in England, but only

one hundred of these are brought under legislative supervision. Why? Because the law provides that only those yards where fifty persons or more are employed come within its meaning. The remaining 2,725 are free therefore to riot in child labour, and that they do to an alarming extent. It appears from the statistics, carefully collected, that there are employed nearly 30,000 children ranging from the ages of 3, 4 and 5, though this seems incredible. So far as the smallest are concerned, we might reasonably ask what can such little dots of workers do? Here they are placed in the very slough of ignorance and despond, the light of life and hope shut out from those condemned to this unnatural toil that is forced upon them by kicks, cuffs, oaths and curses of the most brutal and revolting kind, which stamps the very look of childhood from their faces. The old-men monkey like faces, the shrunken, shivering, cowering, scared looks of many of the children are things not to be imagined. I myself have seen over and over, the black eye, the unhealed sore, the bruised body in little, very little children, that proclaim sorrowfully their experience, to be filled up by cruelty, murderous violence, impetuous passion and punishment within not an inch, but a hair-breadth of life. I hesitate not to say that the Society for the Protection of the Lower Animals would not allow a tithe of the cruelty perpetrated on the brickyard children to be done to the overworked horse, donkey and the like. These children, even the youngest of them, are kept at work in the yards from eight to ten hours a day, and often from twelve to fourteen hours. Without going into minute details it may be broadly stated that the children, of both sexes be it remembered, who carry the bricks from the moulders, have to traverse a distance of about seven yards 2,000 times per day, backwards and forwards, making a total distance over 14 miles. The brick and the mould together weigh 14 lbs and the empty mould would be 4 lb, which gives 28,000 lbs to be carried one way, and 8,000 lbs the other. Need it be a matter of surprise that placed in the midst of foul talk, of loud blaspheming, of ribald jesting, of depraved morality, of debased passions, of course brutality, of loathsome drunkenness, these children grow up otherwise than those in whose midst they live?"

That account was written in 1871 by George Smith, the manager of the Coalville Brickworks in Leicester, and although we have no reason to question the author's sincerity, I seriously doubt, as did our local press, that atrocities on such a level ever occurred in our district. I have never come across children as young as five years old working in a North Wales brickworks, although the hours worked and the rigours of their tasks certainly tally with local accounts. There are records for instance of 12 year old Sarah Griffiths, who worked in the Buckley district in 1843, toiling from 6 am to 9 pm for four shillings a week, carrying up to six bricks at a time despite her swollen legs and stunted growth; rheumatism being not uncommon amongst these Victorian children.

From the census records of the Ruabon district we find examples of how young our brickyard children actually were.

In 1851 we find such as John Jones and Jonathan Williams, both 10 years old, and 11 year old William Williams. In 1861 Daniel Davies and John Eyton were both 8 years old, and in 1871 we find 9 year old Price Richards; all children working in the brickworks, and these amongst the youngest of many such examples.

Before machinery took over many of the more arduous tasks, the earlier outdoor Summer Yards were scenes of fervent physical activity, and these next reminiscences, again of an English yard, shows what work was like for young children in the 1850s. In this case however, I believe the conditions described to be probably much as we would have seen around Wales:

"I was quite young, scarcely out of petticoats, and had seen only seven summers when I was called to work. In those times, ten and a half hours for five days in the week and six hours on Saturday did not constitute the brickmaker's working week. I shall never forget my first experiences of real work. It was a morning in June that I was awakened early and shouldered by my father a distance of one and a half miles to the yard. There were I believe twelve moulders working in the yard, and it was the custom of the proprietor to give a prize at the end of the season to the man who had performed the feat of making the largest number of bricks. My father did not commence work on this day until 6am, although others had been at it much earlier. My allotted task was to page off, which was not such an agreeable task as I had anticipated. Pug mills were not in general use – the tempering of the clay was mostly done by spade and treading with the naked feet. I had not been at work long before I began to feel the burden of my task. My back ached dreadfully and long before breakfast I was tired and exhausted. Six hundred bricks had been made during the first two hours, so that I had lifted during this time a weight equivalent to two tons. Brickmakers, generally, had no sympathy for boys or girls. They were treated very unkindly – somewhat after the manner I have seen donkeys used. The competition going on between the moulders for the prize caused some jealousy, and it was not unusual to find moulders at 4 am. One moulder, I recollect, had all his own gang in the persons of his wife and children – this gave him a decided advantage over the moulders dependent upon outsiders, as he could demand the services of his own folk at any hour. After a few seasons I was considered capable to pug up and was promoted to the clay pit. We had to cut the clay down in sufficient size for a brick. The dabs were required to be carried and delivered on to the moulder's table without showing a finger print, and woe to the carrier who cut the dabs too big or too small, and I remember I hardly ever escaped the usual mode of punishment. I learned to be a good pug boy and revelled in the work, as with bare feet of course, shoes were not worn either by boys or girls. I could tread down my clay and roll out 2500 to 3000 bricks a day; carrying two dabs a time, one in each hand, and often an additional one on my head".

The term "page off" was his local colloquialism for the more general term "bear off" – to remove the newly made bricks from the moulding table. He also mentioned families of brickmakers working together, and from our own local census records we know that it was not uncommon for boys to be found working with their fathers in exactly the same way.

He also mentioned the blistering pace at which the moulders worked, and I came across another example of this in the British Clayworker journal. Apparently it was the practice of some moulders, loathe to stop work and hold up production, to have their wives pop pieces of food into their mouths as they toiled. Did such things ever happen in North Wales, I wonder?

The employment of children was one of sheer necessity in the days when wages were relatively poor. Families were much bigger than they are today, and even a few more pence coming in made a significant difference to a household budget. Other industries also used child labour, especially the coalmines, and I include these two reports which may be of interest. For those who do not understand the term *banks*, these were the stacks of coal or spoil waste which were brought up from the pit:

Evidence given to the Government Commissioner of Enquiry 1849 –
There are a great number of girls and young women employed – not in the pits, but on the banks. Their employment is to carry coals on their heads to their own families, to remove obstructions from the mouth of the pits, to wind up materials from the bottom and in many cases to load coals. They acquire a taste for this employment at an early age and will often leave good situations in respectable families in order to return to their old occupations

Report on North Wales mining by H M Inspector of Mines 1900 –
There is a feeling abroad that twelve years old is rather early to send boys to work below ground. Personally I don't think they take much harm and they always seem very merry, though some of them are very little chaps. It makes a great difference to a workman's family where there are six or seven young children when the eldest begins to earn.

WORKER'S RIGHTS
The legally recognised rights of children and the working classes in general gradually crept into British law by dribs and drabs over the course of a century. The first rudimentary Factory Act was the Health and

Morals of Apprentices Act of 1802, which was gradually improved upon as a more widespread understanding of industrial conditions grew. In 1831 it became illegal to employ persons under 18 years old for longer than 12 hours per day; an Act which was extended to include women in 1844, although these rulings were intended primarily for the extensive textile industries.

The Workshop Regulations Act of 1869 significantly improved the lot of child labourers, but again it was restricted to a few industries only, and the first universally beneficial Act came into effect on 1st January, 1879. This was the Factories and Workshops Act, which now included protection for workers in quarries, mines, brickworks and other places using any mechanical means of power. No person under 16 years old could now be employed without a Certificate of Health from the District Certifying Factory Surgeon, and employers were required to report any injuries or cases of death to the Inspector of Factories, so that a proper investigation of working conditions could be instigated. Also, no boy under 14 years old could be employed in a brickworks or colliery unless he had passed a required level of school examination – a legislation intended to encourage literacy amongst the young and to restrict the employment of the very young . The Act also legislated for other aspects of working conditions, such as the number of hours worked without rest breaks, Sunday working for children, and other numerous issues, including restrictions as to the use of dangerous machinery:

Wrexham Advertiser 20th June, 1896 – The Sandycroft Brick & Tile Co were summoned under section 5 of the Factories and Workshops Act for neglecting to keep in an efficient manner and properly fenced and protected, the fly wheel and crank of an engine at their works. Mr Lewis, H M Inspector, stated that every part should be securely fenced and maintained in an efficient state. His colleague Mr Hilditch visited the works and found a fly wheel 15 ft in diameter totally unprotected. The works were visited in January and a similar state of things were found. The defendants were fined £2 and costs of 7s 6d.

Chester Chronicle 16th May 1903 – The Wepre

Hall Brick Co were summoned under the Act for employing young boys after hours. Mr Hilditch deposed to visiting the premises at 6:50pm and found work in full operation and four boys working there. The boys had started at 6 o'clock that morning and had been employed from 2 o'clock without a meal and they were apparently going on till 7pm. Mr Darbyshire said the boys were anxious to work a little overtime as it was near Easter. A fine of five shillings and costs in each case was imposed.

But the most beneficial legislation for the working man was surely the Workman's Compensation Act of 1st July, 1898. This allowed that in case of death from injury, a man's dependants could be entitled to compensation equal to his total previous three years earnings up to a limit of £300. If his employment with the company had not lasted three years, the sum was set at 156 times his average weekly wage. And should a worker be disabled by an accident which incapacitated him for longer than a fortnight, he would be entitled to a weekly compensation of up to half of his weekly wage, providing the sum awarded did not exceed £1 per week. Just as a point of interest – the first beneficiaries of this Act in the Wrexham district were the widows of two men killed at the Minera Lead Mines, both women receiving around £150 each.

UNION ACTIVITY

The Trades Union Act was passed in Parliament in 1871, which gave workers certain legal rights which had not been hitherto recognised. The Welsh brickmaking industry however, was seemingly slow in taking advantage of the new rights afforded them, unlike the colliers of the district, who took to unionism with great gusto, and the first unions to which some brickmen affiliated themselves were in fact mining unions. The first mass activity which seems to have galvanised the district occurred on 24th May 1873 when an army of 2,000 Buckley colliers and brickmen – mostly colliers I expect – marched to Mold in an attempt to enlist new membership amongst their neighbours. The first evidence I could find of a separate brickworkers union was recorded in the minutes of the Firebrick Manufacturers Association for 1881, when they reported that *"a sum of over £100 has been lying at the Mold Bank since the Buckley Brickmaker's Union was in vogue about three or four years ago. The trustees are making good use of it by paying it to the men who are stopped by the Davison and Hancock companies in consequence of refusing to accept a 10 per cent cut in their wages. They have now received four weeks pay at 10 shillings a week"*.

Those remarks seem to have implied that the union may have been formed circa 1877, and not much else on the union front seems to have occurred until the 1900s, when activity resurfaced in the Rhos district. On 12th July 1907 Mr Robert Jones, the North Wales Secretary of the Brickworkers and Labourers Union, addressed a large meeting at Rhos and stirred the brickmen into forming a local branch. The month after, he moved on to Cefn Mawr and spoke to the workers at J C Edwards Co, as well as establishing branches in Buckley. Other than this, not much need be said, as so little union activity was reported amongst the brickworkers that it's not worth the mention.

I get the impression that the general feeling amongst the brick companies was that they never regarded themselves as a truly integrated Industry – each works being isolated within its own little world and with its own ways of doing things. Union membership however, certainly did exist on a large scale within the brickworks, although not much seemed to come of it.

HEALTH CARE

We should now consider what means were available to cope with the many injuries caused by the all too common accidents within the brick and colliery trades. The first thing we should realise is that during the lifetime of most of these industries there were no such things as government healthcare schemes, emergency ambulance services, or any form of assistance from the local authorities. Before the establishment of the National Health Service, a doctor earned his living from fee-paying patients alone, and the hospitals which did exist relied on private funding mainly from charitable sources, such as wealthy philanthropic benefactors.

Probably the earliest medical facility in our designated area was the Wrexham Dispensary, founded in 1833 by Sir Watkin Williams Wynn, the greatest of the local landed gentry, and this establishment developed to become the Wrexham Infirmary and Dispensary in 1848 as new extensions became added to it. The trustees of this hospital regularly invited assistance in the form of donations from the local industries, as it was industry's workmen who often ended up being treated there, and collections amongst the local workforces were a regular feature of life in the manufacturing sector. In time, most of the works were persuaded to arrange amongst their men to annually donate funds on a fixed subscription basis, and in 1901, the first year of the scheme, £453-18-7 was raised from local industry. A glance at the scale of some of the donations received is also a fairly good way of judging the relative size of the various works. For instance, the massive Westminster Colliery gave £54-14-9, Llay Hall £26-7-6, Ffrwd Colliery £19-3-0, Abenbury Brickworks £9-16-8 and the modest Wilderness Brickworks at Gresford £4-4-1. It's also interesting to discover that some works helped out by giving gifts. In June 1902 the same hospital received garden flower tubs from Wrexham Gas Co, five tons of stone chippings from Bwlchgwyn Quarry and 40 yards of edging tiles for the garden walkways from Hafod Brickworks. Other gifts forthcoming from private individuals included vegetables, fruit, flowers, cakes, books, eggs, medicine bottles and bed linen, and this donation system continued certainly into the 1920s and probably beyond.

Sir Watkin also established the Ruabon Hospital in 1870 following a horrific accident at the town's Wynnstay Colliery, and being situated at the centre of the district's heavy industries, the hospital's working committee was fittingly made up primarily of the local colliery and brickworks proprietors; 80 per cent of the £270 annual running costs coming directly from works sources. In 1887 the late Sir Watkins's nephew, the then Sir Watkin, built a larger Ruabon Hospital as a memorial to his uncle at a cost of £2,500, furnishing the entire place at his own expense, apart from one ward which was paid for by the great philanthropic brickmaster J C Edwards.

Medical care in Flintshire however, lagged far behind that of Denbighshire. Buckley, Flintshire's principal brickmaking district, surprisingly never had a hospital until well into the 20th century, despite the town's high level of industrialisation. For many years Buckley had to rely on the small Cottage Hospital at Mold, opened in late 1878 and entirely funded by donations which had been laboriously collected over a three year period.

But before the hospitals existed, how did the local works cope with medical emergencies? It had been apparent to the working men for many years that they needed some financial recourse to fall back on in the event of accidents, as the local doctors required payment for their attendance and treatments. To cover these eventualities the workers took it upon themselves to establish "sick funds ", whereby a small regular subscription was collected from each wage packet and retained until the need arose; the masters also contributing in a few cases, and with the financial backing of such a fund the services of a local doctor for that particular works could be assured:

Wrexham Advertiser 27th August, 1898 – The employees at the Ffrwd Colliery met together on Tuesday 23rd for the purpose of balloting for a doctor in succession to Dr Llewelyn Williams, resigned, and who for many years has acted for this accident fund in connection with the works.

At Mr Bower's Penbedw Brickworks however, it seems they had a slightly modified fund system:

Wrexham Advertiser 19th May 1866 – A fact has just come to my knowledge respecting the conduct of Mr H R Bowers of the Ruabon Works. At this works no regular sick fund exists, but a very good plan has been adopted which answers every purpose and is open to none of the objections which may be urged to an accumulated fund. In all cases of sickness, subscriptions are made in the following ratio – in the case of men, the master subscribes 2s 6d and the men 2d each per week. If a boy, half the amount. By these means, something like ten shillings per week for men and five shillings for boys is guaranteed in case of accident or sickness. I know of large works with regularly organised sick funds where a percentage is deducted from the men's wages, but where the Masters give nothing, nor is there

any account rendered of the balance in hand, but I know of no other instance where the employer subscribes so liberally to the wants of his men.

A sick fund could also act like a savings scheme; paying out whatever was left over at the end of the year:

Wrexham Advertiser 26th December, 1903 – On Saturday the annual distribution of funds in connection with the Trefynant Works Sick Benefit Society took place, and about 170 members received 10s 10d, each being an equal share of the balance after paying the sick pay for the year.

Wrexham Advertiser 7th February, 1885 – At the annual meeting of the Brynmally Workman's Benefit Society held last week it was stated that the balance in hand after paying expenses amounted to £117-13-0, being an increase of nearly £20 during the year. Mr T Clayton was elected President for the ensuing year. All the members of the St John's Ambulance classes have been granted certificates for proficiency at the recent examination.

From that last account we see that some of the workers had been trained in first aid by the St Johns Ambulance Society, and virtually all the works had a crew of such men who were proficient in administering whatever aid was immediately required.

Wrexham Advertiser 2nd September, 1899 – Recently through the instrumentality of Messrs J C Edwards, ambulance classes have been inaugurated at Pentre Schools for Trefynant Works. Mrs E Lloyd Edwards has manifested considerable interest in the classes and has promised badges of the St Johns Ambulance Association to the 41 successful students. The instructions gained by these classes will no doubt prove most beneficial in time of accident.

For those injuries which required more specialised care, the individual works also needed the means to convey the wounded to a hospital or doctor's surgery, and to this end the larger factories would have had an ambulance van – horse drawn, of course , such as they acquired at the large Ffrwd Colliery and Ironworks near Brymbo:

Wrexham Advertiser January 1890 – The country in ambulance instruction is far in advance of the town. The Ffrwd works at the instigation of the men and with a view to further alleviate suffering, are having a vehicle specially constructed to remove the injured to their homes or the Infirmary. The vehicle is a four wheeler with place for driver in front. It is covered in, and has glass windows in sides. We believe it is intended to let it out on hire to other places in the neighbourhood in cases of urgency. Some few years ago before ambulance work was to the fore, any method of dragging a sufferer to his home or the doctors was good enough.

To give you an example of how frequently injuries occured in those days, I can quote some figures from the accident ledger of the large Hafod Works at Ruabon, when in the year from June 1899 to June 1900 the colliery saw 475 accidents, and the brickworks 30 – numbers which are well in excess of anything we might expect in today's industries.

In 1894 Llay Hall Colliery bought an ambulance van by levying a one-off charge of one shilling from the men's wages; the shortfall in the purchase price being made up by the company itself, and this was the usual way for ambulances to be bought and kept in repair. Some of the bigger brickworks also had ambulance vans, but in the colliery sector it had become a provision of law that mines over a certain size must have them. This next inclusion explains the system. It is a report of an inquest into the death of a man in the clay pits of the Wyndham & Phillips Delph Brickworks; their underground clay workings bringing the company under the regulations of the Coal Mines Act:

Wrexham Advertiser 29th May 1915 – A juror said he would like to ask if Messrs Wyndham & Phillips had any facilities for bringing serious cases to hospital. This man was brought on a cart and in view of the state of the roads and his serious injuries, he thought it must have caused unnecessary suffering. The Coroner said it was

explained that the man was put on a stretcher and was put in the cart. H M Inspector explained that a stretcher was provided in every mine, whilst where the number of men reached a certain figure an ambulance must be provided. He thought the small companies should make arrangements with the large companies for the use of theirs, or that one should be provided at the hospital. The Coroner was glad attention was drawn to the matter. He was informed that the cost of an ambulance car was £80 to £100.

Buckley district however, was again slightly behind the Ruabon and Wrexham districts when it came to organised healthcare. It seems that the first horse drawn ambulance van in Buckley was acquired in 1902, standing ready to be used by whichever works called for it. It cost £118-5-0, half of which was raised by private committee and half from local donations, the principal monies being £20 from Watkinson's Collieries Ltd, £20 from the Firebrick Manufacturers Association and £10 from the Aston Hall Colliery & Brickworks. At the inaugural ceremony on 15th February the principal speaker explained why the town had purchased it. He said:

"What was really wanted was the means of conveying an injured man to hospital in a vehicle constructed especially for that purpose and which would do away with all that risk and suffering that comes where the patient has to be taken over rough roads in some conveyance not so constructed. Lack of such means may result in a life being permanently crippled; it may even mean death itself. Take what precautions we may, whether in the pits or in the clayholes, where the great majority of us have to earn our daily bread, yet we know that men must face danger every day of their lives. There is one feature in this enterprise which to my mind is of special and particular value. It is that the owners of works in this district have co-operated with the people and cheerfully bore their share".

Watkinson's housed the van at one of their collieries until a suitable station could be built.

In the case of the general public, their healthcare was also assured, in as much as it could be, by the actions of the townsfolk themselves, and great efforts were made in order to persuade trained medical staff to reside in the most heavily populated districts. As a good example of this we can look to September 1876, when the inhabitants of the crowded neighbourhood of the Rhos near Ruabon, finally succeeded in securing the services of Dr H P Jones of Amlwch, and so grateful were they to the local builder Joseph Griffiths, whose efforts had been paramount in persuading the doctor to come to the village, that they presented him with "a purse of money" to show their appreciation of his achievement.

District Nurses were also greatly valued within a local community, as they could attend to the majority of injuries and illnesses, whilst leaving the busy doctors to concentrate on their wealthier patients and the more serious injuries which required surgery. To this end Public or District Nurse Funds were a commonly found feature of Victorian times and beyond, and the local communities regularly held special events such as fetes, raffles, street and works collections to pay for the expenses of a nurse for their town. Buckley established its first public nurse fund in October 1895 as the needs of the population rapidly expanded, and the following report recalls one of the fund raising events laid on by the people of Overton district; by all accounts a rather enjoyable spectacle, which must have been a great crowd puller:

Wrexham Advertiser 2nd January 1909 – For the benefit of the local nursing fund a comic football match took place in the afternoon of Boxing Day between the Overton Football Club and a team of local "heavyweights". The village assumed quite a gala appearance and crowds of people waited outside the Brynypys Arms to witness the advent of the heavyweights who were to be conveyed to the field of play in a large wagon. The procession was headed by a mock drum and fife band, and the players wended their way to the field amid the cheers of the onlookers. The heavyweights team was composed of the largest and heaviest men to be found amongst the tradesmen and others in the surrounding villages. They were dressed in white smock frocks and red caps and were assisted by members of the local christy minstrel troupes, and amongst these were an admiral, two

"ladies" and several Negroes, Japs, Hindoos etc. Master O. Peel kicked off and the game became fast and furious; no particular advantage being obtained by either side. At length however, the club succeeded in penetrating the defence of the heavyweights and scored a somewhat lucky goal. This reverse put the amateurs on their metal and just before half time they registered an equaliser. The second half opened with the heavyweights lying low, the team probably feeling the effects of their unaccustomed exertions. As may be imagined, considering the composition of the heavyweights and their assistants, the match from start to finish was full of amusing incidents. The most pleasing feature of the match however is the fact that the District Nurse Fund will be augmented by considerably over £13.

The poor health of the people of these once heavily industrialised districts is a fact which today is easily overlooked, but when we consider that coal mining, the chief occupation in the area, was a job done with no respiratory protection provided, it's not hard to imagine the risks our forefathers lived with, and we must not forget the effects which our many silica brick factories must have also had on the health of their employees.

As a final thought, I will leave you with this. In as late as 1953 mass radiography tests in the Rhos showed that 222 men out of 1,224 tested were suffering from pneumoconiosis, a fact that led the Government to officially declare Rhos as the worst affected area for this disease in the entire British Isles!

STRIKES AND TRADE SLUMPS

These two factors were undoubtedly responsible for dealing the most crushing blows to the fortunes of the ordinary working family, bringing them in most cases to the brink of starvation. Trade slumps, what we would today call depressions, had the tendency to hit the districts with an all too frequent regularity, some of them lasting only a few weeks and caused perhaps by the knock on effects of slumps or strikes in other sectors of industry, but the more serious ones having repercussions for months at a time. One of the most devastating started in the Ruabon district in the early months of 1878 and affected the Buckley area shortly afterwards. Its cause had been the accumulative closures of the Legacy, Bryn yr Owen and Gardden Lodge collieries amongst others, throwing very many hundreds of men out of work. The subsequent haemorrhaging of ready money flowing throughout the community was hard felt, and reports commissioned as to the social effects in the industry's heartland at Rhos were grim. The Wrexham Advertiser of 22nd June 1878 said:

"Many houses are without any bread and children crying for the want of it; the children naked, no fire in the grate, illness in some families with no means whatever to meet it. There were 68 families comprising some 320 persons who are entirely destitute, having been out of employment for six, eight, twelve, sixteen weeks, and having no relief of any kind excepting charity at the doors of their neighbours. There are again some 60 families where say a boy or a girl works, and so is able to bring something that contributes to the family support. But that is so small that they again may be considered as suffering great want. Although the neighbourhood has never been seen in the state it is in at present, we have only to look to the capable and kindly disposed in these localities to render the assistance that will keep parents and children from actually dying of starvation. It is feared some have actually done so in the past week".

A Relief Fund – one of many seen throughout the Victorian era – was established to financially assist the most desperate cases; Sir Watkin Williams Wynn donating £100; a massive sum in those days. On the commercial front it was principally the mining trade that was most seriously affected, but the productivity of the brickworks also suffered. By April the Coppy and Llwyneinion brickworks at Rhos had ground to a halt, and the pinch was being felt by others; the beleaguered Penbedw, Ponkey and Plas yn Wern brickworks ending up in court for non-payment of rates. By the end of the year rumours of impending closures in the Buckley bricklands abounded, and their workers had to submit to the inevitable reduction in their rates of pay or face their works closing. The newspaper recorded on 14th December that " the

brick trade has until now kept its activity in surprising contrast to the coal trade of the district, yet it is feared that a more gloomy state of things is approaching. Three of the brickworks have already ceased working and the stocks of those in operation are increasing rapidly. In consequence of this all the brickmasters have given notice on the last pay-day of reductions in wages. It is almost certain in the face of the present state of trade that the men will accept it with demur".

As in the Rhos, a Relief Fund was established and a soup kitchen set up by the wealthier local notaries to alleviate the worst effects of the widespread unemployment; the brickmasters being amongst the principal fund donors.

The principal factor causing these trade slumps in both the coal and brick sectors was the sheer number of firms competing for the same market. The years of industrial expansion during the 1860s and early 70s had secured a good trade whilst the rate of growth was on a roll, but once the boom in building had levelled off, the plethora of new brick and coal companies found it difficult to continuously sustain their previous outputs. Competition became ruthless amongst the firms, each of them desperate to undercut their neighbours in a bid to secure orders, and this resulted in their producing at such a loss that their recourse was to either reduce their workforce, cut their rates of pay, or as many eventually did, close down entirely. It was in this way that the slumps in trade would inevitably lead to strike action by a workforce desperate to maintain their standard of pay – the consequence being one social burden born of another. As I previously pointed out, the Buckley brickmen were much more inclined towards strike action than their Denbighshire brothers, but the colliers on the other hand were just as militant whichever district they worked in, and it was the stoppage of the coalmines in Denbighshire which led to their brickyards suffering the consequence of the miners' actions – as no coal meant no fuel for the kilns. The only brickworks which sometimes managed to escape being brought to a standstill were the very few which had workable coal seams in their clay pits. You may remember from an earlier chapter that the majority of the good clay seems in Ruabon district lay beneath the coal measures; this subsequently resulting in many of the district's brickworks obtaining their clay from underground pits. However, it seems that many of these brickworks were not geared up to work their coal seams properly – perhaps it was just as economical to buy in supplies as to pay miners to work the seams on site, or perhaps their coal seams might have been too small to have proved productive.

1893 was the year of the great miners' strike, brought about by the coal owners pressing for a massive 25 per cent reduction in pay, and the brickworks were not alone in having to bear the brunt of the miners' actions. The consequences of the great strike were far more devastating than those felt in the slump of 1878, and it was at this time that the districts witnessed a most striking social phenomenon. As poverty gripped the neighbourhoods and awareness of it became widespread, the mine owners began to allow the population to pick coal from the colliery spoil banks, but this act of charity soon escalated into people taking matters into their own hands and actually opening small coal pits for themselves on open areas of land. This of course was totally against the law and was in effect trespassing, but the landowners rather prudently turned a blind eye, initially out of a concern for the people's welfare, but also perhaps because they were all too wary of how a cold, hungry and desperate army of hundreds of aggrieved workers might react if they were turned away by force. The developments which followed illustrate just how different the world of yesteryear was in comparison to ours, and I will leave it to the Victorians themselves to describe the scenes which occurred:

Wrexham Advertiser 2nd September, 1893 – The collier's strike is having a serious effect on the brickworks. The blue brick men at the Ruabon Brick & Terracotta and Monk & Newell works were stopped on Wednesday and the men employed in the clayhole have also been stopped for the want of coal.

16th September – The coal banks at Plaspower Colliery present a most animated scene every day. Hundreds of men, women and children are raking up the old banks and picking out every scrap of coal for sale. The work continues night and day. Fires are lighted for those who stay all night to watch the coal picked during the day.

23rd September – Probably not half of the brickworks' hands are now able to follow their employment owing to the want of fuel. The coal strike is affecting the bricklayers who are at work on the Wrexham and Ellesmere railway construction, as it is difficult to procure coal to make the bricks.

7th October – The talk of Rhos just now is the Grango Colliery which is situated near Ty Gwyn Farm. Scores of people who are not colliers visit the place nightly. The glare of countless lights give the place a strange appearance. Rhosites have found that money can be made at Grango and there has been a rush for the black diamond. "Very much like the gold diggings in Australia" was the remark made by one who had once experienced the gold fever. About 200 pits have now been opened. In some of them the coal is three yards in thickness. As a help to live in the crisis, the colliery has been of very great benefit to the colliers. At least £200 has been realised by the sale of coal dug here. Brewers from Wrexham and farmers from Bangor Isycoed have sent their carts to fetch the coal. Brick manufacturers have also been supplied with fuel from the miniature colliery. No less than 29 carts laden with coal awaited the opening of the gates at Coppy brickworks on Saturday morning.

Two old coal pits at Trefynant were reopened and coal sold to the local manufacturers. The old Brandy pits were also exploited. The Grango site (referred to in the text as a "colliery " only because people were digging for coals) was becoming so overworked that the landowner Colonel Meredith appealed to the strike leaders to arrange that the people not disfigure the land any more, and policemen were posted to ensure the diggers kept to their agreed limits. So much coal was being got that on one Saturday morning 50 cart loads went out before 10 o'clock, but the downside was that the ground began to subside and one digger narrowly escaped death when he was brought up just before his pit fell in. So many people were working on the site that their fires could be seen at night from Wrexham church tower. "I have made more money in a week at the Grango than in the same length of time at the Hafod Colliery" said one miner.

Wrexham Advertiser 4th November – Another "Grango" on a small scale has been found at Cefn in an old stone quarry belonging to Mr Dennis. Coal has been found in abundance and several miniature pits have been opened and the popular landlord not only allows the men to work the coal but has also signified his intention to buy and utilise all the coal raised.

18th November – At Cefn, the pits in the old quarry afford employment to about 200 men. There are about twenty pits sunk about 10 ft deep. Mr Dennis not being able to buy the coal, the labour of the men has increased considerably, as all their output has now to be carried to the road in sacks, and with the exception of sinking new pits, no night work can be done as the conveying of the coal over the rocks from such high elevation is too dangerous. The men have now stocked coal on the old siding and have a man watching during the nights. The coal is sold at sixpence per hundredweight, and tons are carted away daily.

Government itself finally resolved the situation by announcing on 24th November that the miners could return to work at their old rates of pay.

The 20th century also saw its fair share of imaginative local speculation. The national coal strike of 1921 gave rise to local activity similar to that of 1893, when over 30 tunnels were opened by striking miners in the Glascoed Woods near Brymbo. At Cefn Mawr the speculation for coal took place beneath the rock outcrops; numbers of different "sets" being claimed by each group of diggers:

Wrexham Advertiser April 1921 – The latest edition in this quarter is an aerial railway – quite an ingenious piece of work. The coal is got up the pit; then transferred into a bucket which travels some 50 or 60 yards overhead to the top of the rock. Before this contrivance was erected the men had to carry the coal on their backs to the top. This concern only affects one "set". Others still have to carry the coal. The construction of this " airo flight", as named, would surprise a great many and it saves the men concerned a lot of hard work.

Over in Buckley there was similar activity:

Chester Chronicle 16th April & 7th May 1921 – Many of the miners are now getting coal in the disused clayholes around Buckley. Day and night shifts are being worked by some of the gangs who are working as partners. In the clayhole near the Silica Works, Drury Lane, the coal runs to nearly 5 ft thick, but the men have to work very hard to clear the stuff on the top of this coal. In the Mount clayhole the men have drifted underneath and propped the roof up in real mining fashion; candles and bike lamps being used when they work. The owners of these clay holes allow the men to get these seams of coal free. During last week a grand seam was discovered in Old Ewloe Works clayhole near to Buckley church. The firm have only the last year finished getting clay from this hole and in some parts of it the men had not much difficulty in clearing the dirt which covered the coal. Carrying the coal to the top is very hard work; the men having to carry it on their backs in sacks. The different gangs have their own piles of coal which are placed in rotation on the top. Two

"Unemployed miners of Rhos rushing for the coal as the tubs are emptied on the waste tip at Hafod Colliery. Hundreds of the men keep their daily vigil at this spot". Photo and text: Wrexham Advertiser of December 1933 / British Library.

or three hundred tons are placed in heaps along each side of the roadway. Nearly everybody in the district has turned temporary miner, and tradesmen of all crafts are trying their hand. In most places the men are working in three shifts so as not to lose the places after opening them out.

The nearest we have approached to such scenes in modern times was during the National Coal Strike of 1972, when hundreds of local folk dug for coal on the spoil tips of the old Llay Main Colliery, now the site of the Llay Industrial Estate, but these efforts were a far cry from the more adventurous enterprises of those tougher men of earlier days.

VIOLENT DEMONSTRATION

The "rough and tumble" behaviour of the hard working men of the 19th century was legendary in its day, especially in the areas of densest population; Buckley and the Rhos figuring in particular, but within the sphere of the working environment, violent actions shown towards the employers and their agents was fairly rare. Some examples however did at times occur. In 1842 some of the Buckley brickmen, worried by some new local competition, stirred themselves into action against a small brickworks set up by Sir Stephen Glynne:

Chester Chronicle 6th May 1842 – On Monday night a number of men and boys at least two hundred, stating themselves to be from Messrs Rigby and Hancock Brickworks, assembled in a field adjoining the dwelling-house of Mr Joseph Higgs, agent to Sir Stephen Glynne, but on finding that Mr Higgs was not at home, they prowled around the premises for a considerable time and after some of them had made an ineffectual attempt to force open the doors into the yard, they marched off and proceeded to near the village of Broughton where Mr Higgs had erected some buildings for the purpose of manufacturing tiles or draining shells for the use of the tenants on Sir Stephen's estates, which they quickly demolished, scattering the materials about in all directions. It appears by a written document left on Mr Higgs premises, they had taken umbrage at his erecting these buildings and threatening if he persisted in

going on with the works as he proposed, they would again visit him.

The next troubles of which we are aware occurred in November 1880, when some of the brickmasters at Buckley received threatening letters, illustrated by a sketch of a coffin with skull and crossbones. The anonymous letters turned out to be the work of only a few individuals, but were the result of a more widespread dissatisfaction over wage cuts, but they were nevertheless of a threatening nature and ended by saying "I warn you you had better be careful when and where you turn out. Good night. Take advice before it is too late".

Those two previous events, separated by 38 years, are the sole examples I could find of any such violent or threatening actions from our brickmakers, but if we were to look for some more "colourful " behaviour, we should not have to look further than to their brethren the colliers – but who knows for sure how many brickmen working for the colliery companies might not have been actively militant themselves. Messrs Rigby & Hancock at Buckley were such a company who had many brick and coal concerns, although most of their brick production was probably restricted to their Lane End Works. In 1842 their colliery agent Mr Staley introduced a new work practice at one of their collieries' pit heads, which although intended as an improvement, led to more than 80 disgruntled miners congregating outside his office. The newspaper takes up the story:

Chester Chronicle 29th April, 1842 – Mr Staley after vainly attempting to pacify them tried to pass through the mob to mount his horse, when he was violently seized and carried towards the railway formed for carrying coals to the River Dee at Queensferry. Here he was thrust into the bottom of a railway wagon and conveyed very much bruised along the line towards the river, the men on their way telling him he had not long to live, as they intended to drown him in the Dee. On arriving they stated that his life would be spared but only on condition of banishment to England. He was then placed in the ferry boat; the colliers threatening revenge if ever he dared to return.

Mr Rigby learnt of the incident and took Staley into

his house, but he had to sneak away by night when the men became suspicious; 300 of them surrounding Rigby's home, and others of the company's superintendents were also threatened, leading to four of them fleeing the district in fear.

Violence was not always the collier's first course of action however, although they did seem to have a preference for expressing their opinions in a physical way, and it was not unheard for them to escort a disliked colliery agent or manager to the nearest railway station and see him out of town. Of the Denbighshire miners, those employed at the various works of the huge New British Iron Co were definitely the most militant. In December 1868 they attacked the house of Mr Evans, the company's manager, leading to other of the managers sending their families out of the neighbourhood in fear for their safety, and this was by no means an isolated occurrence for the men of the New British.

On 1st August 1855 a "tumultuous assemblage of riotous colliers" ransacked the house of the company's underground manager Mr Hynde; the ringleaders on that occasion being discovered and dismissed. For them it would have been difficult to obtain work elsewhere and many were reduced to begging in the streets of Chester, where they were less likely to be recognised. The attitude of respectable society during that period in history was indignant indeed towards such rebellious characters, and this comes over well in the following diatribe from the Chronicle, which remarked *"If they have disputes with their masters they can be settled in better ways than by breaking all the windows and plundering the manager's house. Their being out of work now is their own fault. There are about twenty of them in Chester, most of whom draw a wagon of coal with ropes, while two go hat in hand to the houses in the street, and their voluntary degradation to their present position reminds an observer that those human beings who won't use or listen to reason deserve to be employed only as horses – as beasts of burden".*

The Transport of Material

I am sure that the question of transport is one which the casual observer might never consider as being of relevance to the subject of brickmaking, but nothing could be further from the truth, as the movement of goods from manufacturer to customer is a principal which in former times, as it is today, was of paramount importance. What would be the point in establishing a brickworks if the cost of moving the finished products exceeded the profit margins to be made on them, and this principle was recognised by the Colliery Guardian, which remarked in 1862 that *"the transport of material for bricks from one part of the country to another would be impractical on account of the expense attending its carriage, and the necessity of brick-making at a distance from the site of building would be equally objectionable on the same ground"*.

The dreadful state of Victorian roads was the single reason why many early brickyards were restricted in their ability to expand from being only small concerns, and why there were so many of them dotted around the country, serving the needs of their easily accessible local communities. The only early brickworks which managed to grow in importance were those which built their own horse drawn tramways connecting to canals or docks, or which connected with the few main line railways then laid, and the brick industry only took off in a big way when rail communication began to expand in the 1860s. We will cover this subject a little later, but for now it would serve us well to understand why Victorian roads proved so restrictive to the moving of heavy loads such as bricks.

Firstly, if we could imagine what our landscape looked like at the time of the establishment of the major brickworks of our district – circa 1860 – we would see a mainly agricultural vista, dotted here and there with quarries, brickyards and small collieries, and a number of towns and villages. Connecting these would be the roads, which would have been mainly hedge lined dirt tracks, which for the most part would have been kept open mainly by the volume of horse drawn cart traffic passing along them. The best maintained roads would have been seen in the towns themselves, upkept by the Local Boards – the councils of the day – who would have also overseen the roads between closely connected centres of population. As to the main highways, these were mainly upkept by the Turnpike Trusts, but again, these roadways were not much better than dirt roads.

TURNPIKES

The first of the Turnpike Acts was passed by Parliament in 1663, and these Acts were enabled as a means of providing the degree of roadworthiness needed to keep the main highways of Britain free to the passage of stagecoaches etc. The Acts allowed for Turnpike Trusts to bid for the privilege of letting stretches of roadways from the local landowners, and the contracts for operating the Turnpike Roads would be regularly competed for at auctions. Once a Trust had won a contract they would be obliged to maintain the road and fund their operations by setting up Toll Gates and Toll Bars at all major junctions, which is why the entrance to most towns were marked on Victorian maps with the symbol T P (Turnpike). Turnpike Roads were therefore the best kept roads in Britain, and allowed traffic to move more speedily along them. *"However incredible it may appear, this coach will actually arrive in London four days after leaving Manchester"* boasted a stagecoach advertisement in the mid-18th century, but as the quality of Turnpike Roads improved with the funding from the tolls levied on carts, animals, coaches and pedestrians, so did the speed of journey times, and by 1860 it took only ten hours to travel from Shrewsbury to Aberystwyth. Turnpikes became big business – statistics from the 18th century list 7,800 toll gates in England and Wales, with 20,000 toll keepers or "pikemen" looking after them. The public however, bitterly resented having to pay to use roads which hitherto had been free rights of way, and in late 1876 Parliament abolished the Turnpikes, and the newly created Highways Boards took over the maintenance of the country's roads, funded from the local rates.

ROAD CONSTRUCTION

Whether the roads were in the town or the country (if given any attention at all in those latter places) the methods of Victorian construction were basic, and had unchanged for centuries, and to get a good idea of what materials were used we could do no better than look at the advertisements placed by the Local Boards to tender for road maintenance contracts. From these it becomes apparent that the basic materials used in road construction were stones, pebbles, gravel, broken bricks, cinders and ashes; materials which featured throughout the period and into the early 20th century:

Wrexham Advertiser 1881 – To contractors and others. The Wrexham District Highways Board invite tenders for the making of a new road at Five Fords. The road will be required to be properly formed to the width of 20 ft ; 15 ft of the same to be metalled with clean gravel (available from the brook) 6 inches deep, well rolled with a roller and afterwards covered with small gravel.

From that advertisement we can see a perfect example of the Victorian economy in logistics – why cart gravel when you can find it in a nearby river? I often used to wonder why when travelling along country roads there seemed to be the scars of small quarries dug into the countryside alongside the road, and these quarry workings, seemingly isolated from any adjacent civilisation, were most likely the source of the stone originally used in the road's construction. For a society whose heaviest everyday road traffic was laden, slow moving horse carts, the only requirement was to coat the surface with stones large enough to prevent the cart wheels from sinking into the ground, a system which no doubt was perfectly fine in dry weather, but which caused problems after persistent rains:

Wrexham Advertiser 24th February, 1872 – We would wish respectfully to call the attention of the authorities to the Mold and Wrexham Turnpike Road, which is in a very bad state of repair, especially between Mold and Caergwrle, the ruts being in some places from three to six inches deep. Where stones have been placed on the road, it has been done by sprinkling a stone here and there as if they were worth their weight in gold, and in no place along the six miles has a proper covering been placed, which is in places quite hollow, and water lodging in the holes to the depth of several inches.

An Observation by a Manchester Man, 1887 – It is surprising to find how reluctant the authorities of rural parishes are to avail themselves of the use of steam rollers for road making, and they still resort to the old practice of putting stones upon the highways and trusting to the carts and pedestrians slowly treading in the stones, the consequence being that the roads are never in good repair.

Even in Wrexham itself, the most prestigious town in all of Flintshire and Denbighshire, this basic method of road laying was used, but during dry weather, when the dust of the road had been blown away, the stones would be exposed causing hindrance to wheeled traffic and giving rise to such complaints as the following:

Wrexham Advertiser 20th May, 1905 – Many are the complaints of the state of the roads in this district, especially in the main street, High St. The dry weather is accountable for the raising of the stones which have been laid down during the winter, and these lying all across the roads together with heaps of dirt, give pedestrians a right to seriously complain.

I should say that the state of the roads were one of the most commonly found cause of letters of complaint to the local newspapers throughout the decades of the latter 19th century, with the problems caused by mud and dust featuring uppermost. Before the use of tar, the drier months were a constant source of annoyance to the folk living in the towns, as the next inclusions, a few of very many, will illustrate:

Wrexham Advertiser 30th June, 1877 – Our attention has been called to the evident enjoyment experienced by the Wrexham street arabs in their proflable enjoyment of kicking the dust about the Rhosddu road, to anything but the enjoyment of the general public. At the beginning of the week several large heaps of dust were carefully and neatly swept up at intervals along the road and left there instead of being properly carted away. The heaps however are now pretty well cleared away by the feet of the juvenile scavengers, but not so the dust, which when raised by wind almost blinds the unfortunate pedestrian.

Wrexham Advertiser 16th June, 1906 – Holt fruit growers, market gardeners and farmers have a real grievance. Daily clouds of dust are raised by private motor cars which rush at a terrific speed along Wrexham Road and through the streets of Holt. When the wind is high the dust is diffused far and wide over the strawberry, vegetable and hay fields, causing much damage. Persons have often to open their umbrellas to protect their clothes and for scores of yards no object can be seen owing to the trailing clouds. The inhabitants of Holt are about to appeal to the council to furnish the town with a watering cart to lay the dust. Furniture in houses along the route is covered with the dust when windows are opened. It is high time some stringent measures should be taken to abate the nuisance and compel motor drivers to proceed slowly when they pass along the streets in both towns.

The advent of the faster moving motor cars particularly exacerbated the dust problem, and ladies especially found it increasingly necessary to stay at home wherever possible, to protect their billowing skirts from getting dirtied. The motor traffic also caused particular annoyance to the agricultural trade, a necessary and economically lucrative business in the days when all groceries were locally grown. To alleviate the problem in the towns it was the common practice to send out the "watering cart" during the summer months, which sprayed the roads wet to lay the dust, and by 1914 Wrexham had eight water columns placed around the town, from which the carts could refill. In time, the advent of spraying tar onto the road surface became more widespread ; a practice originally invented as a means of binding the surface stones together and preventing the rise of dust. The first local use of tar spraying *"to the*

most approved principles of John Macadam" appeared in Charles Street, Hope Street and High Street in Wrexham as early as 1857, but this was an experiment unique to that town, and was certainly not widely embraced even there. Most other districts had to wait until the next century before experiments with tar were undertaken – the first tar spraying in Buckley having been tried at Lane End in mid-1911.

All this is, I hope, serving to illustrate the problems which most brickworks would have faced if presented with the prospect of exporting their wares exclusively by road, and if the preceding information failed to impress that point, then the following should help to clinch the argument. If dust and loose stones proved an annoyance to practical transportation, then mud served as a positive hindrance. Again, the best method of illustration is to employ direct quotations of the problems experienced, and notice how the public's weariness with this all too oft annoyance was highlighted by their use of sarcasm:

Wrexham Advertiser 7th May, 1887 – During the week and after the late copious rains, very loud and unnecessary complaints have been made as to the state of High St, Mold to the effect that it was nigh impassable owing to the mud and water. In order to satisfy ourselves, we made a minute inspection the other morning and now declare that with the aid of a few stepping stones and a good boat, together with the exercise of ordinary caution and perseverance, a skilled person might cross the street with comparative safety at any point between Pendre and the Cross. We hope that after this simple explanation no further complaints will be heard.

Wrexham Advertiser 1871 – For the most part of last month King Frost has held rule, and the streets of Mold have been in beautiful condition, being as hard as adamant. But on Thursday night a thaw set in and King Mud ruled in his stead. Up to Wednesday no rebellion was attempted against him, and the streets were in a state highly creditable to the authorities, the mud not being more than knee deep anywhere, especially near the crossings.

Wrexham Advertiser 24th January, 1874 – There

is no doubt but that Buckley is blessed with the queerest roads in the county. If they had been invented for the purpose of preventing people from travelling along them it would have been impossible to construct them with better effect. The ruts are about a foot deep in places, and the rest of the road about five or six inches deep in mud. We had the painful duty to walk along them this week. Of course, the turnpike roads are a shade better, and only a shade. That portion from Penbrigog to the gate has, we are told, not been scraped for two months.

Chester Chronicle 16th March 1878 – Connah's Quay. They are called roads, but that is quite a misnomer. They are only mud tracks. On Wednesday as a cart load of timber was passing, the wheels sunk at least two feet in the mud and could only be got out with the assistance of a screw jack. The foundation is worn out and now there is a concave surface which becomes a ditch in rainy weather. It has been suggested that a light draughted boat should ply in wet weather between Wepre Bridge and Coffin Row.

The Mold to Gwernymynydd road was described in the 1870s as resembling "more like a ploughed field than anything else", and a Wrexham tradesman in 1874 said that to negotiate the muddy and rutted road from the town to Kings Mills, he was obliged to incur the extra cost of hitching four horses to his wagons instead of three.

Now we can see why the country brickyards remained so small, whereas those better placed factories with direct or nearby access to the more efficient railways could profit and expand. Its also worth remembering that the poor state of the roads existed well into the 20th century, and the following comment made by the Advertiser in 1922 perfectly highlighted the commercial drawbacks of road transportation: "Some who have travelled along the main road between Ruabon and Cefn consider it to be a danger to traffic, and that any vehicle attempting to travel at more than 5 or 10 mph is asking for trouble".

Let's now look at a description of the most popular method of public road transportation once found in the rural districts, and apart from it being a joy to read, it should serve to illustrate how much more difficult it would have been to cart the more heavier loads of bricks throughout the hilly districts of Buckley, Rhos, Mold and Brymbo – the centres for our major brickworks. You will also notice the author's direct reference to how railways were developed primarily for industrial traffic:

Wrexham Advertiser 5th October, 1872 – A ride in a Brymbo Tax Cart. Many of our readers see driving into Wrexham, what a few years ago, were and are still called, tax carts. These carts come and go laden with the lower classes from the districts around the town, and really form the only means of intercommunication between the town and these districts. The immense loads they carry and the rate at which they are driven, coupled with the fact that they rarely have lights, renders it marvellous that serious accidents are not more frequent. Having an appointment at Brymbo a few evenings since, the thought suddenly struck me. Hieing to the Talbot at 6 o'clock I saw an empty cart in charge of a middle aged woman. Having secured a box seat, I waited for a few minutes and watched the process of taking in cargo. Two men besides myself occupied seats on the front, and the body of the cart was filled with women laden with baskets. I occupied the end seat and on counting noses found there were twelve of us besides two extras under 12 at half price and the driver. On inquiring where he was going to sit, he said, "You will see", and perched himself on the shaft at one time and at another across the horse's back with a foot on each shaft. My seat was none of the pleasantest. In the old coaching days, sixteen inches was the space allowed by law for each person, but I had barely six. Moreover I had to hold on by the outer rail for fear of being pitched overboard. All the occupants of the trap were quite sober, and the conversation, mostly in Welsh, was innocent and amusing. A young lady we passed wearing a dolly varden hat afforded a text for a good deal of fun. Most of the journey was up hill work, and the horse, which was a good strong one, soon showed by his condition what hard pulling it was. In fact I felt that as a member of the Society for the Prevention of Cruelty to Animals, I was in a very improper position and guilty of the crime the society was formed to prevent. Before reaching Southsea there is a very sharp hill, and the men all got down and lit their pipes and walked on, chatting to the owner. When we got on the level again we took our seats and merrily jogged on past Broughton Colliery and up again to the Lodge where we paid our fare – four pence. Having done my business, when it was quite dark, I started back, but got into such a maze of light and shade, hill and dale, road and railway, and after two narrow chances of rendering myself chargeable to the Accidental Death Insurance Company, I retained the first guide I met to see me safe out. This being done I again slipped into a trap bound for Wrexham. The journey back was not so pleasant. We had no lamps and it was quite dark. Vehicles were continually meeting us, and the only guide for safety was the driver's loud " ya-ap", indefinitely prolonged and repeated. Once I fully expected a collision. A cart load were coming, singing and bawling, and their driver could not hear our noise for his own. The road was very narrow and we had to come to a full stand for them to pass. The jolting and shaking I got on the return journey was a thing to be remembered, and it has required a series of warm baths to alleviate. I got out at Wrexham never no more to ride in a tax cart if I can walk. With me this ride was an experiment – with hundreds it is a necessity. From the Moss, Brymbo, Coedpoeth, Minera, Rhos and intermediate places, thousands of people are brought to Wrexham by these traps, while lines of railway for the conveyance of minerals intercept these places, which could be at comparatively small cost made available for passengers._

As an amusing footnote to this subject, we should take into account the fact that the absence of any local authority's guidance during the formative years of town planning led to haphazard irregularities in street naming etc. Rhos Parish Council, for instance, didn't organise its street naming and numbering policy until 1895, and Wrexham was much the same:

Wrexham Advertiser 22nd January, 1881 – A correspondent in writing upon the subject of the repainting of the names of our streets wishes the council would pay a little attention to prevent owners of property changing the names of courts and alleys according to their own whims and fancies. There have been a number of liberties taken without sanction. Jones Court was changed to Turner's Court, and Harrison's Court was changed to Broughton Buildings. The numbering of the houses in many streets is a regular muddle. In Tuttle Street there are three sets of numbers. Anyone in search of number 10 would likely have to wander into three different points in the street before he found the No. 10 he wanted. Before the demolition of some old cottages there were actually four houses in the street, all of which could boast of being No. 1. Farndon Street is in much the same plight. Until the recent removal of some old cottages, No. 5 occurred five times over.

RAILWAYS

The single most motivating factor which assisted the development and rapid growth of Britain from an agrarian society into a powerhouse of industry and commerce was the spread of the country's rail network. The decades of the 1840s to the 70s saw the growth of new lines taking off at a particularly high pace, and the expense incurred in building them was testimony itself to the faith which was placed in their being able to prove profitable. Between 1845-7 no fewer than 576 potential new rail routes were presented to Parliament for consideration, and those to be granted the go-ahead would have been the lines considered most likely to realise a consistent profit – particularly the mineral lines which serviced the requirements of the growing Industrial Revolution. Consider this next report, which typifies that principle from the Victorian point of view:

Wrexham Advertiser 6th January, 1866 – In no branch of our local manufacture has progress been so manifest since the opening of railways as in that of Fire Brick and Glazed Earthenware in the neighbourhood of Ruabon. Within the memory of comparatively young men, one firebrick yard supplied the demand for nearly all

Rail operations at Trefynant Brickworks on 16th August, 1957. Photo: Hugh Davies.

Alex Hughes and his horse Sam pulling empty brick shipping boxes on the narrow-gauge Buckley brickworks tramways circa 1925. Photo: FRO.

purposes home and export, and that we believe with but one kiln. Since then a vast change has taken place. Three large manufactories containing the most improved machinery are in existence, and the increased demand is still causing new works to be commenced. Those already in operation are adding kiln to kiln, shed to shed, to a degree that would have astounded our forefathers.

The original genesis of railways themselves started within the industrial landscape as a means of speeding up production. A contemporary explanation written in 1767 explained *"The manner of the carriage is by laying rails of timber from the colliery to the river exactly straight and parallel, and bulky carts are made with four rollers fitting those rails, whereby the carriage is so easy that one horse will draw down four or five chaldrons of coal and is an immense benefit to the merchants".*

You can see that horses pulled the trains before the introduction of the crudest steam locomotives, such as the famous Puffing Billy, which hauled coal at Wylam Colliery near Newcastle from 1813. Once Parliament had realised that these new lines would inevitably begin to change the face of Britain they set up a special House of Commons Committee in 1842 to investigate their impending impact, and its findings gave rise to some interesting facts. A specialist contributor by the name of Mr Hornblower explained that, in his opinion, the first railway ever built was a "wooden way" constructed at Newcastle upon Tyne circa 1672 to transport coals down to the river barges; the earliest railways being made of wooden, not iron rails. Hornblower believed the first use of iron rails began circa 1767, when the Coalbrookdale Ironworks fitted iron strips onto the head of the wooden rails at their own works, to reduce the expense of continually having to replace the damaged wood, and this idea caught on and eventually developed into the wholesale replacement of wooden rails in favour of iron. Many of these early industrial railways were narrow-gauge tramways, particularly prevalent within the Buckley district, where in the 18th and early 19th century many horse drawn tramways existed to connect the brickworks and collieries to the River Dee, but the volume, speed and regularity of traffic along them was extremely limited. William Catherall said of his tramway *"The length of the journey from my brick bank twice a day, six days a week with two tons on each wagon was plenty of work for a horse. For the driver to hand out eight tons of rough bricks is a heavy task – no man in years likes the occupation".*

One of the principal Buckley routes was the Aston Tramroad, which connected a number of sites on its journey to the river wharf near Sandycroft. Although one of the better-funded railways, it was still quite a precarious feat of engineering, with its rails having been very poorly laid and maintained. As one contemporary noted *"It was bad in construction and gets filled up with dirt and snow. In snowy weather it is impassable; in consequence in 1859 the tramway was closed. Some of the rails have no spikes to keep them in their place. I could push my foot against them and put them out of shape"*. The great Mr W E Gladstone said of it *"It is very old and is worked by horses. It is so imperfectly constructed that it is as much as the horse and wagons can do to keep upon it"*. These little tramways could in no way be relied upon to cope with the amount of coal and brick traffic which was beginning to emerge from the Buckley works in the mid-19th century, and a more productive and better engineered alternative was desperately needed.

The first standard gauge line to service Flintshire's major brickmaking district was the Buckley & Connah's Quay Railway, opened on 7th June, 1862 as a five mile long single track mineral only line to connect Knowle Lane Brickworks with the main coast line at the port of Connah's Quay, calling at the other principal brickworks and collieries along its way. Its benefit to the owners of these works proved immense, and many of them practically backed the project; the brickmasters Charles Davison and Edward Parry having become directors of this new rail company. Oddly enough the great brickmaster Mr Catherall was reticent in supporting the new line, fearful of offending his landlord Sir Stephen Glynne, who would have lost his land rental on his well-established tramway, but Catherall's partner William Shepherd would not allow the benefits of the new steam hauled main line to pass him by, and ripped up the old tramway without consulting Catherall. The Buckley Railway originally didn't even possess any trucks of its own; the individual companies along the line supplying their own rolling-stock to carry their produce to the port. The following description from 1877 outlines the working of the line: *"The line was single track and the works alongside it each had branch spurs to them. Five to six mineral trains ran down to Connah's*

Quay daily, and the operations to move trucks onto the line was called "packing up". The engine would detach from the train, run up the branch to collect each line of trucks, bring them back onto the main line and shunt them onto the main train. Then off to the next works' branch line".

Pleased with the new railway, the surveyor John Palin, who had been employed by Ashton's Knowle Lane Brickworks to evaluate its impact, reported *"The Buckley and Connah's Quay Railway commences close to Mr Ashton's works, and a siding has been made into the yard which is a great convenience and saving in expense of carriage, and enables the works to send off his goods so that he has no occasion to stop making for want of room in his yard, which I understand he has formerly had occasion to do. This facility is of course a great advantage to the trade, and it enables the manufacturer to do more work and facilitates the consumption of clay"*. No better testimonial to the advantage of rail communication could be imagined, but by a strange and ironic twist of fate, the rate of the aforementioned consumption of clay meant that their clay stocks depleted so swiftly, that the works actually had to drastically reduce its productivity!

In the same year that the Buckley & Connah's Quay Railway was opened, a petition was presented in Parliament for the proposed Wrexham, Mold & Connah's Quay Railway, which was intended to link the industries of Denbighshire in the south to the port at Connah's Quay via a new line through Buckley – the Denbighshire works only having had the more inconvenient Great Western Railway link to the smaller port at Saltney. *"The proposed line for that reason met with the cordial support of all the owners in the district, who found that at the present time they were hampered to an intolerable extent"*. Again, the W M & C Q Rly's committee was composed of men eager to see their investments flourish – James Sparrow of the Ffrwd Ironworks, Thomas Clayton of Brynmally Colliery, and the principal partners of collieries from Mold, Hope and Treuddyn. Mr Sparrow even had the proud honour of laying the first stone of the line's viaduct at Cefnybedd in September 1864; a silver trowel having been presented to him by the line's contractor as a memento. The great Buckley brickworks had for many years their connections to the main ports of the River Dee as their greatest advantage, but the landlocked industries of Denbighshire could never properly grow until the coming of the railways expanded their trade routes. As a Buckley industrialist explained, Ruabon *"was entirely and altogether made by railways. There was nothing done before the railways were made at Ruabon for the coal. It was drawn (previously) by donkeys".*

The first rail communication into the Wrexham and Ruabon district had arrived in 1848 with the opening of the Shrewsbury and Chester line, and this railway had gone a fair way to increasing the trade of the district:

Wrexham Advertiser 14th August, 1880 – The Shrewsbury and Chester line passing over the portion of the North Wales Coalfield past Ruabon and Wrexham gave the industries on the route a powerful impulse. In former days the consumption of the various products was limited to haulage by cart and boat, which it seemed kept the trades within short compass. Works were on a small scale and there prevailed an impression about the capabilities of the ground to the effect that no commodities could be raised or manufactured in sufficient quantities to recoup the money provided to extend them. The introduction of the railway altered this state of things. New and enlarged markets became reachable on all sides, infusing new life into all industry.

The new connection to the sea via the Wrexham, Mold & Connah's Quay line was one of Denbighshire's greatest boons to its trade, and it wasn't only the brick and coal owners who welcomed its coming. The general commercial trade also saw the line as a potential benefit, and the people of Wrexham eagerly awaited the news as each stage of the W M & C Q's bill was granted official approval:

Wrexham Advertiser 18th June, 1864 – On the arrival in Wrexham of the telegram that the railway bill, in which Wrexham is so much interested, had passed the House of Lords, the news spread like wild fire. Tradesmen came to their shop doors. Everyone shook hands with his neighbour, then shook hands with himself. Smiles and congratulations became the order of the day.

About half past four the bells sent forth a merry peel, which was taken confirmation strong that the news was true.

It's no surprise then, that the necessity of railway communication became an important consideration for the prospective industrial entrepreneur. For instance, when the mineral agent Walter Eddy was advising a client on where best to rent land for a proposed new works in the 1880s, he wisely advised that "the principal point for the success of a brickfield there is being able to get to the branch railway". Even into the 20th century the importance of good rail links still held true, and when a London syndicate purchased prime clayland at Penycae in 1901 for a new works, their first priority was to petition the GWR for a branch line to the site. But the rail company rejected their proposals, and despite their having troubled to buy the land in the first place, they were wise enough to realise the futility of proceeding with their plans any further, and the brickworks was never built.

CONNAH'S QUAY DOCKS

As you will see from reading other passages within this book, the export trade via the Dee estuary was of considerable importance to the brickworks of Buckley in particular; Ireland especially having represented a key market for Buckley goods since the early 19th century. In fact, many of the shareholders of the earlier Buckley works were themselves Irish merchants and speculators, particularly from Dublin – the destination for many of the Buckley companies' brick schooners.

The Buckley Railway originally only had links to the main coast railway which passed close to Connah's Quay Docks, but when the W,M & CQ Rly took over the Buckley Railway in June 1866, they set about extending the Buckley line into the dockside itself via a steep incline, built to run beneath the main coast road. As the Chronicle of 1900 described the system, the trains *'were brought from Buckley to a position called the Bank at Connah's Quay where the engine uncoupled and left the trucks. From here to the docks the wagons were lowered down the steep incline by brake-sticks'* The incline still exists today as a footpath and cycle track.

Prior to the rise of Connah's Quay docks in importance, all kinds of goods were dispatched and received at many small ports along the River Dee and its estuary – from Queensferry, Flint, Sandycroft and Saltney. The following letter dated July 1808 was from the shipping agent James Brough to the brickmaster Jonathan Catherall: *"I have now the pleasure of having engaged the Hope to load a full and complete cargo of Fire Bricks from King's Ferry, Chester River to Limerick at 24 shillings. I am on the lookout for a vessel of 80 to 120 tons for you to load for London, but at present can't procure one, but shall not give up that business till accomplished".* Queensferry was then called King's Ferry, and note how the River Dee was referred to as Chester River. In its day Chester had been a thriving port since Roman times, but the accumulation of river silt had eventually rendered it unable to accommodate the larger vessels.

Connah's Quay eventually became the favoured position for the district's major seaport due to its being closer to the sea, and the channel therefore being deeper and wider, but in earlier times it was King's Ferry which had handled most of the district's sea traffic. King's Ferry however had one major drawback, in that the larger ships being built to accommodate the increased brick and coal cargoes found it difficult to navigate the shallower channel. Ships at Connah's Quay could float free at the same time as those at Kings Ferry were grounded, and the great brickmaster Charles Davison was extremely disillusioned when one of his heavily laden brick schooners had to wait nine days at Kings Ferry for a tide high enough to float it off the river bed.

Connah's Quay had originated in the 18th century only as a scattered collection of cottages inhabited mainly by local fishermen, and The Old Quay House pub, dated 1777, still exists where the original quayside developed. But by 1857 however, the traffic moving through this small quayside had grown to include bricks, sulphur ore, lead, vitriol, scrap iron, limestone, coal, soda and timber, and it was not long before the quay and it was not long before the quay had to be extended. Charles Davison, one of Buckley's principal brickmasters, was to feature prominently in the port's development, as his firm not only heavily relied on its seafaring trade, but his family had themselves been long connected with the commercial life of the port. Amongst all the Buckley brickmasters and coal owners Charles became known as the most enthusiastic promoter of the docks' expansion programmes and the improvement of its rail links, and as the Chronicle described him, he was *"a gentleman who takes a great interest in the welfare of the Quay, and to whose exertions a not inconsiderable portion of the prosperity which has attended the place is due".*

But it wasn't just the local brick and colliery masters who took an interest in the welfare of the port. The W,M & CQ Rly also did much to assist in up – grading the docks in order to accommodate the increased rail traffic from which the company earned much of its revenue, and in early October 1866 a new and extended docks, which they had helped to construct, berthed its first vessel.

Wrexham Advertiser 30th March 1878 – Of all the places in Flintshire which are increasing in population there is none which is making more rapid progress than Connah's Quay. New houses are continually in the process of building and from being the obscure fishing village of twenty years ago it is now becoming quite a town and an important seaport. Wharfs and quays have been erected and at times there are as many as 40, 50 or 60 vessels discharging their cargoes or embarking goods for other ports.

The most significant expansion of the port was begun in May 1884, when the building of a much longer quayside was begun. This improvement was desperately needed to allow the traffic from the Wrexham districts to have better access to the quayside – *"the brick and tile traffic of Buckley together with the collieries nearest the port having taken up all the available space",* and once the new dock was opened in September, Connah's Quay was assured its position as the principal port on the Dee. The brick traffic moving through the port continued to thrive well into the early 20th century ; a typical list of ships carrying bricks for the week ending 26th October, 1895 showing that eight shiploads departed that week for Fleetwood, Newquay, Newry, Point of Ayr, Bangor and London. But by early 1951 there were serious rumours that the docks might close ; it no doubt having suffered from the improvements made in road transportation, as well as the interruptions to trade caused by the recent war, apart from the fact that industry in general had significantly declined throughout the 20th century. The Chronicle for February 1951 reported:

"Mr Dennis Griffiths, chairman of the Buckley Fire Brick Manufacturers Association, said the closing of the docks would be a serious blow to the industry. It was well-known that they were amongst the earliest users of the port, and they were shipping from there long before the docks were opened. He could remember when 55,000 tons a year were shipped from Connah's Quay. He admitted that there had been a decline in tonnage, and they never envisaged that a war would interfere with trade. There was substantial evidence that in the years just before the war, things were beginning to pick up again. During the last 12 months the Irish trade had increased tremendously. The retention of the dock facilities was vital to the clay goods trade of Buckley. Mr G R Oates for Standard Buckley Ltd said that there had been a great increase in the number of inquiries and in the actual business done. His firm had established quite a good connection, especially with Dublin and Belfast. Mr Oates added that they had had quite a considerable tonnage awaiting shipment and it was not a question of closing the docks, but improving the facilities. Mr E V Villar representing Castle Firebrick, Buckley Brick & Tile and E Parry & Sons said that two or three years before the war they had established a sound connection with the Isle of Man, but in post war years that market had suffered because Flintshire housing had enjoyed a priority. Their Isle of Man agent would tell them that he would take six cargoes immediately. He revealed that in 1939 the three companies he represented sent 6,780 tons from Connah's

Ships moored at Connah's Quay Docks circa 1904-12, with a brick schooner awaiting loading in the foreground. The railway wagons bear the name of William Hancock & Co of the Buckley Lane End Works and carry loaded shipping boxes full of bricks. Photo: FRO.

Quay. If Connah's Quay were closed the trade with the Isle of Man would be entirely eliminated. The cost of sending bricks from Liverpool was prohibitive".

The docks themselves were, and for most of their life always had been, owned and run by the firm of Messrs Coppack, Carter & Co; the Coppack family having had many sea captains amongst their lineage, and the eventual termination of their connection with the docks heralded the beginning of the end. In January 1956 British Railways had effected repairs to the quayside's pilings, and in 1962 they purchased the docks outright, closing them shortly afterwards, but only temporarily. However, the level of available trade in the early 1960s could not seriously justify the port continuing to operate, and on 6th April, 1964 Connah's Quay Docks finally officially closed, the last ship to commercially leave the port being the Dutch ship "Merwestad" carrying scrap iron from a local breaker's yard.

Today the quayside looks in very good shape, but only serves to moor small pleasure craft and fishing boats. A small industrial estate has grown up alongside it, but the only activity on the dockside itself comes from leisure walkers, fishermen and cyclists.

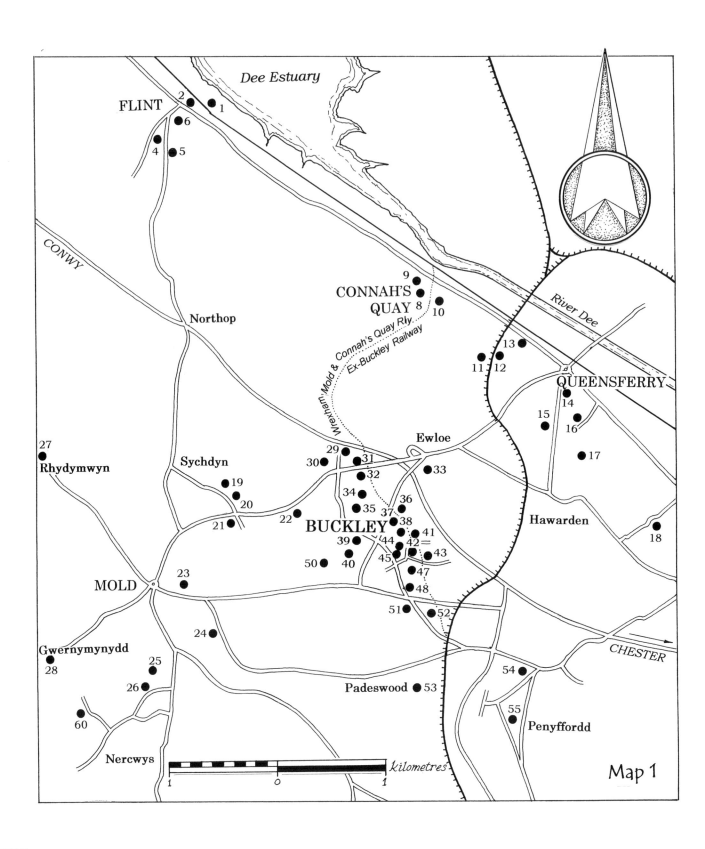

Dee Estuary

FLINT

CONWY

Northop

CONNAH'S QUAY

Wrexham, Mold & Connah's Quay Rly.
Ex-Buckley Railway

River Dee

QUEENSFERRY

Rhydymwyn

Sychdyn

Ewloe

Hawarden

BUCKLEY

MOLD

CHESTER

Gwernymynydd

Padeswood

Penyffordd

Nercwys

kilometres

Map 1

FLINTSHIRE WORKS

Flint Area

Our journey through the bricklands begins in the north of Flintshire at the town of Flint on the Dee estuary.

Before the boom in manufacturing during the early Victorian age, the town was principally a small fishing village and holiday resort. The Chronicle of 1839 referred to it as "this delightful watering place" and a year later Robson's Trade Directory described it as "an irregularly built town seated on a well wooded flat. The gentle sea breeze renders it particularly salubrious and it is resorted to by many respectable families for sea bathing. Since the erection of the new baths on the Flint shore, both comfort and convenience have been afforded". Mr Hall's Hot & Cold Baths were sited near the shore at OS 2475 7319 just west of the present lifeboat station, and by 1848 the Chronicle could say that " those who at this delightful season would recreate themselves and in addition to the luxury of a bath enjoy the picturesque beauties of Welsh scenery cannot do better than sail down the river to Mr Hall's establishment. The delightful rural walks in the vicinity of Flint are much increased in interest by extensive marine views". By the time the 1861 census came around, Joseph Hall was still living at the Baths; by then converted into a private dwelling.

Indeed, before the coastal railway opened up the more expansive beaches of Rhyl and Llandudno further up the coast, Flint was the nearest accessible destination for the more affluent middle classes who would travel by boat from Chester and even the Midlands to holiday here and bathe in the waters which then used to lap the towers of Flint Castle.

Even at this time there were a few very small collieries on the outskirts of the town, which in those days would not have been very noticeable, but they soon became a major exporter of coal from the little wharf which still exists today. In 1850 Flint shipped out 29,076 tons of coal; more even than the larger Mostyn Docks further up the coast, and before the establishment of Holyhead, Flint was also a principal embarkation port for passengers to Ireland. As a fishing town it probably always had a boat repair yard, but certainly by 1858 a more respectable ship building facility was in operation and it was here that in 1864 the great Buckley brickmakers Catherall & Co chose to have built the 74ft. long schooner "William Shepherd"

to accommodate their Irish markets.

By the 1870s however, heavy industry had seriously begun to take its toll on the fabric and appearance of Flint. If the smoke from the newer and larger collieries was not bad enough, the greater culprit was the chemical works just to the west of the castle. Originally opened in 1851 it had grown to gigantic proportions and became the scene of very regular accidents of a most disturbing nature. On the fortunes of the town, the Chronicle by 1879 could paint a picture far removed from that of 31 years previously, and they reported that " at the best of times Flint does not wear a very attractive appearance, being generally enveloped in a halo of sulphurous smoke and wearing a general aspect of dirtiness".

SITE 1: PENTRE BRICKYARD

"I went over to Flint and there is a field belonging to your Lordship near the Tollgate on the road leading from Flint to Pentre Ffrwrndan and adjoining the railway as a convenient place for obtaining good clay, well adapted for making bricks and draining pipes. I have circulated the report that the field is to be let for that purpose. A brick maker from Flint has just made an application for it. I may perhaps be allowed to let the ground on the usual terms – bricks 2s. per thousand and three inch draining pipes 5s."

That letter was sent to the landowner Lord Mostyn by his land agent in June 1855. Although today we cannot know to which field he was referring, on the 1878 OS map there is a kiln and claypit just to the east of the tollgate at the reference 2509 7275 in the district still now bearing the name Pentre Ffwrndan. We may assume that the Flint brickmaker may well have taken the land, but failed in his venture, as five years later an advertisement ran in the Chronicle offering "on the brickfield at Pentre near Flint several thousand of excellent slop bricks with 5 three inch planks, moulding table, tub and wheelbarrow which are sold under a distress for rent". That auction took place on 29th May 1860, and from the meagre catalogue of possessions it is clear that operations were on a very modest scale. The next clues to the fortunes of this site can be traced in the Flint rates books. No works at Pentre were entered in the 1869 listings, so perhaps this site was unused by this time, but in 1873 a William Pierce is shown as occupying as well as owning "a brickworks at Pentre", but three years later, although he still owned the site, it was marked as being unoccupied. As the only brickworks listed in existence at Pentre, which in those days was a very undeveloped area outside the main town, this has to be the brickworks site shown on the OS map, and it was still there on the 1899 version, but by then marked as an "old brick kiln".

The field is still there today, although minus any signs of its industrial past. For such a small town Flint had six established brickyards that I have managed to find, and despite most of them being only small affairs, it shows just how rapidly the place was growing in the 1860s and 70s, and the brickmakers took natural advantage of that fact. To illustrate this, we can refer to the following report of the establishment of Oakenholt paper mill – one mile down the road from the Pentre site:

Chester Chronicle 8th July 1871 – Messrs M,Corquodales new paper mills are proceeding with great rapidity. One noticeable feature is the impetus which has been given to brick-making, as no less than six fresh places have been commenced employing more than 50 hands, with a view of finding a market at the above works.

SITE 2: BATH COLLIERY AND EDWARD BOWER

The main protagonist in our next story was Edward Bower. Originally from New Mills in Derbyshire, he spent a good few years of his working life earning his living from the mineral resources of Flint. The earliest mention of his name which I came across was on a scrappy piece of paper written in 1848 and listing the amount of coal gotten at Bower & Williams Marsh Colliery. The Marsh Colliery itself was a little way out of Flint on the site where the sewage works now stands, and it was here where the 1851 census shows the 41 year-old Edward working as a "coal transporter" and living in a cottage at the colliery. The term "transporter" may be somewhat misleading by today's standards. Bower was after all a co-partner in the company, and

Slater's 1850 Trade Directory lists him as a coal agent, a position which would have seen him occupying the post of organising the sales and transportation of coal from the colliery.

Edwards' other speculation was Bath Colliery, which stood on the main road into Flint, almost opposite the present day Swan Inn. The 1844 tithe map shows nothing here except fields, but Bath Colliery was definitely in existence by 1853, when on 15th November the Ship Inn became the venue for the sale of its assets. Edward had by then moved into a cottage built alongside the colliery, and the little works had become very much his personal responsibility. He must have acquired it at the 1853 auction sale, because in October 1859 both the collieries were for sale, with the Marsh listed in the holding of Mr Williams, and the Bath in that of Edward Bower. Neither men could have become anything like wealthy from their speculations, as the lists of assets were piteously small, and of the Bath the sale prospectus noted that only "a small portion of the coal under the land has been gotten". I believe that this 1859 sale probably marked the end of both sites as collieries and the rebirth of Bath as a new brickmaking site. In the census of 1861 Edward is now a brickmaker living at 36 Chester Road – probably the same cottage he was in eight years previously. Further evidence for the existence of a brickworks here comes in the very detailed maps drawn in 1863 when the railway company built a new road bridge over the line to make a safer crossing. The old road shown on the plans as Brick Kiln Lane had up to this time abutted the old Bath Colliery on its eastern side and crossed the railway on the level, but Brick Kiln Lane disappeared when the crossing was modified to become the bridge we see today.

Edward remained on this site for years to come, but suffered a slight setback in April 1864 when "Edward Bower of Flint, a brickmaker" was declared a bankrupt, and another railway plan for this year shows the site marked as an "old brick field", so we may assume that he might have been experiencing difficulties for some short time previously. Not deterred though, he is seen in various Trade Directories as carrying on brickmaking at Chester Road from 1868 until 1883, and the site is shown clearly on the 1871 OS map as a brickyard, but had disappeared altogether by 1899.

The actual working surface area of Bath Colliery

was very small and was centred at OS 2465 7295, and the later brickfield lay alongside it on the colliery's unused land, centred at OS 2475 7288 where the fire station and adjoining industrial units now stand.

SITE 3: EYTON'S BRICK KILN
SITE 4: FLINT BRICK & TILE COMPANY

"At the Flint Brick and Tile Works the purple mottled marls are used, but as they are not stiff enough when used alone, the weathered shale from the spoil heaps of the old adjacent Pwll y Mwg shaft of the Dee Green Colliery, or sometimes the red surface soil, is mixed with them".

That account was published in The Geology of Flint, written in 1924 at a time when this site, the largest of the town's brickworks, was the only one left in operation, and it is also interesting for giving mention of part of the area's much earlier history. In fact, from an industrial viewpoint the district forming the triangle between the Halkyn and Northop roads is probably one of the most varied and ancient in the town.

The earliest brickmaking site I could find in this area is shown on an 1845 railway map – a brick kiln alongside an old coal pit bank in the holding of the Eyton family – John, Robert, Edward and James, which is shown on the accompanying plan of this area. The Chronicle in 1843 refers to the Eytons as being "large mining proprietors" with collieries at Bagillt and Flint and two years later they also took over the Rhewl Pit at Mostyn. The Eytons figure prominently in newspaper reports of the time, and when Robert Eyton, respected in the town for being a great philanthropist, died on 19th May 1848, all the ships in Flint Wharf lowered their flags to half mast, and on the day of his funeral every shop in the town closed as a mark of respect.

In those days before widespread mechanisation, the Eyton's brick kiln would most probably have been a small scale affair, manufacturing crude hand made bricks for use in their various coal pits nearby. Another feature of interest on the map is the horse drawn tramway which was shown on an 1854 sale plan drawn by the surveyor Mr Leifchild. The rails from the various collieries in this district ran down Halkyn Road and skirted around the then western perimeter of the town, to cross the main coast road to the left of the

Little Ship Inn (then called the New Anchor) to end up at the wharfside and the nearby Lead Smelting Works. An old description of the smelting works says that "coal is brought to the doors of the furnaces by a railway from adjacent collieries".

Come the genesis of the Flint Brick and Tile Works, the Eyton's industrial glory had by then become only a memory. On the 1871 OS map nothing but their old coal shafts are shown here, but in 1873 the rates books show that a Peter Bibby was running a brickworks here on land rented from Adam Eyton, a descendant of the earlier dynasty.

Peter had formerly been a joiner; the son of Thomas Bibby, a reasonably well heeled property owner in the town. Besides the brickworks, Peter had other financial concerns to occupy him, so he took on John Bithell as a managing partner with a one-third share in the brickworks, but in August 1881 the company was up for sale as a "lucrative business". No sale was immediately forthcoming, and a month later the advertisement appeared in the papers again, this time offering an option to purchase either the whole works or the managing partner's share. Whether it was Bithell who was keen to get out is not clear, but from the next report we can see he was still there a year later.

Chester Chronicle 12th August 1882 – Five young men were charged with having wilfully damaged the roof of a shed, the property of the Flint Brick & Tile Co. Richard Birk said he was a brickmaker in the employ of the company. He was in a hut at the works and saw the defendants come in. They afterwards went outside and threw stones onto the roof. They knocked a hole through the roof which was a slate one. Witness went every Sunday afternoon into the works. Mr John Bithell said he was in the managing department. He had notices posted forbidding trespassing. A deal of trespassing had been going on.

As we have seen in an earlier chapter brickworks were a mecca for tramps, and the local police had numerous complaints from this works concerning kilns, huts and bricks being damaged. Even the census record for 1891 lists two tramps as being "resident" at these works, although it was not specified whether it was on a short or long term basis.

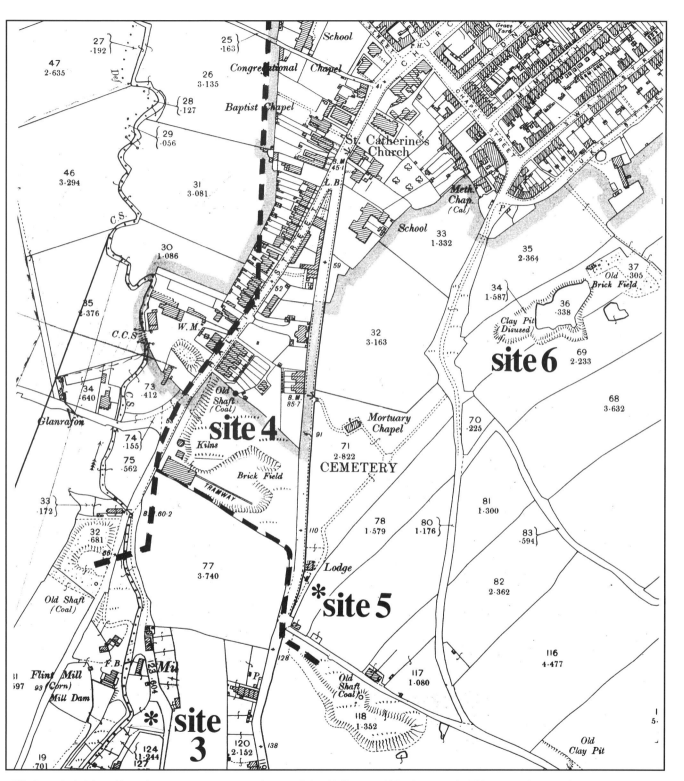

Flint's main brickmaking sites were concentrated around the Halkyn and Northop roads. This map of 1899 shows site 4 as the only one left in production, whilst the heavy black lines delineate the route of the earlier tram lines of the 1840s which linked small local coal pits to the wharf on the Dee. The old shaft marked at site 4 is the earlier pumping pit for the Eyton's colliery workings.

By 1883 Peter Bibby was being reported as "being a man of money", and by 1891 he had managed to purchase the freehold on the brickworks land. He also owned a timber yard business in Salisbury Street. Whether Bibby retired or not is unsure, but by 1895, nine years before his death, the works were held by Messrs Birks & Jones, but this new company must have headed into difficulties shortly afterwards. The rates listings for 1897 show a void where the brickworks was formerly included, and the Chronicle for that year also advertised the sale of the entire works by auction on 17th June – even down to the contents of the office. Messrs Birks & Jones probably managed to purchase back their company's works, as Birks, according to his later obituary, gave up his interest in the company a few years before his demise in January 1913, and from the incomplete run of rate books available we do know that by 1912 the style of the company had changed to Messrs Jones & Davies. By this time the company also had a small iron foundry opposite the brickworks on Halkyn St at OS 2403 7276, and the directory for 1922 also lists Jones & Davies as being the brass and iron founders here.

In what year the works finally closed is not clear, but it must have still been going in 1924 when a geological reference book happens to mention that the Eyton's old pumping pit "still remained in the brickyard of Jones & Davies". When closure finally came the works was demolished, and the land remained derelict and overgrown for many decades, until in the late 1990s a new housing estate was built here – the very aptly named Kiln Close.

SITE 5

This small brickyard which was clearly an established business and not some temporary affair is the only one of which virtually nothing is known. The only evidence for its existence comes in land sale documents for May and November 1853 which show it on the plans attached and name it as "the brickyard on the Flint to Northop road", but by the time of the 1871 OS map it had disappeared.

It stood at OS 2416 7248 which corresponds today to the back garden of the house on the corner of Northop Rd and Coed Onn Rd.

SITE 6: JACOB DAVIES BRICKWORKS

This was the second largest brickworks in Flint and stood on part of a field referred to in those days as Ladies Two Acre Field, which was part owned by William Pierce, a brewer in Bagillt. Knowing of the presence of clay on the land, Pierce decided to profit from that fact, and in 1872 advertised for a suitable man to take the site. A Ruthin brickmaker named Jacob Davies responded and an agreement was made in December of that year for him to work the clayland and *"for that purpose to sink, drive, make, set up, work and use any pits, engines, works and contrivances for finding, winning and manufacturing such clay into bricks, pipes, tiles and other things usually made by brickmakers "*. The annual rent was set at £30 with a royalty paid of 2s. for each thousand bricks made. The works steadily grew, and in May 1874 we find Jacob advertising for tenders to be submitted for the building of three new kilns – a clear indication that his business was flourishing. A few months later he was selling off a small nearly new drain pipe moulding machine, very probably because his increased orders required the need to invest in a larger model.

By 1876 Jacob was still in sole control of the works, but at some point along the way he went into partnership with perhaps his brother, under the style of Messrs Davies. Perhaps this move was to shore up the business by bringing in more capital, but whatever the case, the venture was by then in trouble and soon folded, but rescue eventually came from the nearby brickworks of Peter Bibby, and the company's transformation was duly reported in the local press:

Chester Chronicle 22nd March 1879 – The brickworks late in the occupation of Messrs Davies and which have been standing for some time, are about to commence operations. A large new boiler drawn by a number of horses passed through the town on Wednesday to be placed in the works.

Chester Chronicle 24th May 1879 – The Flint Brick & Tile Co having purchased the works late in the occupation of Messrs J. &J.P. Davies and enlarged considerably, they are now in a position to receive orders for various kinds of builders and fire goods. Articles for chemical and ironworks made to any pattern to order.

Under the guidance of its new masters the works acquired the capability to manufacture what it called "bricks and tiles of superior quality" and this continued certainly until 1891, after which time no documented evidence can be found until its reappearance in the next available rates book of 1897, by which time it was listed as being "dilapidated". By the beginning of the Great War, the maps show it as being only an " old brickfield ", and by 1922 it had vanished completely.

The brickworks stood at OS 2438 7274 which is now occupied by the houses in the corner between Prince of Wales Avenue and Gwynedd Drive.

Shotton & Connah's Quay Area

Brick workers at an unidentified Connah's Quay brickworks in the early 20th century. Photo: FRO.

SITE 7: A. RENEY CONNAH'S QUAY

Moving down the coast from Flint we arrive in Connah's Quay; the home to four well established works, the least documented being that of Andrew Reney. When it was founded is unsure, but the 1870 OS map shows a small "brickyard" with its claypit fronting onto the main road. By the turn of the century it had gone; to be replaced by a more substantial works just south of it at OS 2936 6963, and it is this later site which we know to be that of Andrew Reney. Whether the smaller site was its predecessor is only supposition. On the 1912 map Reney's works was not even marked as a brickworks any more; most of the buildings having been demolished, and the open cast clayhole was described as an "old clay pit". The clayhole was bulldozed flat by the Urban Council in 1951, and today the site is now the scout's football pitch at the corner of Chapel Street and Tuscan Way.

SITE 8: T.J. RENEY, CENTRAL WORKS

An advertisement in the Chester Chronicle of 1897 offered machine made wire cut bricks to be had from Lloyd's Connah's Quay Brickworks; the works which was later to become known as Central Works. It was established by William Henry Lloyd, who in 1889 had purchased the Top y Fron estate and began farming there. After three years he decided to begin a brickworks to capitalise on the demand for bricks following the boom in housing which resulted after the establishment of the Hawarden Bridge steel works in 1896, and he engaged Thomas J Reney to erect the sheds and kilns and take on the running of the works. After two years however Lloyd decided to take control himself and he erected a further two kilns, bringing his total expenditure on the place to £2,200, but in financing his new works he had also become indebted to Reney to the tune of £1,400. Had his works been the only source of bricks in the district, he might have been sitting pretty, but unfortunately three other major brickworks in the immediate area had proved to be too serious a competition, and to ensure his company's survival the only course of action left to him was to hand it back to Reney, who practically bought out Lloyd's interest for the paltry sum of £100. Lloyd had speculated well above his financial means, not to mention showing a serious lack of practical experience, and by 1905 he found himself bankrupt. Asked by his receivers "why on earth he should have embarked on a business of which he had no previous experience", he said that "brickmaking seemed to be a craze just then".

Wrexham Advertiser 12th May 1906 – Mold County Court. Thomas Edge aged 10 and John Quinn aged 11 appeared on charges of felony. Frank Baird said he was brickworks manager to Mr T J Reney. At 1 o'clock on Saturday he made the storeroom at the brickworks secure. He went there on Sunday at 3pm. The window had been broken and the hasp damaged. Upon entering he found that several boxes had been broken open and a quantity of fuse taken. A powder – cask lid had been broken and a tin containing powder had been tampered with. Sergeant Hill said the defendants broke into 20 or 30 places during the night and actually took out and harnessed a horse belonging to Mr Nock, which they rode away. The boys admitted the charges and the father of Edge said he was unable to control him. Last month he was charged with stealing a horse and was discharged. The Bench ordered that six strokes of the birch be administered and that they be detained in a certified industrial school until the age of 16 years.

The works is listed in trade directories of 1914 but not afterwards, and was supposed to have closed by 1916, which given the problems caused by the war could well have been the case.

The works was sited at OS 2930 6955 with a clayhole extending southwards. In the decades which followed closure this flooded hole was known locally as Reney's Pond, and in 1967 was filled in with 37,000 tons of ash procured from the old Connah's Quay power station. It is now home to a football field, and at its southerly side can still be seen the banks of the old clayhole rising up. The Deeside Naval Club now stands on the site where the factory buildings once were.

SITE 9: JOHN WILLIAMS BRICKWORKS, CONNAH'S QUAY

Chester Chronicle 27th August 1881 – On Wednesday John Hughes, about 13 years of age, after being out in the morning gathering mushrooms, called on his way home to see his brother working at Mr John Williams brickworks, when his clothes got entangled in the machinery and crushed him so severely that he died from the effects on Thursday morning.

That report is the earliest reference I could find to this site, along with the verification of its name on a railway map of the same year.

In April 1900 the works was put up for sale as having been "worked by the late John Williams of Buckley for the last 20 years", so perhaps it's establishment can be placed circa 1880. From the advertised details we can see that it was of a fairly respectable size with four drying sheds, five kilns, an engine shed, boiler shed, a separate drying kiln, office, cottage, workman's cabin and three chimney stacks.

What happened to it in the following years is uncertain, but the rates book for 1912 lists it as being "redundant". By the late 1930s however, the works had been acquired by the building contractor Alun Edwards of Cefnybedd, who used it to make the bricks for his construction work. There still exists a letter from the Wrexham Brick & Tile Co, which at the end of

December 1935 wrote to Alun Edwards regretting that they could not supply him with 240,000 bricks which he had requested, and perhaps it was this event which persuaded Alun Edwards that he should acquire a brickyard of his own. Mr Edwards himself explained in a newspaper report that in 1938 he had spent £3,000 on providing new machinery at the Connah's Quay Brickworks, but because of pilfering and vandalism, he had by 1951 realised a loss of £8,000 on the place.

It's not hard to imagine that he may have given up on it soon after, because in 1953 we find a report of the Urban Council leasing the works clayhole to the local cricket club. The site was re-landscaped as a cricket pitch and the works' old engine house was converted into a pavilion, but it has since been replaced.

The factory itself was at OS 2926 6968 on the site of the present Old People's Association club house, and to the south the banks of the old clayhole encircle the cricket pitch.

SITE 10: PRINCE'S BRICKWORKS CONNAH'S QUAY

This was the largest and most successful of the brickworks in the Deeside district and was founded around 1879 by James Prince, but the earliest documented evidence I could find for it was an 1890 advertisement for his Brick & Pipe Works, at which time he was also promoting himself as a builder.

Chester Chronicle 13th October 1894 – A horse attached to a cart belonging to Princes brickworks ran away on Tuesday. The cart was being loaded with bricks when the animal became frightened and bolted. The cart came into contact with the Office and was overturned. Part of the office was knocked down and the horse, while endeavouring to free himself, kicked so violently that he sustained serious injuries.

A gradual enlargement of the works took place over the following years. In June 1896 a complaint was made to the council that Mr Prince "had erected a new brickyard across a footpath" and he corrected his error by constructing a new path around his site, and it was in this same year that the works benefited from a siding onto the Wrexham, Mold & Connah's Quay Rly.

In 1901 we even find him having to turn down orders because of the time he was spending on his improvement works. A letter of 17th May from Mr Prince to a firm of Manchester architects reads: "We thank you for your esteemed favour to hand the tendering for a new church, house and shops here, but we are very busy with our own works buildings just now and cannot see our own way to tender." By November though, it looks like the works was back in full production. In a letter to Point of Ayr Colliery he quotes for an order of bricks and pointedly mentions: "We wish to say that the quality of the bricks we are now making far exceeds our previous manufacture". That one line suggests that new improved kilns had been installed.

Flintshire News 2nd July 1914 – Five boys residing at Connah's Quay were summoned for malicious damage. It was stated that they entered Princes brickyard, pulled the plug out of a barrel of tar,

QUALITY IS THE FINAL TEST

OUR BRICKS ARE MADE TO STAND THIS TEST

We Make : Hand-made Facing Bricks "Alltones," in Rough or Smooth, Sandfaced, Antique, Multi-coloured, Reds.

MAKERS OF "ALLTONES"

We Make : Wire-cut Rustic Bricks (any size or colour). Red Wire-cut Facing Bricks, Wire-cut Sandfaced Rustics. etc., etc.

JOHN PRINCE

BRICK MANUFACTURER

CONNAH'S QUAY

CHESTER

Greys, Old Gold, Ginger Brown, Purple Brown, Heather Brown, Plum, Blue, etc., etc.

Also Briquettes in all shapes and colours, for Fireplaces. Air Bricks, Pressed Facing Bricks in all thicknesses, etc., etc.

JOHN PRINCE'S BRICK WORKS AT CONNAH'S QUAY, Established 1879

Telephone : Connah's Quay 9.

Telegrams : " Prince's Brickworks, Connah's Quay."

Shipping Port : Connah's Quay.

Private Siding : per L.N.E.R., Connah's Quay.

Road Transport Anywhere.

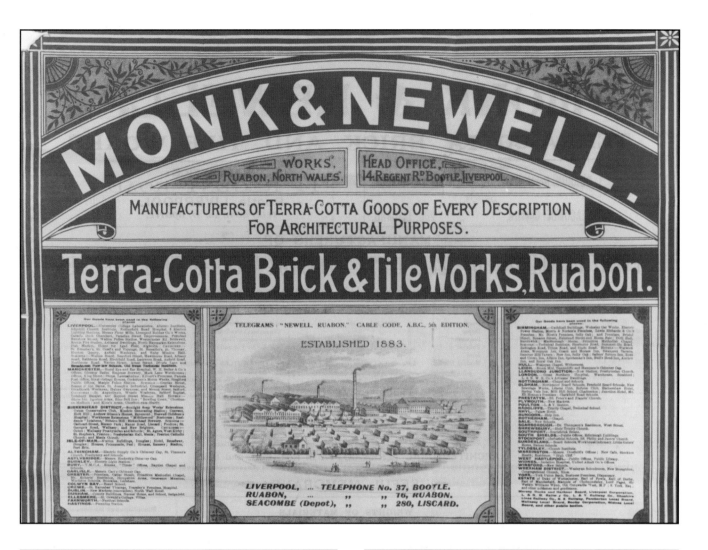

Monk and Newell was one of the three large works in Ruabon, and this is the top half of the Company's calendar of 1915. Bricks stamped with the company name are still quite easily found . Thomas Monk died in 1889 and some of the company's bricks were thereafter stamped "Newell Ruabon", but such examples are extremely rare. The works was acquired by Capt. Stubbs in the early 1920s and became one of his North Wales Brick and Tile Company holdings, with the reverse of his Ruabon bricks bearing the trademark "Rubric". Photo: DRO.

"The Brickmakers" by Ralph Hedley, RBA (1848-1913). Working methods varied even within local districts and although these field brickmakers are depicted working at Cleveland in 1899, their methods were not much different from those used in our district. A girl turns out bricks directly from the wooden mould onto the bare ground, so the weather must have been very dry, as bricks were normally placed on planks. In the right background is a "scintled" hack of bricks – a term used in the industry to describe stacking the drying bricks with gaps between them to allow air to pass through easily.

The Trevor Works of Roberts and Maginnis was in the 1970s a stark contrast to the practices of the earlier field brickmakers. The track leading to the back of the works once led to a driftmine worked by a donkey hauled tramway, giving the works its earlier nickname of "The Donkey Works".

Pant Brickworks was owned by the wealthy industrialist Henry Dennis, who developed the site into one of the largest brickworks in North East Wales. This illuminated address was the employees' presentation to Mr George Till upon his leaving the position of works manager in 1902. Photo: DRO.

The opencast clayholes in the Glascoed Valley near Brymbo show a beautiful yellow fireclay striated with bands of red. From the clays in this valley Ffrith Brickworks made its characteristic yellow bricks.

Site 57. The small yards belonging to the agricultural and landed estates made bricks mainly for use on estate building projects. This example is unusual, as such minor yards hardly ever produced machine-stamped bricks, and name stamping was even rarer.

Site 94. Joseph Collins and his son Daniel had a short lived tenancy at the Marchwiel Brickyard, so this is again one of the district's rarer found bricks. This country brickyard was one of the larger of many small yards to be found on the clay rich lands of Wrexham's Maelor district.

Site 68. The Ffrwd site was principally a large iron works alongside a colliery, and its brickworks was founded to supply the growing demand for bricks to furnish those works. The brickworks eventually outlived the two earlier sites.

Site 116. Giller & Co probably mixed their clay with the waste from the earlier Plas Issa Ironworks, which would account for the brick's distinctive rust red mottling.
This example is a stable brick -- one of the company's advertised products.

Was this brick made at the Wynnstay Colliery? It comes from an old engine house on the colliery site itself, but although the colliery was not documented as having a brickworks of its own, it was the later owner of the Plas yn Wern Brickworks, where this brick could have been made.

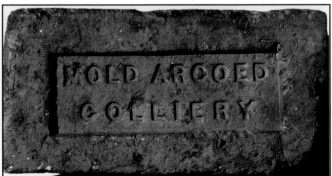

Site 23. The Argoed Colliery was not Mold's largest, but in its day it was certainly the most prestigious. Not many collieries seemed to name-stamp their bricks, and this surviving example is no better tribute to the brickmaking activities of the Victorian colliery industry.

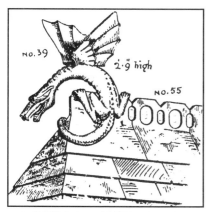

Another fine example of local terracotta modelling adorns the Nags Head at Rhos.

An impressive J C Edwards terracotta dragon sits atop a roof in Chester. The accompanying illustration of the dragon comes from the Company's trade catalogue of 1903.

The Delph Works of Henry Wyndham were originally founded by Thomas Seacome and became the largest brickworks in the Acrefair district. Wyndham acquired the works in the early 1880s and Mr Phillips, the works manager, later became his partner.

The important J C Edwards Trefynant Brickworks at Cefn Mawr closed in 1958 after 100 years of production. Over 40 years later large terracotta blocks litter the overgrown ruins.

Summer 2001. Old machine beds lie in the woods which were once the site of the Wepre Hall Brickworks at Shotton. What once stood on these beds were likely the works' brickmaking machines.

The ruins of an original coal-fired round kiln lie overgrown by trees and ivy on the old Ruby Brickworks site in February 2003. This view shows one of the kiln's two loading doors. A kiln from the demolished Abenbury Brickworks has been rebuilt and preserved at Kings Mills near Wrexham, but this is the last original kiln to remain in situ anywhere in the district.

Many examples of the local brickworks' productions are still to be seen throughout the district. The ornate design of a house in Chester illustrates some fine architectural terracotta from the factories of the Ruabon district, as does the red brick portico of one of Wrexham's grander town houses. On a more modest scale, a beautifully detailed door arch in buff terracotta decorates a house in Sandycroft; probably the product of one of the nearby Buckley factories. All these buildings were constructed around the end of the 19th century.

The first large scale brickworks advertisement to feature in the local press appeared in late 1909 for the Wrexham Brick & Tile Co, shortly after it had changed ownership. This colourised version shows the same illustration of the factory which was used on much of the company's literature.

Site 91. Wrexham's two most prestigious brickworks lay at the south of the town on a spur of the first rate Ruabon Marl clay bed. The Wrexham Brick & Tile Co could equal the product quality of the Ruabon works, and they capitalised on this fact by stamping some of their bricks with their trademark Ruabon District Marl Beds.

Site 92. Davies Brothers Works lay alongside that of the Wrexham Brick & Tile Co. Unable to benefit from the association with the Ruabon Marl name they settled for the trademark Abenbury Marl Beds, named after the local district and the name of their works.

Site 126. Besides the Dennis Company, the three principal works of J C Edwards were the most prolific in Denbighshire. The Trefynant Works existed for just over 100 years, and produced every conceivable item of clay and terracotta manufacture.

Adamantine was one of the many brands to emerge from the Davison Co's two main factories at sites 32 and 38 at Buckley. Davison's clay beds were some of the finest in Flintshire, and the company liked to advertise their products' specific properties.

Site 34. This unusual stamping comes from the Brookhill Works of the Buckley Brick & Tile Co. So respected was the manager Mr J M Gibson that the works became known as Gibson's Works, but his name had nothing to do with the official company title.

Site 41. The Standard Company lasted well into the 20th century. During the Victorian era the works established their Buckley Glazed Brick Co brand to capitalise on the growing fashion for glazed and enamelled wares.

tapped one-and-a-half barrels of oil and smashed seven chimney pots, doing damage of £4. The case against one was dismissed and the other defendants were ordered to pay the costs.

It seems that the last days of struggle to keep the works in production were not helped by the mood of its younger employees. In 1960 a fight between two 17 year-olds resulted in one of them being stabbed with a penknife, and the following report is particularly revealing:

Chester Chronicle 28th January 1961 – The story of five youths who on five occasions deliberately damaged a brick cutting machine at Princes brickworks where they were employed, in order to get time off, was told at Connah's Quay Court. The damage cost the company hundreds of pounds in lost production. Apparently the method used was to throw a bar in. The machine went bang and stopped and the bar was then pulled out and thrown in a corner. Michael Sephton, 18, was charged with malicious damage. He affected the production of 48,500 bricks, enough to build two substantial houses, and John Hargreaves, 17, affected the production of 23,000 bricks. The cost of repairs was £97. Mr Kerfoot Owen for the juveniles said it was agreed that it was senseless behaviour and could only be attributed to so many working in consort with no adequate supervision. There were no fewer than thirteen boys employed at the works where their basic wage was £3-10-0 with a bonus after 42,000 bricks. The atmosphere where they worked was very hot and extremely dusty and they returned home filthy and exhausted.

By the end of that year all was lost:

Chester Chronicle 9th December 1961 – Although the average output was 3 million bricks a year and there is a claypit rich with clay, Princes brickworks has ceased production. Only four of the original 30 employees remain and when the last of the bricks in stock have gone, the works will close down for an indefinite period. The reason for the closure is the need for modernisation. The works was founded 82 years ago by the late Mr Prince and has been carried on by his son Mr John Prince, grandson Mr

Sidney Prince, and great grandson the present owner Mr John L Prince. Mr Prince told the Chronicle that the depth of the clay in the pit was 65 yards. "We have only taken about 18 inches a year over all the floor and there is 120 years left". Mr Prince is now concentrating on a new venture, the Connah's Quay Concrete Co. Ltd, the site of which adjoins the brickworks.

The works stood at OS 2935 6926 and has been replaced by a group of houses called Isabella Court. The extensive flooded clayhole to the south-east was filled in December 1971 following the tragic drowning of a child, and looks much today like it probably did in the days when this district was nothing more than rolling fields.

SITE 11: WEPRE HALL SHOTTON
Further down the coast lies Shotton, which like Connah's Quay is today an extensive district of housing estates. In Victorian times however it was much smaller and just on the brink of expansion, and by mid-1903 the Chronicle was describing the growth of these two towns as "little short of phenomenal". In the case of the establishment of Wepre Hall Brickworks we have an historically unparalleled record of the event in the form of the diary of James Hampson, which catalogued the process almost step by step.

Hampson was one of the main players in the enterprise, the others being Robert Price and Richard Darbyshire. At 7pm on 16th November 1899 they met to hear the results of Price's bore hole tests at this site, and on hearing that he had discovered a bed of clay up to 21 ft thick the decision was taken to write to the W.M. & C.Q. Rly. Co. and apply for a branch line to be layed into the virgin field. The following diary entries continue the story:

Tuesday 21st November 1899 – A letter from Mr Blane (Wepre Estate's agent) asking me to make a written application for the land at Shotton for the purpose of starting a brickworks. Wrote again to the railway company asking for a reply to my letter. Got an acknowledgement of my letter next morning saying they were giving our application for a siding their consideration. Have got two test bricks – one from Seth Heaton at Mount Pleasant Brickworks and the other from Tom Shaw Aston Hall Brickworks – I have also got a brick from Sandycroft brickworks and one from Mr Rowley's Shotton brickworks. The brick that Shaw has burnt for me is very much like Mr Rowley's bricks and these have a very good sale – in fact I think the clay that we have is the same bed that Mr Rowley is working, it is not far from it and has the same appearance and our test brick is very similar.

2nd December – Mr Darbyshire met Mr Cartwright from the railway company and walked down the line next to the proposed site; the railway agent pointed out that the siding would be on an incline and would need manning, which cost would seriously compromise the amount of capital outlay to set up the works. Suggested spreading the cost over some years.

Friday 8th December – I received a letter from agent to the Wepre Estate confirming our application for land at Shotton for a proposed brickworks.

Saturday 9th December 9pm – We met Mr Blane's secretary at the Glynne Arms Hotel and he says if we can make arrangements with the farmer Mr Charmily we can enter upon the land at once and start casting clay.

Saturday 14th April 1900 – Messrs Darbyshire, Price and myself met to decide about a brickmaking machine. After considerable discussion we agreed to purchase Mr William Johnson's No. 2 pug mill – if this proved satisfactory after seeing one at work. We agreed to go out to Mr Lloyd's brickworks (site 8) on Tuesday to see mill at work. Mr Price says it is always reckoned among brickmakers that a foot of diameter of kiln equals 1000 of bricks so I think to be on the safe side it will be wise to make the kiln 18 ft inside diameter, this will enable a little more space to be left between the bricks.

Estimate 420,000 bricks to build boiler house and chimney and shed foundations, kilns. Bricks cost £294 and with all other building costs £695-10-0.

Brick-making machine with table and hoists £400
Second-hand Lancashire boiler   £150
Second hand steam engine   £150
Railway company siding   £250
Donkey pumps to bring water from
stream on site   £30
Wagons, rails and tools   £100

Hampson estimated the total outlay for the works to be £2,095-10-0 with a projected annual profit of £1,326. On 1st July 1900 a legal partnership was drawn up between the three men with the company to be styled as The Wepre Hall Brick Works, but Price left the business at the end of August. Mr Darbyshire became the managing partner, and in a trade directory for 1914 the works was by then being referred to as Darbyshire's Brickworks.

There is some suggestion that the works was bought by the building firm of Alun Edwards Ltd of Cefnybedd circa 1930, but I personally doubt this. It does seem unlikely, as Alun Edwards Co placed an order with the Wrexham Brick & Tile Co for 240,000 common bricks in December 1935, which would suggest that Alun Edwards had no brickmaking capabilities at that time. A letter dated 1936 also exists from the Wepre Hall Brickworks which is signed by the managing director Mr Hampson, so the company must then still have been under its original ownership. On 24th February 1949 however, the works went for sale at auction at the Blossoms Hotel, Chester to Fred W Jones at a cost of £4,275, for which price he got the following – a triple span drying shed, 4 beehive kilns, a workman's shed with a fireplace, an elsan toilet hut, store room, boiler house, office, machine house, 2 tipper lorries, 21 acres of clayland and the railway siding. Initially Fred had a battle with the local council who wished to purchase the site under a compulsory order and convert it into a recreation ground, but the works remained open mainly making common red bricks, and by 1978 they were turning out 50,000 per week, which was 30,000 fewer than the kilns' total potential.

The site of the brickworks is at OS 3036 6837 which is now a copse of trees, but within it lie a few remains of the factory – a chimney base and two engine foundations. The extensive clayland has been filled in and is now scrubland.

SITE 12: ROWLEY'S SHOTTON BRICKWORKS

The second of Shotton's brickworks was Rowley's. Not as extensive as Wepre Hall, it was situated at OS 3065 6832 between Shotton Lane and the main railway line and the whole site was owned outright by Rowley himself – an unusual state of affairs for those days. Harry Butler Rowley founded the works circa 1898, and a year later we find the Shotton Brickworks up for sale as a "new wire-cut brickworks making and burning 45,000 per week". It didn't sell however, as the rates valuation records of 1912 confirm his still occupying the site.

The next piece of historical evidence is one which is quite revealing – an advertisement for the sale of the works by auction on 7th June 1919. Part of it reads " offered by Captain Rowley in consequence of war disablement. The clay produced a well known first class brick famous in pre-war days".

That text strongly suggests that the works had been silent during the Great War whilst Mr Rowley himself had been in uniform and receiving his injuries – note particularly the past tense "produced".

We lose track of what happened next, until the 1930 rates listings showed the brickworks on Shotton Lane as owned by a William Astbury and apparently not qualifying for any due payments, strongly implying that it was defunct, but the Trade Directory for 1932 lists Mr Astbury's brickworks at Shotton, so perhaps it was in production at that time. The factory was sited on what are now the houses on the south side of Strickland Street, whilst the 10 acres of clayland is now a football field. The banks of the clayhole on the west and south are still discernible.

Queensferry Area

SITE 13: ELEANOR COLLIERY QUEENSFERRY

Chester Chronicle 30th July 1870 – " It may be stated that the Eleanor Colliery which belongs to the Prestatyn Colliery Company is at Queensferry. The land has been taken on lease from Earl Spencer and Sir Stephen Glynne. About three years ago the company began operations by sinking the necessary shafts. In the sinking of the first shaft very little difficulty was encountered, but in the second shaft an immense bed of quicksand was met with. To get through, cast iron cylinders had to be brought into operation and at the present moment the shaft is perfectly watertight – bricked up to the surface – and no less than 500 tons of coals may be drawn up per day. Through the skill and perseverance of Mr Gilderoy the able manager, one obstacle after another was overcome and the colliery is now in first class working order. The take consists of 500 acres and in addition the company have spent from £15-20,000 in opening out the colliery.

On Saturday a demonstration of an interesting character took place on the occasion of the opening of a branch line nearly a mile in length to connect the Eleanor Colliery with the Chester and Holyhead line. About 2 o'clock a number of the proprietors and other gentlemen assembled and after the works had been inspected, a wagon containing 10 tons of coal was drawn along the new line, followed by a band of music. The wagon was decorated with flags, and bunting was also exhibited from several houses and prominent places in the locality. The line having been formally opened, an adjournment took place to the Hawarden Castle Hotel where a sumptuous dinner was provided. After dinner an adjournment then took place to a large tent erected in a field fronting the hotel, where the workpeople employed at the colliery were regaled with an abundant dinner. The men and boys numbering about 150, all respectably attired and some wearing rosettes, walked to the tent in procession headed by the band. An interesting circumstance occurred in the proceedings when one of the colliers asked permission to address the meeting and he called upon all present to join him in offering up their thanks to God for his gracious protection of them in their dangerous avocations and to implore his protection hereafter. The assembly immediately and with greatest reverence knelt down and a prayer was offered with great zeal and earnestness. The remainder of the day was spent in innocent amusements".

That evocative report places the establishment of the colliery and its subsequent brickmaking operations at around 1867-8. The earlier of the shafts and surface buildings stood at OS 3130 6845, which is some 100 metres west of the footbridge over the main road coming out of Queensferry, whilst the second phase of workings show up on later maps at OS 3110 6847, which is the present location of a petrol station opposite a large D.I.Y superstore.

It was at this second site that evidence of Eleanor's brickmaking comes to light. Written as late as 1924, The Geology of Flint records that "on the west side of the road a small brickpit shows the outcrop of coal". Although the remnants of that brickpit had survived even until that date, the colliery itself had by that time been closed for many years. Those early rejoicings of 1870 did not last long, as Eleanor was for sale and under liquidation in August 1872 and early 1873. Only 15 of the 500 leased acres had been worked, and we can see from the sale offer that fireclay was listed as one of its assets.

The colliery did survive until certainly 1881, as plans of the coal workings show. They would most certainly have made bricks for their pit linings right from the start, and brickmaking continued certainly for some years, as the Chronicle of 1879 records the evidence of their manufacture:

Bricks. On sale by private treaty, seven kilns containing 7,000 to 40,000 in each kiln. 16 s. per

1000 at the Eleanor Colliery on the ground. Apply to Mr Lowry on the premises.

Those kilns, by the way, would most likely have been of the clamp variety, and not large permanent constructions – Eleanor was only a small scale operation and had disappeared by the close of the Victorian era.

SITE 14: QUEENSFERRY COLLIERY

Coal mining in the Queensferry district goes back to pre-Victorian days, as the tithe map of the early 1840s shows on this site three separate Coal Pit Fields. Coal mining on a larger industrial scale started here in 1856 when Isaac Thompson leased the fields from Admiral Dundas at an annual rent of £300, with a royalty of 6d. payable on each ton of brick and fireclay. The rates books list Isaac Thompson's Colliery, Brickworks and Railway up until 1863, but after that the brickworks are not mentioned, although detailed plans prepared for the W.M. &C.Q. Rly. in both 1863 and 64 clearly show the brick kiln and clayhole just to the north of the pit buildings.

In November 1869 Dundas sold the colliery site, at which time it was being operated by Messrs John and Frederick Thompson. Perhaps bricks were still being made here, but no evidence for such exists. In 1876 it appears that the Thompsons had wished to cease all operations. In a report then written by the agent of the new landlord, W H Gladstone, the course of events was noted thus:

"Bearing in mind the vast amount of coal still lying in a virgin state at the colliery, I am of opinion that the Right Honourable W H Gladstone would not be justified in giving his consent to an abrupt termination of the lease unless greater inducement were held out by the present company.... a new company were formed able and willing to work the mines".

That new company was probably formed to raise the capital needed to keep the failing venture from collapsing, but it did not last long. The colliery was officially acquired by the Aston Hall Colliery Co in June 1878, and was able to continue operating

until, in 1909, Aston Hall itself found its finances in difficulties. Horace Mayhew, the senior director, planned to concentrate coal production at Aston Hall and erect a new brickmaking facility at the Queensferry Colliery site if enough clay could be proven to exist there, but the scheme never went ahead, and in July 1913 all the assets existing at Queensferry were sold off and the buildings demolished. In the detailed description of the lots sold, no brickmaking plant was mentioned.

The colliery was centred at OS 3175 6773, where a mobile home park now stands.

SITE 15: PETER GRIFFITHS ASTON BRICKWORKS

This was the only independent brickworks in the Queensferry district; all other works having been connected with collieries. The 1899 OS map shows it in its mature years, but even then there was little more than a drying shed, kiln and machine house sitting amidst a small area of clay workings along the western side of the Queensferry to Hawarden road at OS 3150 6720.

A good chronology of its development can be traced using the census, the rates listings and the royalty ledger of the Hawarden Estate. Nothing shows up prior to 1861, when 69 year-old George Griffiths had a three-quarter acre brickworks here employing two men and a boy. Five years later George was dead and his widow Ann took on the running of the works until 1870, when her son Peter, then aged 37, became the owner.

Wrexham Advertiser 7th May 1887 – Two children named Lily Billingsley and John Hughes were charged by Mr Peter Griffiths of the Ferry Road Brickworks with being in a shed on his property breaking drain pipes. He saw the girl running out but was not sure of the boy. The damage done was 3s., but he did not wish to press for them; only that the children should know that they were not to go there at will.

The output of the works was fairly modest. In 1891 171,000 bricks and 28,000 drain pipes were made and this figure gradually climbed over the years, with the works production peaking at just over half a million bricks in 1905.

By 1916 Peter would have been 83 years old, and it is at this time that we see his son George take over. George however was 58 years old himself, and for whatever reason the brickworks disappears from the records after that date, but I should think that the war would have had a lot to do with its demise.

The overgrown ruins of Griffith's works still exist today, but only in the form of a few humps and bumps sheltering underneath a copse of trees at the edge of the field.

SITE 16: GREAT MANCOT MAIN COLLIERY

Despite its grand sounding name, this colliery had a very short life. Work on it was begun in 1861 by the ironworks owners Messrs Plant, Rose and Plant. They leased 40 acres of land along Mancot Lane where a disused coal shaft had existed from many years before, but the visible surface buildings of their new colliery, including a small brickyard, took up only four acres. Once the preliminary explorations had proved satisfactory, an official Indenture of Lease was granted to the company by the landlord Sir Stephen Richard Glynne in December 1862.

We know a brick kiln existed from its marked position on a railway map of 1863, and it was in that year that the colliery proprietors gave the running of the brickyard to Edwin Sutherland, although he was only listed in the rates books as holding that position for two years. Whether he stayed on or not is unsure, but by March 1865 we have the first evidence of the company's bricks going on public sale. A letter to Henry Beckett, Sir Stephen's mining agent, reads:

"I write to inform you that we are selling brick from the last kiln, as we are not likely to make use of them. In fact the quality is such that would not do for colliery purposes and whatever we sell, the statement shall be handed to you and we will pay royalty on same".

In May 1867 the final stock of 31,000 bricks was sold for £2-6-6, and Mr Beckett added a footnote to his accounts reading "made up to the closing of the colliery and to the conclusion of the workings in 1866".

We might ask why the colliery existed for such a short period, and the answer probably lies in the fact that it was the only colliery in the area not to have had main line railway connections, although in 1863 the company had built a shipping stage on the Dee at OS 3258 6842 in lieu of what would have been a more efficient rail link. This wharf was connected to the site by a tramway which ran down Mancot Lane and Chemistry Lane. The colliery site is now a strip of narrow woodland on the roadside, with the pit head having stood at OS 3195 6725.

SITE 17: MANCOT BANK COLLIERY

In the early days of Mancot district's industrial awakening, the landscape was much more rural than it appears today. In 1855 the Chronicle recommended a visit to see the construction of the iron ship "Royal Charter" at Mr Cram's Sandycroft shipyard and noted that " the neighbouring country abounds with interesting objects. There are numerous manufactories to examine". Another such manufactory was to be born a year later; William Thompson taking a lease in September of 1856 on the coal, fireclay and brick clay on this site, and he worked it until its acquisition by Isaac Thompson of Queensferry Colliery in Jan 1860. By 1862 it had been given the title of Mancot Bank Colliery and Brickworks and was connected by a 1 1/4 mile branch railway running around the south of Moor Farm to join the main coast line at Sandycroft. This branch was called the Moor railway, or the Mancot Banks railway. A report made in July 1865 explains "surface clay for brickmaking is subject to a royalty of 1s.6d. per thousand. A branch railway is laid up to the pits. The freight is only 3d. per ton for coal". At the same time the company was advertising for sale "a large quantity of excellent bricks at a moderate price".

By October the whole concern was up for sale with its two pits, railway and bricksheds, but no change occured until Feb 1867, when Isaac signed over the works to John and Frederick Thompson – presumably his sons – but some time between May 1869 and 1870 Isaac again held the lease, although John and Frederick seemed to be in working control. A document dated 1st December 1870 states: "Sir Stephen Richard Glynne shall allow the said John and Frederick Thompson sufficient sand, stones and clay for making brick for use in building shafts, tunnels and other works in or about the colliery".

The clay at Mancot Bank was certainly not difficult to come by, as trial borings showed 14 separate seams of various clays between the coal measures.

The rates books show that the works continued up until 1871, after which it appears to have closed. The position of the surface buildings are now replaced by houses at the far end of Woodland Court at OS 3204 6642, but the old overgrown spoil heaps still exist on either side of the site.

On the tithe map an earlier "Brick Kiln Field" is shown to have existed just east of Moor Farm at OS 3270 6615.

SITE 18: RAKE COLLIERY

The area of Mancot was in 1856 alive with entrepreneurs prospecting for suitable coal fields to develop. Mancot Bank at site 17 was just coming into existence, and Mr Darby of Brymbo Ironworks noted in his diary that he had made trials at the "Mancot Colliery" but had found his respective take to be full of fault lines. The term "colliery" had a dual definition in Victorian days – it could for instance, as in this case, simply refer to an area of land under which coal was known to exist.

The enterprise at the Rake was undertaken by James Darlington of the Ince Colliery at Wigan. He was a mining surveyor by profession who had taken a lease on part of the lands around Mancot in September 1856. By December word of the Rake Colliery's progress had gained the attention of the Chronicle, which reported that Darlington was "engaged in skilful and extensive operations for the speedy development of the coal".

At this point let's take a foray into the more colourful behaviour of the men whose lives imbue the sites we are investigating with a more human quality. It is in the form of a letter dated 31st Jan 1860 and sent to Mr Burnett, the commercial agent to the colliery's landlord Sir Stephen Glynne. Was the spelling an attempt to disguise its author, or a genuine sign of an understandably poor education? It read:

> "Sir I take the liberty of rightin to inform you a little of that manager at the Rake Colliary it is a sin and a shame to harbor such a man he cant leve anthar mens wife a lone and he is at Joseph Morris the publican every day the banksmen is oblidge to tel you a un truth wen you wil cum to the colliry to enquiar for him the will tell you that he is down the pit or gon to sum arrant and at the same time he is at the Wite House or at Joseph Morris is house if you heard what the cuntry taulk about him you wood be suprise it is a disgrace to keep such a man about the place then is a nautha purson gain to right to Mr Gladstone on this a count and the colliars seas he nos nothing a bout colliary this manager as ben with a nothar mans wife in bed all night and hir husband workin down the pit at the Rake it is tru what I sea and that man liv under you in Hawarden."

Who that manager was is unknown, but it probably wasn't Mr Darlington himself, as he would most likely have been referred to as the owner or proprietor.

In October 1860 negotiations were underway with Sir Stephen for a branch railway to be made from the main line "to the Rake Lane Pit with needfull sidings and conveniences", and construction seems to have begun in Jan 1862. It was funded by Sir Stephen, who on completion charged a rent on the line of 3d. for every ton of coal transported on it.

By 1863 Darlington was worried for the colliery's future and wrote to Mr Burnett saying "I have again the pleasure of reporting that the success of the colliery has continued. If this mine will last six quarters (one and a half years) at the present rate of profit, the outlay will be recouped, but I much fear that this pit will be exhausted by June 1864. Every effort is being made and our only difficulty has been the limited extent of the operations".

Darlington held on to the Rake until it was taken over by Isaac Thompson of Mancot Bank Colliery circa 1866, but the place seems to have ceased functioning by 1870. A brickyard was certainly part of the colliery's operations, but evidence of it only appears in railway maps of 1863 – 4, which showed the little brick kilns around a clayhole, which today has flooded to become a pond. The colliery buildings stood at OS 3325 6565 behind the present day Rake Lane Farm, and the pond is just to the south.

On the tithe map of the early 1840s there was also a "Brickfield" 200 metres north east of the colliery at OS 3340 6580.

Site 9

Site 10

Site 24

Site 27

Site 29

Site 30

Site 31

Site 33

Mold Area

SITE 19: OLD FFERME COLLIERY

Chester Chronicle 6th August 1853 – A great passion has sprung up of late for exploring the mineral resources of Mold. The present mania is confined entirely to coal, in places where the mining operations are carried on with as much vigour and alacrity as digging after gold in California. The imaginary richness of the coal field is such that its fame has reached the far county of Durham and attracted the attention of the coal proprietors of that bishopric. From their experience they have commenced a new work upon the Tyn Twll land, which the "knowing ones" of Mold say only contains a thin bed of coal. A few weeks will suffice to put to the test the geological views entertained of the absence of the black diamond in large districts of the neighbourhood.

Despite the doubts of the "knowing ones", a 3ft seam of the valuable Main Coal was discovered, and the Tyn Twll Colliery was established at Nercwys. Our site 19 was some miles away at Mynydd Bychan, but was owned in its heyday by the Tyn Twll company. When exactly site 19 was established is uncertain, but it must have been in existence from at least 1857, as the Chronicle then mentioned a sale of the assets of New Firm Colliery at Mynydd Bychan, between Sychdyn and New Brighton.

This site was probably defunct for many years after that sale and certainly did not exist on the 1871 OS map. It appears that the Tyn Twll company took it over in September 1889, and two months later a lease on the brick earth and clay was taken, probably to enable the bricks for the colliery buildings to be made, and a colliery plan confirms the pit site as having been constructed some time in 1890.

The Tyn Twll company was reformed some short time later and site 19, then renamed Old Fferme, was further developed from March 1893, when new coal and clay leases were obtained for it, and by November that year the workmen had gathered at the Star Hotel in Mold to celebrate their latest achievements with the toast "Success to the Tyn Twll Colliery Co".

A report on the company's holdings was made in Jan 1894, from which we can see that the parent site at Nercwys had no brickmaking facilities itself, but at Old Fferme there was " good fireclay 2ft. 6in. thick and this is used for making buff bricks and glazed bricks. The Old Fferme Brickworks make good common bricks which at present are used chiefly at your Tyn Twll Colliery for lining the shaft, putting up the buildings on the surface etc". A suggestion was made by the author of that report that a rail link might be connected between the two sites, as there was very little prospect of the brickworks being able to survive on its own because of poor local demand for bricks, but this scheme never went ahead.

In March 1894 the company found itself in receivership, and all assets were sold by order of the Court on 19th September, including the brickworks with its drying shed, two kilns, pugmill and tools.

Tyn Twll's main colliery site at Nercwys survived for some years later, but site 19 was probably left abandoned. The 1912 OS map showed the buildings as having disappeared and become overgrown with trees, and all that was left was an "old clayhole". Today the site sits amidst an area of lush countryside, and some bumpy ground at OS 2507 6583 marks where the brickworks once was. The adjacent clayhole is now a pool, and the coal shaft a little way to the north west has been capped with a concrete block.

SITE 20: NEW BRIGHTON COLLIERY

Very little evidence for this site exists. It is shown on the 1871 map, and we know that it was sold at auction on 20th Feb 1877 under a distress for rent, with the list of assets showing it to have been a very modest colliery site. It did however have quite a reasonable brickmaking capability, with brick presses, a brick-making machine, bench, trestles and moulds, together with an impressive surplus stock of 20,000 slop bricks, 500 pressed slop bricks and 250 white firebricks.

The 1900 map shows it marked only as a "disused brickworks" with no mention of its colliery affiliations at all. The colliery buildings stood at OS 2526 6568 where a large new house now stands.

SITE 21: NEW BRIGHTON BRICKFIELD

This small site was at OS 2540 6537, shown marked on the 1871 map as a "brickfield" with a shed and kiln just south of the Rose and Crown pub.

In the rates books from 1868 to 1872 a brickyard at New Brighton is listed in the holding of John Jones, and we can only assume that this might refer to site 21, although it is more than likely, as very little else existed in that area in those days.

The 1871 census also shows that an Edward Jones lived with his family two doors along from the Rose and Crown. Edward was recorded as working as a brickmaker together with his 13 year-old son George. Perhaps as the rates say, John Jones owned the site, but Edward actually lived there. Could John have been Edward's father? By 1875 John had died, and in 1882 the exact same site was still a brickyard, but now being run by Edward Melling.

The little works had gone by the turn of the century, and has today been replaced by housing.

SITE 22: ALLTAMI KILN

This very small site remains somewhat of an enigma. It is not shown on any OS map, but a railway map of 1865 places a kiln at OS 2674 6549 in a field, although no occupier is listed. Was this a recognised brickyard?

The Chronicle in 1882 mentions a scant reference to the Alltami brickmakers Messrs Davies & Co – could they have reworked this earlier site, or were they a firm of journeymen brickmakers with no established works?

SITE 23: MOLD ARGOED COLLIERY

In the days of the old township districts, Argoed stretched from the Bridge Inn below the Bailey Hill over to the western side of Buckley, and consequently many industrial sites from times long forgotten even in Victorian days have borne the name Argoed. For instance, of the Rhydygaled Colliery situated in Argoed township, the Chronicle in November 1867 reported that *"a shaft has been sunk near some old workings of the ancients, said to have been stopped 150 years. Some old men in the neighbourhood, 90 years of age, remember hearing their grandfathers stating they had been working there".*

Quite a few collieries were named Argoed – there was for instance an early Argoed Colliery near Buckley, shown on the 1840 tithe map at OS 2725 6415, where the young William Shepherd, a later partner in Catherall's Brickworks, was believed to be working as a clerk in 1826. This was situated in a small field, encompassed by others bearing such romantic names of the industrial age as New Engine Field, Old Engine Field and Coal Banks. Also on the tithe map is an early Argoed Hall Colliery at Mold at OS 2485 6390, and we know that this works was sold on 25th Jan 1842. How long it might have survived after that is unknown to me, but it doesn't show at all on the 1871 OS.

Putting aside these other workings, our principal concern is for the site which proved the largest and most enduring, although throughout its history it was worked by various companies under differing names. It was here that in 1837 21 men and boys perished in a pit flood at the time when the works was referred to as Plas yr Argoed or Little Argoed Colliery.

In November 1863 the Argoed Colliery Company Ltd. was established to work the coal and fireclay on this site. At this time three pits were already in situ, although only two were in use. The Secretary of the new company, Richard Owen, the postmaster at Chester, had tests made on the clay found here and reported "it is found of such excellent quality that practical men consider it superior to any in the district. They therefore propose to erect sheds and kilns for the manufacture of firebricks, white bricks and tiles for building purposes. Hence from this source alone the company will reap a good dividend".

The Chronicle later got wind of this new undertaking and reported on its progress:

Chester Chronicle 23rd April 1864 – Being in this locality on Tuesday last and somewhat interested in the undertaking, we paid a visit to the colliery and had ocular demonstration of the great progress which has already been made, the company having only completely registered in November last, and were conducted over the place by the intelligent and obliging steward. We observed a pit in full work on the eastern boundary, near to which another pit was being sunk and an engine erected. On the west of the property a great number of workmen were busily engaged in erecting two very large boilers and a 40 h.p. engine by which means the two pits will be at once brought into work.A pit is also about being sunk on another part of this extensive field and there is every reason to believe that by mid-summer the colliery will be throwing into the market a large supply of the finest coal in Flintshire, which will be a great boon as the demand for coals for shipping purposes is so great as to exceed the supply by thousands of tons weekly. Besides coal there is a very valuable bed of fireclay 16 ft thick which can be worked at a slight expense to a good profit.

By 1866 however, the company found itself in liquidation, perhaps because of the increasing competition which had recently developed. Only the year before, the Chronicle had noted how "collieries and brickworks are now being opened and erected with the utmost rapidity in every part of the neighbourhood surrounding Mold".

A further change of ownership soon followed and a new Argoed Hall Colliery, Brick & Tile Works was established. The new company appointed a surveyor to report on their acquisition and in June 1868 his notes included the remark "the pit gear still standing, but neglected". This strongly suggests that the colliery might have been unused since the 1866 bankruptcy, but yet again, change was in the air. The following account explains what happened next:

Wrexham Advertiser 13th Jan 1872 – The Mold Argoed Colliery Company is being organised for the purpose of acquiring and working the Argoed Hall Colliery. Mr John Marley of Darlington, the eminent engineer, has carefully inspected the property, and his estimation is that the estate contains nearly 2 million tons of coal. In addition the property contains a bed of fireclay of the most valuable description and with the machinery and plant already fixed, there could be obtained a profit of £750 a year. The amount paid for the existing plant and machinery on the whole estate is £13,400, but such is the confidence of the vendors, they have accepted payment of £10,000. The vendors have been induced to sell solely on account of an insufficiency of capital to fully develop the property.

It must be noted here that although there had previously been much hype concerning the profits to be had on brickmaking at Argoed, I have never found any evidence of such actually being undertaken, although it surely must have been, but in May 1874 the Wrexham Advertiser ran an article which stated that "the whole of the surface works including clay grinding pan, drying sheds and kilns are now completed ", and perhaps this marks the time when an improved brickworks had been fully established.

The colliery's output in 1873 was 14,000 tons, which rose two years later to nearly 50,000. By early 1875 the supply of bricks from the works could not equal the local demand and new plant was later installed to the point that it was looking like the brickworks side of the business might turn out to be the most profitable. "Taking everything into consideration, there are few better properties than the Mold Argoed Colliery anywhere in the district" said the Advertiser.

In September 1876 the first recorded advertisement ran for the sale of bricks to the public. 150,000 first class red bricks were available for land sale at the works or to be forwarded by rail. The brickshed at Argoed was not only large enough to ensure a good output, but was put to other good uses aswell. September 1876 saw the manager of the colliery, Mr G. Cooke Williams, leave to take up a post at Aberystwyth University, and the shed was used as the venue for the presentation of a testimonial from his workmen and friends. "The brickshed was nicely decorated for the occasion" commented the Advertiser. The shed had other uses – the previous year saw the mine badly inundated when water burst in from old abandoned flooded workings. Many men were trapped underground and hundreds of local people flocked to the pit to await the outcome:

Wrexham Advertiser 13th March 1875 – Everything was prepared in the way of refreshments for the poor men, provided they were found to be alive. Medical assistance was also ensured; Mr Edward Williams being present throughout Monday afternoon and night. While these arrangements were being made in the Black Lion, the crowd on the pit bank continued to increase, and as several of the Non-conformist ministers were present, another prayer meeting was held in the Brick-shed, which was attended by several hundreds.

After three days all the miners were brought out alive, and later that month the entire workforce of nearly 200 were treated to a celebration dinner at the Black Lion Hotel in Mold.

The company's fortunes continued until a serious economic slump forced them into liquidation. In March 1880 the company was sold at auction to Mr E J Bartlett of London, and the works was saved from redundancy until, in April 1884, it was forced to close again amongst serious fears that it would never reopen, but by August the workforce received notice that work would shortly be resumed.

The final blow however came nearly two years later:

Wrexham Advertiser 15th May 1886 – We understand that the Argoed Colliery will be finally closed in a few days; the seams which can be worked at anything like a profit in the existing state of things, being exhausted. The rails etc are being brought to the surface and the engine and plant generally will be shortly offered for sale unless previously disposed of by private treaty".

During the dismantling of the colliery a wooden board was discovered in the workings at the spot from where the entombed miners had been rescued in 1875. On it was a scriptural text which had been scratched in with a nail. Argoed Colliery was remembered for many years after – even in 1913, when a nearby colliery was extending its workings, the Advertiser remarked that they would "run in the direction of the famous old Argoed Colliery at Mold".

Little remains of the colliery today save some remnants of the waste banks, and the site now rests peacefully on a wooded slope overlooking the town near to the Rhyd Alyn nursing-home. The brickworks itself stood a little way south of the colliery at OS 2471 6403 atop a steep bank of the river Alyn.

SITE 24: TYDDYN TILERY AND COLOMENDY BRICKWORKS

This modestly sized brickworks was on the western side of the Mold to Chester Road and SSW of Tyddyn Farm. The first mention of it appears in a sale of the Tyddyn Farm estate in July 1847 with the description "all that parcel of meadow land together with the Tilery thereon lately erected and the buildings, works and machinery thereto appurtenant and used therewith. All which were formerly in the tenure of Jonathan Hobson". The text goes on to describe the site as being in the occupation of John Catherall. We also have a good description of its function – the Chronicle mentions it as "for making drainage tiles for the use of the estate and for sale".

By Feb 1854 the Chronicle tells us that William Jones, the proprietor of an ironmongers in Wrexham Street, Mold, had acquired the works and he was advertising for an experienced maker to manufacture bricks, tiles and drain pipes at the works, which was styling itself as Tyddyn Brick & Tile Works. The account books of the Gwysanney Estate mention purchasing drain tiles from the Tyddyn Brick Co in the same year. The 1847 sale map shows the tilery as a small building with no permanent kilns, but a railway map of 1866 has it named as Tyddyn Brick & Tile Works and on a slightly grander scale. William held the works for some number of years until Henry Bragg & Co took it over in 1875, and in Sept 1876 the newspaper ran an advertisement announcing that "manufacture has been resumed at these works lately occupied by Mr William Jones".

It is at this point where we reach a conundrum. A

concern called the Colomendy Brick Tile & Clay Co, described as carrying on their works at Tyddyn just below the town of Mold, starts to get mentioned with a Mr Abbatt as one of the directors in 1876. Our problem is this: was the Colomendy company a separate concern from the Tyddyn works – was the Colomendy company the official nomenclature of the Tyddyn works – was Henry Bragg connected with Mr Abbatt – and how are both concerns mentioned in the same year? Perhaps Henry disposed of the works almost as soon as he acquired it, or perhaps he went into partnership and helped form the Colomendy company. All the available maps show only one brickworks in this district, so perhaps we must assume that both concerns were one and the same. Whatever the case, we really shouldn't make the mistake of assuming that the Colomendy Co was necessarily situated at the Colomendy near Gwernymynydd, although it may be true that the company had other workings there.

The Colomendy Co. of 1876 went into voluntary liquidation in July 1878 and exactly one year later a new company was formed to purchase the defunct works. The chairman of the new Colomendy Brick & Tile Co Ltd was James Ashworth, a mining engineer from Southport, who had also been the managing director of the previous company. Any further documentary evidence cannot be found until 1882, when the Tyddyn brickworks again appears in the rates listings, this time as occupied by James Griffiths.

On 20th August 1884 all the works plant was sold at auction, even down to some scrap iron on site and the office furniture, and we must assume this heralded the end of the works. By Jan 1899 it is referred to as "the old brickworks" in a newspaper article.

The brickworks was the neighbour of Tyddyn, also called Bronwylfa,Colliery, which was also on the same side of the road a little to the north. This was established by Richard Isaac, probably in early 1849, and passed through numerous hands until its closure, which I believe came in 1881. No brickmaking activity had ever been documented here,but we do know that 20 tons of fireclay was included in the inventory of a sale at the colliery in 1877.

The 1871 OS map shows the brickworks at 2523 6307 with two sheds, three kilns and a large clayhole on the opposite side of the road. A branch railway ran from the nearby main line a little to the east, running behind the brickworks, and on to the colliery.

A few years ago there were still some wall foundations to be seen on an earthwork platform on which the works was built; the landscape being a slight gradient here – but today the site has been mostly levelled off.

SITE 25: OAK PITS COLLIERY

The site of the Oak Pits Colliery today illustrates dramatically how much the town of Mold has expanded since the Victorian era. This area was then regarded as being well outside the town, and the colliery sat almost alone amidst acres of surrounding farmland. Nowadays the sprawling industrial estate which has replaced the Oak Pits is very much a part of Mold. Modern transportation has shrunk our perceptions of geographical distance,and the passage of time eradicated the traces of the landscapes of the past. Who today, for instance, would know that somewhere in Mold in the 1830s, at a place not even recorded, there was a 1 1/2 mile long racecourse complete with four hurdles, and after the races the crowds would retire to the Leeswood Arms in Wrexham Street to celebrate or console the outcome of the day's sport.

The Oak Pits site was begun in 1858 and was acquired in 1863, according to some court proceedings, by a new concern called the Welsh Coal, Mineral & Oil Company. In March 1868 the company advertised that "the proprietors of the Oak Pits Colliery beg to announce that having completed the extension of their works, they are now able to supply the Welsh Main Steam and House coals". A great impetus to the trade from here came on Monday 15th March 1869 with the opening of the branch railway which connected the pits to the new Tryddyn branch line, and in October a year later the company leased further lands to the SW to extend their operations. Oak Pits may only have been a modestly sized colliery, but by 1872 it was sending out 400-500 tons of coal daily and, for its size, its productivity became legendary. It's not surprising that at the height of production in 1878, 750 men and boys were employed here.

As was often the case in those days, one of the all too frequent trade depressions gripped the district in December 1878. The local coal owners gathered in Mold to debate the situation and one of the Oak Pit's senior managers stood up and voiced what everybody present must surely have known – there had been too much over-production by too many producers – the classic scenario of boom and bust. The men at Oak Pits were given the choice of accepting a wage reduction of 20 per cent to offset the losses caused by the drop in coal prices, or the works would have to close. They wisely chose the reduction.

In April 1879 the Welsh Coal & Mineral Oil Co. changed its name to Oak Pits Colliery Company, but a continuation of poor trading conditions and the costly outlay on timber needed for the roof supports in the extended workings, meant that by September 300 men had to be laid off.

The great days seen by the colliery were over. Bankruptcy followed, and in May 1881 the entire concern was put up for sale over a three-day period, even down to the nuts and bolts from the stores. A nominal bid of £7,000 was made for the whole estate and the sale was cancelled, as it was clear that no bids would reach the figure of £150,000 which the owners estimated they had spent on the colliery.

Who owned the works in the subsequent years is unsure, but in Dec. 1881 there was a rumour going about the district that the Nerquis Colliery was on the verge of resuming operations at the Oak Pits. Whatever the outcome , the colliery did continue,but trade never again reached the dizzy heights of the previous decade and by 1887 even The Times of London made comment on the conditions which had by then afflicted the district of Mold: "*At the present time the mining interest is in phenomenally low water. The workmen are taking their departure for other districts and a significant proof of the depression is to be found in the fact that some 200 houses in Mold alone are devoid of tenants*".

The colliery's fate was eventually sealed by a natural disaster. Flooding of the workings had been seriously affecting the work's profitability, and on a Sunday night in 1887 a flood broke in which was so persistent that it resisted all attempts to drain it. In May of that year the colliery was sold for scrap, and by July it was being demolished. In a cruel twist of fate, 79 year-old Robert Roberts, whose son had bought some of the second-hand materials, was on site during the demolition when a wall fell on him and caused his death.

Wrexham Advertiser 23rd July 1887 – In a few weeks it is only too probable that a heap of rubbish will be the only momento of this once prosperous colliery, where over 600 men and boys were employed and where fourteen years ago about £1,500 a week was earned.

No written or printed evidence has ever been found to suggest that Oak Pits actually conducted brickmaking , but the 1871 OS map clearly shows a brickworks near to the colliery and connected to it by railway. The colliery buildings stood at OS 2380 6280 and a new house now stands on the site of the coal pits themselves, whereas the brickworks was a little way off at OS 2395 6262, which now corresponds to the eastern parts of the present Broncoed Industrial Estate.

SITE 26: BRONCOED COLLIERY

Apart from the dirt, smoke and clamour which once must have been in evidence here, the surrounding landscape of the Broncoed Colliery will have changed little over the years; the urban growth of nearby Mold still being some distance away. Our first reference to this colliery was found in the Chronicle of 22nd February 1848 when Messrs S Williamson & Co held the site. In 1851 the place was up for sale, and a plan of the site showed it to be only a little coal bank with a lime kiln and a railway called the Broncoed Branch connecting it to a point on the main line at OS 2490 6300. This branch connection was then probably only a horse drawn tramway. The colliery was at this time acquired by Cynric Lloyd, a local landowner, and William Shepherd, the Buckley industrialist.

By early 1858 Mr Shepherd, the principal partner in the works, had put it about that he was looking for somebody to take it over, and this next report not only verifies that fact, but also reads as a great story:

Chester Chronicle 24th April 1858 – An Ingenious Swindler at Mold. On Thursday one of those accomplished gentleman who go about to beguile the unwary with fair words, arrived at Mold. He was dressed as a mechanic with square and callipers sticking out of his pockets. Having gleaned sufficient information to warrant him in experimenting on the credulity of some of the mining population in this district, he proceeded to the house of an engineer employed at the Broncoed Colliery, and informed him that he was the son of one of the gentleman who intended taking the colliery, and was to be the manager. He then depicted in glowing colours his plan of future operations at the colliery and enquired of the engineer what wages he got. "A pound a week" was the answer. " Oh, I will get you 23s. a week". The bait took, and the engineer jumped to the conclusion that a good dinner would further advance him in the good opinion of his future master. An excellent dinner was provided, and the stranger congratulated him on the delicacies laid before him. It was proposed that they should see the blacksmith, and it being a piercingly cold day, the engineer offered the stranger his son's new fashionable overcoat and an umbrella. The offer was gladly accepted. The blacksmith was met with, and the same promises of an advance of wages made to him. The three friends partook freely of John Barleycorn and then came to Mold, where from the excitement produced by the glad tidings on the engineer and blacksmith, they found the streets scarcely wide enough to proceed along them. They did however reach the Cross, and the stranger requested them to go to the King's Head, and call for glasses of what they pleased at his expense, whilst he went to the railway station for a box of tools he expected by train. They both went, and having sat down there drinking for some time in momentary expectation of the return of the stranger, their patience became exhausted. Enquiries were then made by them, but the mysterious stranger had disappeared from the scene of his operations, with the new overcoat and umbrella, and has not been heard of since.

By then there were four pits in operation, but two were nearly exhausted. One year later, Shepherd found his purchaser for the works in the guise of the North Wales Smelting & Reduction Company, and he said his goodbyes to the colliery in grand style:

Chester Chronicle 23rd April 1859 – Mr Shepherd having disposed of Broncoed Colliery on Tuesday last, regaled the numerous colliers employed there by him for many years with a plentiful supply of good cheer at the White Lion Inn and the Black Horse Inn. There they were met by workmen employed by him at his extensive brickworks (Catheralls Buckley) and also colliers from his Spon Green Colliery. Good feeling was noted between workmen and their long respected employer.

By the start of 1860 the new company embarked on the task of replacing the earlier rail link with a proper standard gauge line, and this was completed in August. A notice in the Wrexham Advertiser of November 1861, reproduced below, gives us the evidence of a brickyard at the works, which the company were letting out to a sub-contractor. Brickmaking at Broncoed would have been an almost certainty – even from its earliest times – as its relative isolation would have made the carting of bricks to the colliery from works further afield an expensive obstacle:

Wrexham Advertiser November 1861 – To Brickmakers, Contractors etc. The Smelting Reduction Lime & Coal Co Ltd, Broncoed Colliery near Mold. To be let for the purpose of brick-making – the Brickfield belonging to the above company. The company to have the right to purchase such bricks as they may require, and the lessee to purchase from the company all coal and slack at the company's prices at the pit mouth.

Chester Chronicle 21st November 1863 – On Sunday last the old shaft of the Broncoed Colliery fell in, carrying with it the engine and buildings erected on the bank, leaving a considerable quantity of debris scattered about the yawning gulph. The place had been drowned in some time ago and divers were engaged to descend the shaft to examine the state of the pumps and timber at the bottom. It is supposed that the occurrence was caused by the removal of the pumps two or three days before, as they lent considerable support to the brickwork of the pit. As the company have sunk a new pit, this accident will not check their operations.*

The proceedings from a court case show us the next steps in the work's history. It seems that from early 1868 the colliery was acquired by the nearby Oak Pits Company. The former owners had spent £100,000 on the works, "and had never realised one farthing of it". In the three-and a-half years until July 1871 the Oak Pits Co had also seen no profits at Broncoed, mainly because of two factors – the annual wages bill on the 598 persons employed at Broncoed was £30,000, and the colliery had been dogged by continuous and expensive litigations, mainly arising from their mine pumpings polluting farmer's streams.

How long the works survived after 1871 I cannot say, but it was marked as an "old colliery" on the 1878 map at OS 2390 6225. A few stone walls still remain, but the site is now part of private land.

SITE 27: RUBY BRICKWORKS RHYDYMWYN

The Ruby Brickworks was fairly unusual for Flintshire, in that it produced a hard, dark red facing brick which didn't fall far short of the quality of the famous Ruabon factories.

The story of the works begins around 1867, at which time coal had been mined here at Rhydymwyn on a small scale and had resulted in thousands of tons of clay being raised and left unused. The landowner of the site, B.G. Davies Cooke of Gwysanney Hall, later became aware of this fact, and from November 1890 to May 1891 he employed a surveyor to study the site and judge the feasibility of erecting brickworks to capitalise on this valuable mineral reserve. In May 1891 the Cambrian Fireclay Co. was formed to supply clay from the site to a proposed electrical insulator factory in England, but if anything came from this venture, it must have

been extremely short lived.

On 15th August 1892 however, a company was registered which did make proper use of the minerals:

British Clayworker August 1892 – The North Wales Brick & Tile Co Ltd near Mold commenced operations nearly three months since. A permanent roof upon wood has been erected and walls will be built with the company's own bricks as soon as the machinery is running. The first bricks will be burnt in a common clamp. The works are situated on a meadow adjoining the Mold and Denbigh railway. The company possesses one of the finest coal measure shales resting on a splendid plastic clay 12 yards thick.

British Clayworker July 1893 – The North Wales B. &T. Co. whose works are situated at Rhydymwyn celebrated the completion of ten chambers of their kiln on the 24th June by a tea party to their workmen and their wives. From 70 to 80 sat down to a substantial tea in the new kiln which was tastefully adorned with flowers. Mr James Beresford, a shareholder, said "it is a pleasure to be present on such an occasion, and to note the beautiful manner in which the extempore room has been laid out by the manager Mr Hetherington. It is something novel in the history of a brick kiln to be made to look so attractive, in fact I think never in the history of brick-making has such an event taken place". Mr Alderman Parry said " I very heartily congratulate Mr Hetherington and his company upon the excellent and extensive works that they have succeeded in erecting here in such a comparatively short time. The laying out of the works, the opening out of the clay pits and the securing of the latest machinery and kilns are such that speak volumes".

Joseph Hetherington was the practical managing partner in the firm. His associate Mr Dean, and the other principal shareholders were Manchester businessmen, and the company of Messrs Dean & Hetherington had already gained much notoriety as kiln makers. Consequently, the works had been fitted out with a Hoffmann continuous kiln of the most advanced design.

By June 1898 the company had liquidated and re styled itself as the Ruby Brick & Tile Co Ltd, but Mr Hetherington died in the August. The company must have still been in difficulties by the turn of the century, as letters to the landlord show that they were applying for reductions in their rents and royalties. On 4th March 1901 Mr Davies Cooke's agent informed the company that "Mr Cooke has made no offer for me to submit to you. He has simply expressed his sympathy with you and thinks that if a new company was started it would succeed. Of course we shall adhere to our promise and allow a railway to go over our land to the station if required at a minimal rent".

The following year saw the works in new ownership. Nicholas E Hartley & Partners Ltd took over Ruby and immediately set about improving the work's chances of survival by applying to the board of the Mold and Denbigh Railway to have a siding put up to the factory at a cost of £734.

In 1903 Mr J C Hartley, Nicholas' son, took over the works. By the 1930s the works had ceased its production of high quality facing bricks and concentrated on wire-cut common bricks. The market for bricks had levelled off over the years and capital investment in the works seems to have followed the same trend. In 1944 the Castle Firebrick Co, perhaps contemplating a purchase of Hartley's works, commented that in their opinion *"the works operated by Mr Hartley could not be described as being up to moderate standards, though it must be admitted that he produced at low cost"*. It is a popular misconception that Castle

Employees at the Ruby Brickworks. Early 20th century. Photo: FRO.

Firebrick bought out the Ruby Works, but in fact it always remained in the Hartley's possession, and to the date of this text's completion in summer 2003 the Ruby Brick & Tile Co still officially exists as a holding company in the hands of the present day Hartley family.

In October 1963, with the use of bricks as a building material having fallen off considerably, Hartley had to make his 40 workmen aware of a possible closure. He had also had to suffer the bitter irony of watching a new and extensive housing estate being built in the nearby village from bricks brought in from afar, and this despite the Ruby works being just minutes away.

Reports of its closure seem to differ. The Chronicle says that production ground to a halt by August 1965, but lothe to close the works, Hartley ordered that the Hoffmann kiln be kept fired in anticipation of any new orders. Under these restrictions and with only a skeleton staff left, the final end came soon afterwards. On the other hand, Thomas Jones, a former worker at Ruby, stated that a decision was taken to change the direction of quarrying the clay, resulting in their clay stocks having become contaminated by lime, causing the bricks to crack in the kiln.

Perhaps both stories put together paint a more complete picture as to why Ruby closed.
Ruby was the largest of the brickworks in the Mold district, and the site remained in the hands of the Hartley family until the late 1990s. For nearly four decades the abandoned remains lay derelict, becoming overgrown by trees and ivy, like some lost jungle temple, but by the year 2003 much of its demolition had begun. It stood at OS 2051 6773 with its quarry to the north east.

SITE 28: CAMBRIAN BRICKWORKS GWERNYMYNYDD

Gwernymynydd today could be as aptly described as it was in the Chronicle of 1863 – "a quiet mineral neighbourhood". Quiet, however, is hardly the word to describe the tangled web of financial and practical dealings connected with the history of the Cambrian Brickworks. Although the documented evidence left to us can be somewhat confusing, the following account seems to encapsulate the basics.

The first evidence of any activity appears on the 1878 map, where at OS 2037 6197 a fireclay pit was marked deep in the countryside south west of the village. It appears that the landowner Mr Davies Cooke had bought some works in Gwernymynydd in about 1870, although it is not quite clear which works these may have been. Perhaps they were the stone quarry at the top of the hill above the village, where a large lime-kiln still exists, or they may have been a brickworks – in which case, why were they not on the 1878 map?

Whatever the case, Mr Cooke registered his Cambrian Fire Clay Company in 1881, and the number of shares purchased realised him £8,000, with which he developed the brickworks. Unfortunately, instead of taking on a practical brickmaker as the works manager, he appointed an ex bank clerk, and most of the time spent between the two men was engaged in argument as to how things should be done. Apparently the ex clerk could not grasp the idea that to make bricks saleable, they all needed to be the same size! It looks like disaster was on the cards right from the start.

In 1898 Mr Cooke found it necessary to take a second mortgage on the brickworks from a Colonel Bird, who agreed to help Mr Cooke after seeing a sample of his bricks. The two men formed a new company to work the site, but when the bills started coming in, Colonel Bird found himself unable to meet his share in paying them. As the Colonel had the brickworks as security on the mortgage to Davies Cooke, he decided in 1901 to petition for his partner's bankruptcy. Mr Cooke was by now wanting to dispose of the brickworks entirely,or find a new partner in the venture. In May 1901 he engaged an experienced clayworks manager named Henry Harris to take over running the place, and had been negotiating with Mr Mitchell, a Northop colliery proprietor, who was willing to become his new partner. But, as the cash flow difficulties with Colonel Bird began to bite, the workmen found that their wages were not forthcoming and they struck work, bringing the brickworks to a grinding halt. The entire venture had proved a disaster, and as Mr Cooke pointed out at his bankruptcy hearing in November 1901, it seemed it had been his misfortune to fall in with men he described as "unscrupulous individuals". By this time, the newspapers were describing the works as being "practically dormant."

The Cambrian Brickworks, by order of the court, was put up for sale on 23rd July 1902. It was described as having a frontage of 70 yards on the Mold to Ruthin road. On the ordnance map of 1900 we can see that the earlier fireclay pit had by then been connected to the brickworks by a tramway running behind Aberduna Farm.

The rates book in 1903 shows that the works had ceased production, but from 1905 -7 it seemed to be running again. In the 1912 listings, it was the property of the Cambrian Mining Company and the ordnance map of two years later still shows it with its two kilns, but by that time the tramway had been taken up. The works stood at OS 2123 6239.

I am unable to say when it closed, but housing has stood on the site for many years. There is also no trace left of the fireclay pit, and also no evidence of the tramway.

Buckley Area

SITE 29: CASTLE BRICKWORKS

The works situated on and around the Buckley Mountain represented the powerhouse of Flintshire brickmaking. The following 25 sites are all to be found around Buckley, and the name of Buckley itself most likely had an industrial derivation. It has been suggested that the name might have originated from " Buck-lay" – a grazing pasture for the deer kept by the Ewloe Estate, although the more likely explanation is that it derived from the Welsh "Bwlch y Clai", which means clay hole, and considering the almost universal usage of the Welsh language amongst the Buckley folk of the 19th century, this is the more likely explanation. Indeed, in the mid-19th century the Reverend Elvet Lewis of Buckley always gave his address as being at Bwlch y Clai. Castle works, Buckley's northernmost works, was sited some one and three-quarter miles from Buckley Cross, which is well into the open countryside, and was built on fields which in more agrarian days were called Foulkes Croft and Barn Field. The works were founded with an official Indenture of lease granted to William Malcolmson of the Mayfield Factory in Ireland in April 1866, although construction of the works had begun the year earlier. A great clamp kiln was constructed to fire the bricks needed to build the sheds and kilns, and when the new bricks were eventually removed, the side walls of the clamp were left in situ to form the walls of a narrow drying shed. Malcolmson's partner and manager on site was George Herbert Alletson, who was only 24 years old at the start of the venture, and who rose to become one of the guiding lights of Buckley brickmaking.

By early March 1869 Castle were announcing their new main outlet at Chester General Station:

"The excellent position of the works of the Castle Brick Company for the transit of their goods by rail or water, the very superior description of the material and the newest and most perfect machinery being employed,enable the company confidently to point out to gentlemen using these goods on their estates,

the important advantages to be gained by purchasing from the Castle Brick Company".

The works were connected to the main line railway by a horse drawn tramway; the horses much later being replaced by petrol rail tractors.

On 15th July 1875 the company reformed as the Castle Firebrick and Coal Company, which was registered to take over not only the Castle Brick Co, but also the Plas Bellin and Northop Hall Collieries, from whence the brickworks got their vast supplies of coal. Apart from Mr Alletson, a local Northop man, nearly all the other directors in this new firm, including Malcolmson, were Irish merchants and shipping men.

Flintshire News 24th December 1912 – At Mold

Police Court a man named Thomas McCarthy was charged with sleeping out and with assault. Owing to numerous complaints received with regards to tramps infesting the works on Sunday, Mr Alletson visited the works periodically on that day. He found the prisoner and another man there. Mr Marston, appearing for Castle Fire Brick Co, here interposed that there were nine tramps there the previous Sunday, and they complained the place was not sufficiently warm. Mr Alletson told the two men to go, but the prisoner refused to go until he cooked his food. Mr Alletson gave him time to clear out. Prisoner then said he would go away, but went in the wrong direction. Again Mr Alletson took hold of him and the prisoner, who had evidently had drink, fell and hurt his head. McCarthy asked for his tins, which were handed to him by a workman. One contained hot water and McCarthy tried to throw the contents into Mr Alletson's face, but he succeeded in avoiding it. Mr Marston appealed to the bench to help them to put down what had become an intolerable nuisance.

The next great leap in Castle's fortunes came with their association with John Summers Steelworks. In 1916 Castle had commenced the manufacture of high temperature silica bricks for furnace linings, having just built a special plant for this purpose. Summers recognised the benefits of securing a ready local supply of this necessary material and successfully managed to buy out Castle, and as the fortunes of the brickworks were now so closely linked with those of the steelworks we should examine its origins. John Summers had originally been a clog maker in Stalybridge, establishing a small works there in 1850. The year later he visited the Crystal Palace exhibition, and was impressed by a small nail making machine, which he subsequently bought for £40. He then set up the Globe Iron Works at Stalybridge, and having grown sufficiently wealthy, he looked further afield for a suitable site on which to open up a second works. Choosing the lands opposite Connah's Quay on the Dee estuary, he purchased 43 acres and by December 1896 his new Hawarden Bridge Ironworks were in place for the mass manufacture of nails and corrugated iron.

Having purchased Castle works, his new aquisition was re-styled as the Castle Fire Brick Company, and backed by the capital from the steelworks Castle bought up many of the other Buckley manufacturers, as well as Caernarfon Brick in 1930, Buttington at Oswestry in 1944 and Hooton Brickworks on the Wirral in 1964.

The production of ordinary fireclay bricks continued at Castle Old Works (the name given to the works following the acquisition of the adjacent Elm Colliery) until the end of 1944, when it was transferred to Castle's three other Buckley plants, namely Catherall's, Buckley Brick & Tile and Parry's. This then allowed the Old Works to concentrate its efforts towards increasing its silica brick output for the Hawarden Bridge steel plant.

Chester Chronicle 1st August 1953 – They were singing and laughing in the rain on the Castle Firebrick recreation field on Saturday. The rain did curb things a bit and most of the time was spent in a couple of large marquees, but the fun and games went on with an enthusiasm infused by the management who, as they have done for the past eight years, dug deep into their funds to give their "big family" another communal treat. Conceived at the end of the war, following a welcome home to the workers from the Forces by Mr G.H. Alletson, this fete at once caught on, and as Mr Richard Summers, chairman of the directors, said: "it has become an institution – a part of the Castle organisation, and a part of the Castle friendship and mutual understanding". About half a dozen of the Castle men could not be present, for they were looking after the kilns at the works, but they were not forgotten, and tea was sent along to them from the fete ground.

By 1965 the company could report an increase of £100,000 on their previous year's profits after having spent vast sums in modernising their other works at Buckley. But the spectre of doom was not far away. In 1971 the British Steel Corporation, the new masters of the nationalised steel industry, announced that the Shotton Works had lost £21 million following a collapse in the market. 6,400 jobs went at the steel plant and Castle Firebrick was caught in the wake of a massive financial reorganisation. By that time, the Old Works was the only Buckley factory left after British Steel had sold off the other concerns, and in 1972 the works was sold to the Butterley Brick Co. After 110 years of continuous production the works was closed and demolished in 1976. The site stood at OS 2751 6680 and is now occupied by new industries, but the old brick foundations of the original kiln yard can be seen around the perimeter of the present day yard. The massive flooded clayhole to the east still exists.

SITE 30: CASTLE NEW WORKS – ELM COLLIERY

This site began principally as a colliery and was established by George Watkinson. He was one of Yorkshire's greatest coal and brick masters, and expanded his empire into Buckley in 1872, when he bought the Willow Colliery at OS 276 651.

Buckley Colliery had been advertised for sale in August of the previous year, and he acquired that as well. In 1876 he leased some land at OS 264 667, approx one-and-a-quarter miles west of Castle Brickworks, to sink for coal and brick earth, provided he only used what clay he found to make bricks for use at the pit site. This minor concern was abandoned by him eight years later.

Watkinson's most prestigious undertaking at Buckley also started in 1876 when he took over the Elm Colliery at OS 2740 6625, not far from Castle Brickworks. He added a third pit to the workings in 1894 and succeeded in making the Elm one of the largest collieries in Buckley. At this time the works employed over 600 persons, and by 1896 the Elm's underground workings extended so far that new shafts had to be sunk down to meet them and facilitate easier ventilation and surface access. These new shafts, 1.3 miles away from the Elm, themselves became the new Mountain Colliery.

In 1920 Castle Firebrick bought the Elm Colliery and embarked on a giant expansion programme. A totally new factory at OS 2720 6640 was erected to the north west of the colliery, and we are lucky in being able to date this event. The Buckley diarist George Lewis recorded on 16th Jan 1925 that

"Castle firm started to build a new brickworks by the Elm Colliery", and by August the new works was put into production. Its function was to make common building bricks from clay mixed with the deposits of pit shale which the Elm Colliery had been raising, but had put to no good purpose. The New Works, as it became designated, proved so successful that the following year another kiln was built, identical to the one already in use. Both were state of the art Belgian 30 chamber continuous kilns, and together they could turn out 240,000 bricks every week. Electric trucks removed the finished products from the kilns, and an overhead runway loaded them onto trucks for delivery – this handling technology left most other North Wales brickworks stuck firmly in the Victorian era by comparison. In 1944 the works was extended yet again with a new mill house, a 16 chamber kiln and a further chimney stack costing a total of £10,896.

The collapse of Shotton's steel making profits towards the end of the 1960s took its toll on the works. Castle Old Works had concentrated on producing silica bricks, but the New Works was exclusively designed for the production of building bricks, and as the call for such had been in steady decline for years, the decision was taken not to risk any further investment in the site. The order to close New Works came in August 1970.

As for the colliery at the Elm site, it had ceased by the end of 1929, but restarted in July the following year when a new seam was discovered. How long it survived after that I cannot say, but its demise came many years before that of the brickworks.

SITE 31: PARRY'S BRICKWORKS

Edward Parry was born in Ireland in 1806, although his father was a Buckley man. The family returned to Wales when Edward was still a boy, and he remained in Buckley for the rest of his life. Edward became the manager of one of the local brickworks, and a trade directory for 1850 shows an Edward Parry as manager at Ashton's Brickworks.

On 27th March 1861 Edward met with Mr Dixon, the agent for Davies Cooke's Gwysanney Estate, to discuss his proposals to take a lease on land south of Ewloe Barn Farm to establish a brickworks of his own. This meeting took place at the Ewloe Hall Colliery, where we know that Edward was the manager at that time. Interestingly, it must be pointed out that later company literature for Parry's brickworks has the company shown as being established in 1860, so perhaps he may have officially registered the company at that time in order to raise capital for the intended venture. Whatever the case, the first appearance in the rates ledgers for Parry's Ewloe Wood Brickworks is in 1863, so perhaps this is when the works actually started production. The original lease document is dated December 1864, but this discrepancy between dates is not unusual – official Indentures of lease were usually drawn up after preliminary works had been done in surveying and testing out new sites to establish their practical viability.

Parry's works became particularly noted for their dark blue paving bricks and other specialised products, including the "Acidio" brick made specifically for chemical works. The following description from their catalogue describes another of their products: "Dragon Brand fireproof material is manufactured from an admixture of the various beds of fireclay at our disposal. Unlike the majority of manufacturers who mine or quarry only one or perhaps two, we have the choice of ten distinct clays".

Wrexham Advertiser 12th October 1872 – On Saturday last a dinner was given at the works of Mr E Parry to the workmen by Mr R Parry in honour of his marriage. At an early hour the men were busily engaged in erecting flags and decorating one of the sheds, which they did with great taste. Shortly after five o'clock the dinner was on the table and the workmen and their wives began to assemble. Mr E Parry presided and after the men had been supplied with ale, roast beef, ham etc he rose to propose the health of Mr and Mrs Parry. After dinner the tables were removed and dancing commenced and was energetically kept up until a late hour.

Mr Parry himself was a committed Christian and took a keen interest in helping to establish local chapels. When the New Wesleyan Chapel was built in Wrexham Street, Mold in 1868, he donated all the bricks for its construction.

Like the nearby Castle Works, Parry's was a mecca for the "tramping fraternity" in the Victorian period. Being located well away from town reduced the risk of investigation by a constable on patrol, and consequently tramps flocked to the warmth of Parry's kilns in their droves. In 1893 one particular tramp, James Rae, was recorded as having been convicted of trespassing at Parry's works on no less than 16 separate occasions.

Edward Parry died in November 1879, and the firm was taken over by his three sons, Robert, Thomas Sharp and George Armstrong, and five years later a further lease was taken to extend the clay workings northwards, destroying much of the farmland belonging to the original Ewloe Barn Farm, from whence the brickworks got its name. In July 1902 the family concern became a Limited Company under the new style of E. Parry & Sons Ltd, but not long afterwards the company's fortunes took a sharp downturn. For the year ending June 1904 they showed a meagre profit of only £126-1-0 and from then onwards the losses kept increasing – from a debit of £55-5-11 in 1905 to nearly £3,000 in 1912. If things were not bad enough, a serious fire certainly couldn't have come at a worse time:

Flintshire Observer 20th Feb 1913 – The Buckley district was the scene of another fire on the morning of Thursday 13th, the engine room of the brickworks of Messrs E Parry & Sons being discovered ablaze shortly before 5 o'clock. Within a short time the engine room was entirely gutted, but the Mold Fire Brigade arrived in time to prevent the spread. The origin of the fire is unknown and the damage is estimated at not far short of £1,000. It will however be some time before the works can be restarted, and about 60 hands will be thrown out of employment. This is the first fire to occur at these works which have been established for over half a century. The loss is not covered by insurance.

In attempts to offset the decline the directors kept

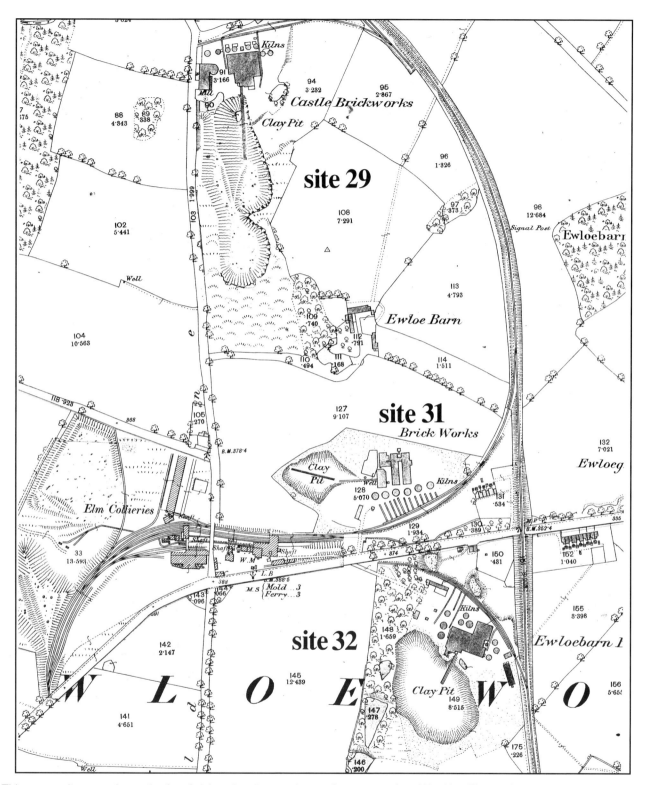

This composite map shows the four brickworks sites on the northern extremity of Buckley. The road traversing west to east is the main Mold to Queensferry road, with Pinfold Lane crossing north to south. Parry's Brickworks at site 31 and Davison's Ewloe Barn Works at site 32 are shown as they were in 1871. The Elm Colliery did not exist at this time, but is shown here as it appeared in 1899, by which time it had incorporated the older Buckley Colliery. Castle New Works was built alongside the Elm in the 1920s. The old Castle Brickworks factory at site 29 is shown here as it was in 1871 with the claypit workings depicted as they were later on in the century taking out further mortgages against the works, and by the end of the 1930s, after many swaps and changes, Alice Parry, the wife of George Armstrong Parry's son, held almost all the shares herself. Salvation finally arrived in October 1944, when the powerful Castle Firebrick Co offered 14s. 1d. for each of the company's shares at a total outlay to Castle of £6,000. A Castle report in 1945 noted "Since this company was acquired in Oct 1944 it has continued to operate on low production. The plant is well equipped to deal with any demands likely to be made for it, having very extensive drying sheds. For a long time past this undertaking has produced large quantities of special lining material for cement kilns. The demand is not great now due to closure of so many cement works, but will improve as soon as these works reopen". With the work which Castle put their way, by 1948 Parry's books could record a profit of £2,694.

Some say that the works closed in 1962, but this may have only been temporarily, as an entry exists in the company's Minute Books for April 1969. During the lifetime of the works the clayhole excavations became so vast that Ewloe Barn Farm was completely eradicated by them, and today we can hardly tell where Parry's clayhole ended and Castle's began – both quarries have merged to become one vast flooded canyon. The factory stood at OS 2767 6634, and was itself swallowed up by more modern mineral excavations by the owners of Lane End Brickworks.

One interesting feature still remains nearby – part of the old Buckley Colliery, perhaps it's engine house, can still be seen abutting the roadside close to the junction of Pinfold Lane.

SITE 32: DAVISON'S EWLOE BARN BRICKWORKS

Across the road from the site of Parry's works there exists today a large area of varied industrial usage. This was once one of two extensive brickworks owned by Charles Davison & Co, and being situated down the slope of Buckley Mountain, it became known as Davison's Bottom Works.

The earliest references to clayworkings at this site appear on the 1839 tithe map, which shows a field called Lower Brick Field in the holding of Robert Teggin. Marl Pit Field lay a short walk to the south east, and the same distance along the roadside to the north east was Little Meadow, which was registered as being used by William Davies as a brick and tile works. Davies would have been running what we might term a cottage industry by today's standards, and he would have been using simple clamp kilns. Davies eventually got into arrears of £33 – one years rent on his site – and the landowner Davies Cooke obtained a court order in May 1847 to seize the assets at his meagre brickworks, listed as "eight firebrick bearers, a quantity of firebricks, a lot of firebrick clay, slop brick clay and a lot of loose timber".

This is where Charles Davison enters the picture. He took on Davies' Little Meadow site by a lease of 24th June 1847, which granted him an annual usage of 100 tons of clay for each kiln erected, provided he built no more than three kilns. He was to pay £3 per year in dead rent and £30 rental for each kiln. Charles also took over what the lease calls "the brick and tile kilns in a nearby field known as Ponds Tile Works", but there is no indication as to where this was, although it must have been in the immediate vicinity.

Charles Davison himself was a shipowner on the Dee estuary, so he had no difficulty in funding the new venture, and his family continued to be connected with shipping for a great many years to come. In the same year he started the brickworks Admiral Dundas, another of the local landowners, provided a wharf to which he could cart his bricks for loading onto his ships, and Charles built a warehouse there to accommodate the products of his new venture. By 1880 he owned fifteen ships and became a vociferous spokesman on the subject of improving transportation. Before the Buckley Railway was built, the Ewloe Barn works suffered much expense in carting their bricks to the port at Connah's Quay by road. Indeed, Charles became one of the port's greatest advocates, and passionately believed that it should have been five times larger than it was, to ensure that all the Buckley works, collieries as well as brickworks, suffered no incumberance to their trade.

Wrexham Advertiser 28th November 1885 – On Monday a three-masted schooner of 250 tons burden was launched from the shipyard of Messrs Ferguson & Baird, Connah's Quay. The schooner has been christened The Empress, and the launch was one of the finest that has taken place at the Quay. The vessel was at once taken into dock and loaded with bricks for London. She is owned by a company of which Mr Charles Davison is manager, and the load of bricks is from the firm of Messrs Charles Davison & Son, Buckley.

Charles needed plenty of fuel to feed his kilns as the works grew in size, and a railway map of 1866 shows us three sites in the immediate vicinity at which he had a partnership in some small coal pits. One was at the bottom of Pinfold Lane at OS 2765 6510. Another was at Great Oak Colliery at 2750 6570, and another two were at Buckley Colliery near Parry's works.

Charles had been running the brickworks from his shipping office at the port, but by the close of 1867 he moved the company's head office to Ewloe Barn Works. Two years later a new lease was negotiated and the works was expanded, and

the landowner, befitting his status as landed gentry, included a clause which allowed him leave to "hunt, course, shoot and fish" on the lands. Nowadays, a busy dual carriageway cuts past the site and housing estates loom ever nearer, but back then Ewloe Barn would have been surrounded by acres of rolling countryside.

By now the company was being run by Charles and his brother Tellett, but Charles decided that a new partner should be employed to relieve him of much of the workload. On 8th December 1873 Henry Hurlbutt officially became a partner in the firm, although he had been involved in a managerial capacity for the previous six months. Henry had been a timber merchant in Chester since 1855, and by 1870 he was running thriving timber outlets at the canal wharfs at Cow Lane Bridge and Tower Wharf, but in 1872 he transferred all his premises to Connah's Quay to take advantage of the docks.

We have already come across a few examples of trespass onto brickworks by children, and Ewloe Barn likewise suffered:

Wrexham Advertiser 30th Jan 1875 – On Sunday evening the offices of Messrs Davison at their brick and tile works were forcibly

Loading the railway trucks at the Ewloe Barn stockyards sidings. Late 19th century. Photo: FRO.

entered by some persons unknown, whose object seemed to be simply destruction. They opened all the drawers, and those which were locked were ruthlessly broken open. Nothing was missed except about a pound of biscuits, and in the offices there were several articles of clothing and some bottles of spirits.

Henry Hurlbutt became the principal guiding force in the company, and on 31st March, 1883 he bought out Charles Davison's shares and became managing director. Charles now went his own way, but one of his relatives, W.A. Davison, continued in the position of works manager, which he had held previously.

Chester Chronicle 29th January, 1887 – On Saturday the employees of Messrs C Davison & Co were entertained to a first class tea by H. Hurlbutt, the principal of that firm. Nothing had been spared in order to make the party an enjoyable one. The tables were loaded with the best of good things, the shed was nicely dressed and a first class string band in attendance. The company numbered about 200 including the workmen and their wives or sweethearts. When full justice had been done to the eatables, the tables were cleared away and the capacious shed set in order for the dance. After the dancing, in acknowledging the enthusiastic vote of thanks of his workmen, Mr Hurlbutt said he believed there was a better time soon coming for them and whenever it would come he hoped they would make the right use of it and do their best to better themselves. It was always his wish to see his men doing well.

Henry, a personal friend of W E Gladstone, became a JP in 1887 and the High Sheriff for Flintshire from 1900. He married one of the Davison's heiresses, and died in 1913.

It's worth mentioning the large variety of products made by Davison's. So great was the variation in the chemical and mineral contents of the works' rock and clay strata, that they could produce over 30 different products of varying properties. Of their brand names there were Bovitron bricks for mild acid environments – Losol with its low acid solubility property – Hysilin for high mechanical strength – Alumantine for lining high-temperature cement kilns, and the famous Obsidianite and Adamantine brands. Of these, one of Davison's catalogues says:

"Read what a prominent American chemical engineer says. There appears to be in the USA no product equivalent to Obsidianite manufactured by Charles Davison Co of Buckley, England. The Adamantine quality can be used for chimney and flue building, and is of particular value in withstanding the action of acid laden gases. It is also admirable for all kinds of foundation work, manhole linings and culverts. For places where wet conditions exist, Adamantine material is eminently suitable".

The clay at Ewloe Barn was much more difficult to reach than at other works; it being beneath deeper layers of surface materials, and Davison originally thought his clay rent should be reduced to compensate for the time wasted in reaching it. This letter to the Estate's agent back in 1867 explains the problem:

"The bed of clay is much thicker than others on the Buckley Mountain. There is an extraordinary thickness of fey, or common clay and soil overlying the fireclay, as compared with other works. The Buckley Brick and Tile Co for instance – where we have as many feet as they have inches. The gradient or inclination of the clay is so much steeper than ours, which make it more difficult to work".

After the Second World War the company was sold to General Refractories of Sheffield, who in turn became part of G.R. Stein Ltd. For many years they concentrated solely on the production of refractory bricks for the cement industry, but by 1976 they reported that "the order situation is desperate. From the middle to the end of February we have a completely blank order book. Orders have simply dried up." By the time the works closed later that same year the huge factory only had 30 employees left.

The Ewloe Barn works complex was centred at OS 2778 6615 with a large opencast clayhole to the south.

SITE 33: ASTON HALL COAL & BRICK COMPANY.

The colliery and brickworks at this site were in their day isolated on the slopes below Buckley Mountain amidst a rural tranquillity of green fields. The area today warrants quite a different description; busy dual carriageways now bordering the site on two sides.

The company's name derives from the Aston Hall Estate, which W E Gladstone purchased from Admiral Dundas in 1861. I have read that a Messrs Leach & Co had a colliery here at the time, but no confirmation of such has been found. What is certain though is that Messrs Lancaster & Fenton are listed in the estate rent ledger as having a colliery here from 1862. They ran trial borings on the site until October 1863, and then formed Aston Hall Colliery Company under a lease running from October 1865. Just to complicate matters, I can also report having come across an Aston Colliery Co formed from 1st January 1864, and an Aston Hall Coal Co in the same year... these two companies most likely being different styles of the same concern. A plan of the colliery drawn in 1865 officially confirms it as "belonging to Hugh Fenton & Co". In regard to the existence of any brickworks at this colliery, we can refer to a court case of June 1866, when we learn that the Aston Hall Colliery had at that time been in possession of a brickworks for a month. It must have been a sub let working, as it ran under the style of Messrs Kershaw & Co, but some short while before, according to the report, it had previously been occupied by Messrs Lawson. The rates listings also show Kershaw & Co's brickworks running from 1866 until late 1868. Kershaw's must have been supplying bricks for the main Aston Hall Co, as an advertisement in Jan 1868 mentions that the colliery company "are now prepared to supply the public with the finest quality of white and colour pressed bricks". This sub letting ended around early 1869, when the rates listings show the brickworks having been taken over by the Aston

Hall Colliery itself, who proceeded to place the brickworks in the throws of an expansion programme:

Wrexham Advertiser 30th January, 1869 – Near to Hawarden on the estate of the Aston Hall Colliery Co a new pit is being sunk in addition to three at present at work. A few yards below one of the seams of coal, a valuable bed of fireclay is being got, and large sheds and buildings have been erected covering some acres of ground, and two of the kilns hold 25,000 bricks each. The works will find employment when in full operation for some hundreds of hands.

Amongst the company's improvements was the laying of a new three mile railway down to the main coastal railway line. This branch line was opened on the 23rd August, 1872, and replaced the little horse drawn tramway which had run down to Admiral Dundas's wharf at Queensferry. The opening ceremony was witnessed as follows:

Wrexham Advertiser 24th August 1872 – Many colliers with their Davys turned out for a holiday. A white ensign was hoisted on the head gear of the pit, and the engine having made a trial trip to see that the line was clear, came back for the first train. The new Tank Engine which is to work the traffic, named the Glynne, was decorated with a tricolour flag and a wreath of choice flowers, and boughs of oak were placed in the laden coal wagons.

By December 1874 however, the colliery company was registered as bankrupt, and was again in liquidation three years later. On 6th June 1878 a totally new company was formed. It was now the Aston Hall Coal & Brick Co Ltd under the general managership of Alexander Ward, the Hawarden civil engineer, who had for some years previously been the old company's works manager. This new firm also eventually bought out the Queensferry Colliery and the Pentrobin Colliery, and new shares were offered to finance the capital needed for the venture. By April the next year the new company could finally announce that "The Aston

Hall Coal & Brick Co having purchased from the liquidator the whole of the works of the Aston Hall Colliery Co are now prepared to supply house and steam coals and Aston buff facing bricks, of which they are sole manufacturers ".

The extremely tough bricks produced by this company were particularly notable. In 1878 the British Architect journal reported them as being "a beautiful rich coloured yellowish brick", and I have even come across an advertisement for a house sale which made particular note that it had been faced with Aston Premier bricks – the only time I have come across a specific brick company's product mentioned in promoting a house sale. The following excerpt is from the company's catalogue of the 1890s:

"The Aston Hall Premier" bricks and terracotta are manufactured from a special clay of exceptional quality and unique character which is recognised by leading architects as producing the first and best manufactured Buff Goods in the kingdom. They are particularly noted for retaining their original colour and for not vegetating as is the case with the soft, common buff bricks. The electric light has been placed throughout the works, and manufacture now goes on day and night.

If you do not find in this catalogue what you desire, send a sketch of your requirements to the Aston Hall Co and they will quote you a price".

A further liquidation came in 1883 and the court ordered the sale of the company on 31st January, but bids fell far short of expectations, and the sale did not go through. Despite this, the company seems to have kept going, excepting a spell in 1894 when colliery operations were suspended by serious flooding of the workings. This stoppage brought the brickworks to a halt once its coal stocks had been depleted, and the opportunity was taken in the meantime to wire up the bricksheds with an electric lighting generator (mentioned above) which succeeded in improving productivity by enabling a night shift to be employed.

The table below shows the brickworks sale sheet for one week during 1904, and its worth noting the comparison between the sale price of the goods and the total wage bill for that week, as the 42 souls working at Aston Hall Brickworks cost the company only £58-7-11 in wages.

	number sold.	total sale price
best buff bricks	49,700	£139-3-3
special moulded brick	4,604	16-2-4
floor tiles	35,120	98-6-9
best glazed bricks	2,280	13-13-7
chimney pots	63	3-18-9
coping	162 ft	5-8-0
balustrades	32	4-14-0
vases	4	4-0-0

Who actually continued to work the company since its liquidation in 1883 is unknown to me, but there was a report that W E Gladstone may have taken a lease on it in 1889. Horace Mayhew, the senior director and manager, explained in a letter dated 9th February 1909 that his partners and himself had carried it on for more than a quarter of a century, so perhaps they had bought it back in 1883. Whatever the case, in February 1909 Mr Mayhew wrote to the landlord Mr Gladstone explaining that the high rates imposed at the colliery were making it impossible to continue the works profitably, and Mr Gladstone agreed in July to a proposal that the colliery be closed, leaving the brickworks to continue alone. But as their clay source had come mainly from the colliery workings they then faced the problem of the eventual cessation of supply. Apart from some good clay set aside, there was a separate stockpile of 10,800 tons which had not been properly screened for impurities as it was brought out of the mine. The plan had been to erect a new brickworks at Queensferry Colliery (still one of the company's holdings), but this would have been a costly affair in time alone, and Mayhew was becoming ever more anxious, as his good clay stocks were dwindling fast. On 5th October 1909 he wrote to Mr Gladstone's land agent explaining

"as you are doubtless aware there is not much remaining of the clay we have raised out of the mine, and the amount that can be safely used of

the old bank of clay deposited by the old Aston Hall Co is quite an unknown quantity. The labour in picking and cleaning it will be very great and I fear the percentage of bad bricks will be abnormal".

Mayhew knew the importance of retaining the prestigious Aston Hall name as an assurance of future brick sales, and he suggested issuing £20,000 worth of shares in a new venture to finance the proposed new brickworks at the Queensferry Colliery, which would operate under the Aston Hall name. Agreement from Mr Gladstone was given, but the venture never went ahead, probably because not enough coal and clay could be found at the Queensferry site.

The final dismantlement sale of both Aston Hall colliery and brickworks went ahead on 24th July 1913.

In 1881 the OS map showed the brickworks with two oblong kilns, but by 1923 it had expanded to possess nine round and three oblong kilns.

The road from the large St David's Hotel to Burntwood virtually passes over the brickworks site at OS 2940 6606, whilst the colliery site is now part of the housing estate at OS 2939 6590.

SITE 34: BUCKLEY BRICK & TILE CO – BROOKHILL BRICKWORKS

The Buckley Brick & Tile Co was formed in 1865 to control two separate works (Brookhill and Belmont) under the management of the same company. Brookhill Works was the the larger of the two and was the adjacent southerly neighbour of Davison's Ewloe Barn works.

On 8th September 1864 Davies Cooke's Gwysanney Estate let an area of 12.5 acres of virgin land to two Cheshire men – the land surveyor Robert Roberts and George Meakin, "the eminent contractor", as The Mining Journal called him. Nothing was done with this site until the Buckley Brick & Tile Company (later referred to simply as The Buckley Company) was incorporated on 20th February 1865 to merge this site with that of the already established Buckley Draining Pipe Works half a mile to the south. Roberts then took out a further lease on the virgin

site from 25th March which allowed him to "erect any kilns and to make and construct all such roadways, railways and tramways as may be necessary". The Brookhill site was up and running, but not without some initial complications. In July 1865, John Palin, one of the company's principal directors, wrote a somewhat sarcastically toned letter to the Gwysanney Estate, complaining that the company had already been charged rental on kilns not yet constructed:

" My dear Sir, I can only say that I fully understood from numerous conversations with you that we would not have to pay for the two kilns until at all events one was erected, and that you should claim from us a half years rent for two kilns before even one was built, is I must say, extremely hard".

Palin went on to explain that they had met with "uncontrollable difficulties". Whatever they may have been, by the same time a year later £8,705 had been spent on building the Brookhill works, and at the beginning of 1866 they had had the good fortune to appoint Major John Merriman Gibson as their manager and company secretary. Gibson was of that breed of men who radiated flair and enthusiasm, and it wasn't long before Brookhill became known locally as Gibson's Works; a name which I can witness from experience remained in the memory of Buckley people even until 70 years after his death.

Major Gibson came from Hexham in the north of England and had been a blacksmith before joining the army, after which he took an appointment with the Buckley Railway, and was later a contractor's agent at the River Dee Embankment Works before he joined the Buckley Brick & Tile Co. His military background led to his later taking command of the 160 strong Buckley Engineer Volunteer Corps – an extremely popular movement in Victorian days, and not unlike our modern Territorial Army.

During their earlier years, water shortages were a recurrent problem for both the company's works – the Upper Works (Belmont) and Lower Works (Brookhill). In 1866 a new reservoir was built at Brookhill, but proved too small to supply their demands, and three months production was sacrificed whilst the workmen concentrated on boring the clayhole in an attempt to hit an underground stream. Finally they resorted to building a supplementary reservoir to the west of the clayhole in some woods, which have long since been eradicated.

In 1867 a slump in the brick trade took hold which lasted for some few years, and to offset the expense of transportation by sea (the Buckley area's chief outlet at this time) the Buckley Co bought their own ship in 1869. Named "Problem", she ensured that a steady, if moderate profit was made on shipping costs... £91 in 1870, £179 in 1872. The expense of refits in 1884 saw her make a loss of £216, but in all, she was a good investment. Her end came in 1907 when she ran aground between Newry and Queenstown on one of her interminable Irish runs. With assistance the ship was helped into Wicklow, where it was determined that the cost of repairs would have proved unrealistic, and Problem went for salvage for £110.

As a backdrop to the work's history, I have included these two entries from the company's Minute Books:

"31st August, 1894 – I this day thoroughly inspected every part of both the Upper and Lower Works, Tramways, Reservoirs, Sidings etc, and I cannot allow the opportunity to pass without placing on record the highly satisfactory state in which I found everything. I was much struck with the respectable outside appearance of both our works compared with others I saw in the neighbourhood, and especially with the

Brookhill employees in 1894. Major J M Gibson stands sideways. Photo: FRO.

splendid new sheds in course of erection at the lower works (Brookhill).

1st March, 1895 – On 13th February a small piece of clay had unfortunately fallen on Thomas Jones the clayhole foreman. It was a fall of only about 8 ft and not more than a barrow load, but it caught him on the back when stooping. An inquest was held and a verdict of accidental death returned. The Secretary said he had paid all the funeral and grave expenses and suggested we should also put up a stone over the grave, which was agreed to. Also that we should allow the widow 2s. 6d. and each of the five children 1s. a week during our pleasure. Secretary said he was determined to make another effort to get the men to insure".

By March 1899 the company had found it necessary to reduce their capital, and a list of creditors was drawn up, presumably in anticipation that they might go bust. Lean times must have followed, if their correspondence with the landlords is anything to go by. It seems that the company was trying to reduce the expenditure on clay royalties by requesting that the neighbouring Catheralls works be allowed to sub-let one of their clay fields to the Brookhill works. We can only assume that things got better by the fact that the works managed to stay open!

Their great managing director Maj. Gibson died on 17th Feb 1927 after having suffered from declining health following an accident at the works the year before. The men ceased work at 12:30pm to attend his funeral, which was one of the biggest the town had ever seen, and the Chronicle's obituary was probably very near the truth when they reported that "it can be said of him that he did more for the brick and tile trade in Buckley than any other man in his day".

The following years of the 1930s saw bleak times for the company. The Belmont factory had been sacrificed back in 1912, but even this rationalisation could not protect the company from the vagaries of market forces. In 1930 only seven and a half months were worked, and despite a slight upturn in 1933 further losses had been realised by 1938. In September the following year the then managing director, Richard M Gibson, the son of John Merriman, began negotiating the sale of the works to Castle Firebrick. Castle bought the works in May 1940 for £11,000, and five years later they could report that "in spite of early difficulties encountered in this plant, the demand for acid resisting material has steadily improved. We have installed a power operated press at this works which will take the place of the small hand operated machines. As at Old Works, a small canteen has been opened for employees. This has proved to be helpful and has been self-supporting from the start".

In 1950 Castle then purchased the freehold on Brookhill's land for £3,000 and production continued until 1st April 1961 when the works finally closed; the reason apparently being due to an inability to continue working the clay seam which struck out eastwards under the factory itself. Once the clay bed had become exhausted there was simply nowhere else to go! The works was finally demolished around August 1968, and over the years the ruins became engulfed under trees and undergrowth, until modern excavations eradicated them entirely at the turn of the 21st century. The factory stood at OS 2793 6563 with its clayhole to the west.

As the Buckley Company was one of the town's most famous works, let's look at some of their products:

Company minutes 13th December, 1884 – " The Secretary said that a special kind of brick and tile which he had been making for some time had given great satisfaction and was working its way in the market. He said having given it the name Metalline, it would be well to register it as a trade mark which would cost £5 to protect for 14 years. He was instructed to register it."

In 1887 the Trade Marks BBB (Best Buckley Blue) and FW (Flintshire White) were also registered. One of their most famous lines was the hard BHB (Brookhill Blue) brick, and when the nearby works of Charles Davison & Co began stamping their bricks with HBH in 1903, the Buckley Co saw it as a crafty attempt to imitate their trademark. An appeal to the Patent Controller however saw them lose their case, and they had to pay £50 towards

Davison's court costs.

Gibsonite and Salamdine were also trademarks of the company.

One of the last visible remains of the works to vanish was its clayhole, and before we leave this chapter it's worth the mention that it was once the scene of one of Buckley's most romantic tragedies:

Chester Chronicle 10th September, 1921 – About 10:30am on Sunday morning a man was in the neighbourhood of Buckley Common. He saw two heaps of clothing near to a clayhole of water. He thought it his duty to report his strange discovery to the police. An inspection of the clothing led to the discovery that they belonged to Miss Dorothy Fox, aged 21, and William Robert Williams, aged 18. The police commenced dragging operations. These clay pits are huge craters and contain a great depth of water. In the deeper parts of the clayhole in question there must be easily 50 ft. of water. In a short time two bodies were recovered. They were found to be locked in each other's arms. The dragging operations were watched by an increasing crowd, and the discovery of the bodies, especially the posture in which they were found, created a profound sensation. A note in the man's hat contained a message "from Willie and Dollie". At one time it was thought a sentence could be dimly discerned which was to the effect that the girl stated "she could not stand it any longer and was going to Mammie".

The passage of time has seen some social changes which today would not have resulted in a desperate act such as this. At the inquest it was revealed that Dollie had been pregnant, and without her late mother to turn to for any sympathy and support, the stigma and shame caused by her condition led the pair to take their lives. One of her stockings had been tied around her eyes as a blindfold, and it was believed that William must have done this in an attempt to calm Dollie's fears as the two lovers waded out into Brookhill's deep waters.

SITE 35: CATHERALLS TRAP BRICKWORKS

"Soon after finishing the Canal, i e the new channel of the River Dee, 1737, a native of the name of Jonathan Catherall commenced the burning of firebricks on a small scale indeed, but which has since become a very important trade".

That passage taken from A Memoir of Hawarden Parish, published in 1822, marks the beginning of a business which was to become recognised as probably the oldest established brickmaking concern in the whole of North Wales. In those early days Buckley was already the home to a successful pottery trade, to which brickmaking was of minor secondary importance. The unique fireclays of the region were referred to as "weak clay" by the potters, because of its unsuitability for pot manufacture in their small low temperature kilns, and the legend has come down to us that it was Jonathan Catherall I, born in 1689, who in 1739 began experimenting with the clay by firing it at ever higher temperatures to produce a new harder brick of obvious commercial value, and it was he who became the father to the Buckley brick industry, despite there being other brickmakers at work at this time.

Its hard, if not impossible, to precisely evaluate exactly when Jonathan might have established his brickmaking firm, but Catherall Company letterheads and company advertisements both display the year as 1760, although his involvement with brickmaking would certainly have been ongoing before then. In 1762 Jonathan died, and his wayward son John took over; a man of intemperate habits who was often drunk and liable to lose vast amounts of money on his gambling habit. He held the pottery and brickworks until 7th December, 1777, when on returning from a trip to Chester, and perhaps somewhat drunk, he fell from his horse at Saltney and died. The works could now be taken in hand by his mother Martha, who in truth had been responsible for keeping it afloat during John's tenure. At this time, her 16 year old grandson Jonathan II, a legal student in London, returned home to assist his grandmother until his coming of age. He would later say of his father that he "had his frailties, which were to love bad women, horses and cocks".

Jonathan II was definitely not made in the like of his father, but took after the founder of the company. Hard-working, religious, philanthropic and generous – he was the man who was to steer the firm to its greatest heights, and I think we should learn something of the man himself.

Such was his passion for work that he set himself about to travelling the length and breadth of Britain, and even abroad, in search of new markets for the company's products. Here is an extract from a letter of 28th October, 1808 which he wrote from Swansea:

"I came here this morning safe and well, the horse well too. I left Machynlleth Monday and got to Llanrhystud on Tuesday. It rained so heavily I could not go from here till Wednesday morning – the river was very deep. My cloak kept me dry but I was much afraid the horse would not bear the journey".

An earlier letter shows what pains he would endure on his trips:

"In November 1791 by standing too long in the brickfield I got a cold which increased in December whilst on a journey in Cardiganshire by being very much wet. I was very violent in February 1792 on my journey to London, but was able to attend much to the injury to my health, to travelling and business. In March I went to Manchester on horseback. I was alarmed by losing the proper use of my right leg and afterwards my right side. Being apprehensive it was a paralytic stroke, I got a man to rub with oatmeal and flannel the parts affected. With my left hand I wrote to Dr Taylor, Infirmary, Manchester, who was sent for and came by 1 o'clock. He let blood in my neck. On the 30th I had a stroke or fit. I was now in the inn. By much struggling to get to the side of the bed, I rubbed the linen bandages off the incision in my neck and lost much blood. I could speak though not much nor very correct. My appetite was keen and recollection good but had lost the use of both arms, hands, thighs and legs".

That illness took him a long time to recuperate from, but by 22nd April the next year he could recount:

"Went to Mold in a chair (sedan). Was carried on to the Brickwork to see the men make a pit for the machine". Note how the then insignificant hamlet of Buckley was being referred to as Mold!

The brickworks at some point in its early history had the jawbone of a whale mounted over the entrance. Perhaps Jonathan II acquired it on one of his many trips.

His friend Griffith Jones wrote to him in 1820:

"I am sorry to hear that your lameness is getting worse; I am afraid that you bustle so much about the brickbank".

His religious fervour has been well-documented, but it will suffice to say here that he was a great campaigning non-conformist. He was fined many times for holding religious gatherings in the local cottages, before obtaining a licence to hold services in a pottery shed on Buckley Common, which he did for nearly ten years. The first non Church of England chapel in Buckley was built by Jonathan in 1811, and he also paid for the new minister's stipend for the next forty years. At the time of its construction, he commented in his letters:

"After doing a hard day's work, our workmen set to to make bricks for the building of the chapel, without wages".

He bought a bell for £12 which was brought from Cork in Ireland and installed at the chapel – the clergy at St Matthew's C of E church complained bitterly about this move, afraid that it would lure away worshippers from their congregation, and it was eventually removed and used as the Trap Brickworks timekeeping bell.

Jonathan was always to the fore in setting up free soup kitchens when trade depressions threw people out of work, and at such times when the works had to stop he would keep his men busy and in wages by having them repair and build walls with discarded half bricks.

In 1792 Martha died, and her grandsons, Jonathan II and John, found themselves at odds as to how the place should be run. The following year Jonathan decided to strike out on his own, and he set up the Ewloe Place Works alongside the cottage in which the family had lived, which still exists as the Hope & Anchor Inn. John now held the Trap until his death in 1805, at which point the works supposedly closed. This would seem to have been the case, as the tithe map of 1839 shows the place marked as an " Old Brickbank " in the holding of the landowner Cynric Lloyd. In the early 1840s the 30 acres of Trap lease were bought by the Chester accountant Enoch Gerrard, and on 7th August, 1841 he passed them on at a nice profit to Cynric Lloyd for £2,500. At this point it must be noted that the works would not officially have been referred to as The Trap and in July 1842 an advertisement appeared in the Chronicle stating that "The Ewloe Brick & Tile Co, the property of Cynric Lloyd Esquire, are now ready to supply firebricks and tiles at fair and moderate prices". This clearly heralded the start of a new chapter in the work's fortunes. The term Trap later became associated with the works, perhaps because of a cynical political commentary written earlier in June 1841, which purported that the "new TRAP made in the form of a brick kiln has been established for the purpose of entrapping those who voted for Sir Stephen Glynne. They must remain in the Trap where I shall take care they are kept hard at work at about sixpence a day". This comment was a criticism of the way in which some unscrupulous employers would give work and lodgings to the populace, only to hold them to moral ransom for their votes under the threat of dismissal, and it perhaps should not be taken as a direct criticism of the Catherall family themselves.

The next great man to become involved with the Trap was William Shepherd; once himself a poor collier and later a clerk at Argoed Colliery – probably the Argoed in south Buckley (see the text of site 23). He was supposedly appointed manager at the Trap some time after 1847. He was held in almost the same reverence as Jonathan II, and the following remembrance of him paints a vivid picture of his down-to-earth nature:

Chester Chronicle 4th February, 1893 – I happen to live in the south end of Buckley and it will be the south end people I will attempt to describe. First and foremost was the late Mr William Shepherd, who had pushed his way up to that position by sheer force of ability and strength of character. He was therefore a kind of Lord Mayor of the place. An old workman of his told me the other day that at election times (Shepherd was a leading Liberal, and he a Tory) he would say "A big loaf, Jack lad". " Aye, aye, but mester, but your two and eightpence a day will not buy a very big loaf, mester" answered Jack. But he took it all in perfect good humour. Those were the terms he used to be on with his workmen.

In the rates books for 1852 onwards, none earlier being available, we can see that William was the occupier of the Ewloe Brickworks Co on Cynric Lloyd's land. The lease was renewed in 1861, and the map shows four kilns in situ, but by 1866 a further kiln had been added. The 1865 rates listings show the works in the hands of Shepherd & Catherall, and this continued to be the case in later years, although Jonathan II had died in 1833, so the Catherall referred to must have been his son William. The dealings between the two families are actually fairly complex. William Shepherd died on 26th April, 1866, and his son of the same name took on his mantle, added to which, both families were inter-related by marriage.

By 1880 it appears that the Shepherd family's involvement at the Trap had come to an end, and on 23rd October the works was auctioned at the Green Dragon Hotel in Chester. From the sale details we can get a good idea as to the state of play at the time: "An old established and very valuable Firebrick and Tile Works known as Ewloe Works, now and for many years past carried on by the trustees of the will of the late William Shepherd, together with the good will attached to such works. Six kilns, drying sheds, with claypit, cottage, stables. To view apply to Messrs Catherall at the works". The works at this date were connected to Catherall's Ewloe Place Works (site 39) by a tramway which linked both to the

Site 34

Site 35

Site 36

Site 37

Site 37

Site 41

Site 41

Wrexham, Mold & Connah's Quay Railway. The outcome of the sale ensured the works stayed solely in the Catherall family's possession until 1936, when the Trap was purchased by Castle Firebrick Co for £4,748-8-6.

In 1962 Castle spent £180,000 on modernising the plant:

Chester Chronicle 3rd November, 1962 – Catheralls works, which produce refractory bricks in all manner of shapes and sizes, presents a very different picture through the improvements carried out. The battery of modern intermittent kilns now installed are the largest in the country, yet the installation of them was carried out without loss of production. A feature of the works is that as a result of oil firing and the high degree of temperature control, the life of the ladle bricks now produced for blast furnaces is between 20-25 per cent longer than the type formally produced. The original Catherall went into the firebrick business when he saw the alterations in the method of iron smelting. Little did he realise the wide variety of uses to which the output at his works could be put. In addition to the ladle bricks, Catheralls now produces blocks for lining rotary cement kilns and other materials with exceptional heat and acid resisting properties used in the manufacture of sulphuric acid and fertilisers. The blocks have gone to the West Indies for lining sugar furnaces.

Castle's subsequent misfortunes in 1971 led to them selling the Trap works to the Butterley Building Co in 1972, and the works continued until the announcement in November 1985 of its closure due to the depression in the building industries. The sixty men at the plant were laid off when work finally ceased the week before Christmas.

The Trap works up until its closure had the distinction of having been the longest running brickmaking site in the whole of North Wales. It stood at OS 2783 6531 with its clayhole to the east, and today the entire site has been replaced by the modern Catheralls Ind Est.

SITE 36: GLOBE BRICKWORKS

The Globe was a fairly short lived brickworks by Buckley standards. It is not shown on the 1871 OS map, and the earliest reference I could find to it is the following:

Wrexham Advertiser 5th October, 1878 – The proprietors of the new Globe Firebrick Works gave a supper of roast beef and plum pudding to the men and boys in their employ on Monday evening at the house of the manager Mr Joseph Griffiths. Twenty men and four boys partook of the excellent repast provided. After supper the manager gave to each man and boy a piece of silver in lieu of beer, the firm being unwilling to encourage drinking. Songs were sung and votes of thanks were given to the firm for their kindness, also to Mrs Griffiths who kindly prepared the supper. We are glad that this new company have set such a good example to the old firms, and hope the latter will do likewise.

Even by June 1880 the Chronicle was still referring to the place as "the new Globe brickworks", so I imagine that it's establishment must have been not long before the appearance of the above article, which probably marked the celebration of its recently having begun production. The Globe was a modestly sized works and the earliest rates listing for July 1880 described it as "six acres of land with a brick kiln" in the occupation of its owner Thomas Fogg. His tenure continued until certainly 1886, but from October the following year the Globe was offered for let.

Charles Davison & Co, the owners of the large works at Ewloe Barn and Old Ewloe, leased from 1891 the by now larger Globe, referred to in the agreement as "the Kiln Field formerly in occupation of Thomas Fogg". By then it consisted of a brickshed 36.5 metres by 11 metres, one circular kiln of 6.7 metres inside diameter, three others of 2.6 metres diameter, two chimneys and the other obligatory brickworks erections.

The reason for its ultimate closure may lie in a letter sent to the parent company Davison's, part of which reads "Globe Works – notice of lease termination must be given by March 1904, as the clay is practically exhausted". Whether the clay ran out or not, or perhaps Davison's brought in a supplemental supply, by May 1911 a new pottery works had been set up at the site, and several girls were at work on this new and more delicate side of the clayworker's trade. On 24th April the diarist George Lewis had written "Work began at the Globe Brickyard making Staffordshire ware and a number of Staffordshire men and women have been employed there".

This new venture didn't last long. The newspapers recorded that in August 1912 notices were posted at the Globe Brick & Earthenware Works giving the 50 men and girls a week's notice of termination, and the OS map surveyed in 1912 shows the works marked as disused. The factory stood at OS 2868 6533 on the edge of a very steep incline down into the clayhole, and this flooded pit remains today surrounded by trees and bushes. For many years the locals regarded it as a popular beauty spot; one of them who had lived near it for 44 years saying in 1976 that the claypit had been "transformed into a pleasant wooded valley in which children fished in the pool and people enjoyed walking".

SITE 37: ETNA BRICKWORKS

On the 1839 tithe map, on the site of the future Etna Works, there were three fields in the occupation of John Royle & Son named Clayfield, Brickearth field, and Brickground. These earlier brickmaking sites eventually took on the appearance of a more recognisable brickyard, and it was this which came up for auction on 30th June, 1854. From the sale advertisement we can see it was called Ewloe Brick & Tile Works "now and for many years carried on by Messrs John Royle & Son". This might seem confusing, as we have come across the brickworks name " Ewloe " before, and it seems that many of the early brickworks in this vicinity had almost the same designation. Royle's lease had terminated some time before, and he was continuing the works on a year by year tenancy – perhaps the landlord Philip Humberston hoped another leaseholder might make better use of the place. The ad noted that "the firebrick earth and pot clay found in this locality are held in high esteem in all parts of the world as the increasing

shipments fully testify". Royle held onto the works and in the 1856 trade directory it had by then acquired the name Mount Etna Works, named after the adjacent Etna Hall, which was demolished long ago. This name is also seen on an 1862 railway map, although the designation Mount was eventually dropped altogether.

Chester Chronicle 2nd May, 1863 – Another instance exhibiting the good feeling between employer and employed in this populous and rapidly improving locality, took place in celebrating the marriage of T.R.P. Royle Esq. On which occasion the Etna Firebrick & Tile Works were tastefully decorated with evergreens, flags and flowers, and a sumptuous dinner in true Old English style provided, to which the whole of the workmen, about 80, sat down. Afterwards an excellent tea was enjoyed by the wives and families of the men. The arrangements for the day reflected great credit upon Mr Robert Williams, the worthy and respected manager of the works.

An Indenture of May 1890 shows that Thomas Richard Popplewell Royle, the son of John Royle, and by this time the owner of the freehold on the works land, let the Etna to the Prince Brothers, allowing them time to get the premises into working order. This suggests that the Etna may have been a little dilapidated, and the wording of the lease seems to bear this out, using such descriptions as "the old shed and adjoining tumbledown buildings"... "old working shed"... "six tons of old rails", but there were also signs that the place was still in production... "two working kilns"... "new working shed"... "patent kiln".

In fact, I believe it was the case that the Princes had occupation of the site long before 1890, as the rates listings for the Etna Works show that John Royle & Son let the place to Frederick Prince in as far back as 1879. Illustrated in the book is a brick stamp from this works which bears the initial R from the days of Royle's occupancy.

By 1895 we start to see the Etna Works being referred to as the property of Richard Ashton & Co, and this is only because the Prince family had the right to that name because of their involvement at

Ashton's Knowle Lane Brickworks. In March 1900 the then leaseholder Isabel Prince found herself in deep financial trouble, brought about by the bad trading conditions at the Knowle Lane Works, and she was forced to hand control of her two brickworks to the colliery firm of Watkinson's, to whom she owed large outstanding mortgage payments. The adjacent firm of Davison's immediately realised that their own position in the market might be seriously compromised if the wealthy firm of Watkinson's revitalised the brickmaking operations at Etna and Knowle Lane, so an agreement was negotiated in January 1902 that Watkinson's would not work Etna in return for Davison's paying them an annual compensation of £260.

For a month at the start of 1903 the Etna Brickworks "together with modern machinery recently put into thorough working order" was advertised to be let, and Davison's appears to have jumped in and taken a lease on the works. Railway plans of 1905 show the site in the holding of Davison's, although the works were listed as disused, but I imagine that the plans were drawn somewhat earlier than the completed presentation date of 1905, so it may well be true that Etna was back in production in that year. The reason I make that assumption is because the rates listings for 1904-6 show the Etna Glazed Brick Co in operation. We also know from the Wrexham Advertiser of December 1906 that Charles Price was involved at the works, and the diarist George Lewis recorded on 3rd June 1907 that Charles Price had failed to successfully make salt glaze bricks at Etna. Was Mr Price sub letting from Davison's, or was he more likely acting in a managerial capacity? Whatever the case, he was definitely working the Etna from 1904 to 1907, after which the site was probably left unused. Davison's solicitors got wind of a prospective purchaser in Feb 1910 and alerted the company, who, realising the atrocious state of the brickmaking trade at that time, replied with "We agree it is probably bluff. Anyhow, there is no hurry, and you will know how to play the fish gently later on".

By November 1911 the works and plant was for sale for a paltry £850 – this sale was probably arranged by the trustees of the Royle's estate, who were at that time still the owners of the brickworks land. Davison's lease on the Etna Brickworks was shortly to expire, and on 8th June, 1912 the trustees of the Royle estate contacted Davison's, asking for first refusal when the surrender date came up, should Davison's decide not to continue working the site. Davison's replied that they intended first to test the clayhole to establish if there was enough clay left to justify keeping on the works. Etna may have been partially working at this time, but the 1912 OS map marked it as being disused.

A month later, however, the Royle's estate succumbed to Davison's requests to continue working Etna, and a lengthy procedure of haggling over terms began.

In the meantime, George Lewis recorded that Etna finished working in September 1913. The knotty problem remains as to what degree Etna was actually being used between 1907 and 1913, and its likely that Davison's were merely using it as a clay source for their adjacent works.

Wrexham Leader 18th September, 1936 – The Flintshire Coroner held an inquiry into the Buckley drowning tragedy, the victim of which was Thomas Wyatt, aged 16, a brickyard worker. On 29th August he was seen to jump into the Etna clay pit pond, and disappeared. The police were informed and at first Sergt. Elliott took charge of dragging operations. Day by day the police squad was engaged in trying to recover the body, but without success. Gunpowder charges were exploded at selected parts of the pond, in the hope that the explosions would free the body and it would rise to the surface. The explosions moved all kinds of debris in the bottom of the pond, but no body came to the top. Neither did it on the tenth day after the youth jumped in, so the police persisted with grappling irons. On Monday rain pelted down and the sergeant and his men were drenched to the skin. About 11 am Sergt. Elliott from the boat got an iron on the leg of the deceased and with care the body was dragged up. The next difficulty was to get it to a landing ledge, as the sides of the pond are a sheer cliff drop with no hold for anybody. The police got it on to a stone ledge, but it broke away and shot down into the depths. In the heavy rain the police tried again and about 2pm located the body in 50ft of water about 50 yards from the side of the pond. This time they succeeded in landing it and conveyed the body to a temporary mortuary in the adjoining brickyard. It was here that the Coroner viewed it. The deceased lost his mother last April, whilst his father died some time before that. The coroner said there was no doubt that the youth committed suicide, whilst it was perfectly clear that Wyatt was not of sound mind

It took 16 days to bring up the body. The day after the suicide, a Mold man threw a loaf of bread into the pond, as it was believed in those days that the bread would locate the position of a body by drifting to the point over which it lay.

By 1976 the works still existed, albeit in ruins, and Davison's successors, G R Stein, kept a mechanical digger on site to work the clayhole two or three days a week to supply their adjacent Old Ewloe works. In 1979 all that remained was bulldozed and the clayhole filled in.

The works was of moderate size with only three kilns and stood at OS 2865 6523.

SITE 38: DAVISON'S OLD EWLOE BRICKWORKS

Davison's Old Ewloe Brickworks was the earliest of his brickmaking concerns, but the works had had a much earlier history. In 1818 the Mesham family had leased the site to John Smalley and William and Mary Williamson, and we have references in the press of 1830 as to Messrs Williamson & Co's Brickworks, as well as its involvement with Mr Smalley:

Chester Chronicle 22nd January, 1830 – A dreadful accident occurred on Saturday at the Ewloe Brickworks belonging to Messrs Smalley and Co. A poor man of the name of William Hughes was employed in digging clay from beneath a stratum of rock, a piece of which weighing nearly half a ton fell, and he was

buried. It was some time before he could be dug out, although every possible exertion was used. When released the poor sufferer exhibited a shocking spectacle. The whole of his left hand and arm from the fingers to the shoulders was a complete mass of mangled flesh and shattered bone, and which was immediately removed by Mr Probart, Surgeon of Hawarden. The left side of the head was denuded of its scalp and the skull fractured, besides several of his ribs. The utmost solicitude and kind treatment were evinced by Mr Smalley, through whose kindness and the prompt and efficient means adopted by the medical attendant, very sanguine hopes are entertained of the poor fellow's recovery.

Smalley & Co's Brickworks are also mentioned in Memoirs of Hawarden Parish, published in 1822, and Mr Smalley was probably one of Buckley's most important early industrialists. A map of 1840 shows he also had a colliery at OS 2813 6495, and the tithe map a year earlier apportions a coal bank to him at OS 2825 6525. In December 1842 the brickworks passed from Smalley & Williamson to Walter Pownall, described as "all that messuage, dwelling-house, office, sheds, engine house with the fields late in the occupation of Messrs Smalley and used by them as a brick and tile manufactory". By a separate transfer deal, the engines and machinery of his Ewloe Brickworks were assigned to Pownall by Smalley himself – yet another reference to a Ewloe Brickworks! The details of Pownall's lease also confirms that the site had previously been co-worked by John Smalley & Co and Mary Williamson & Co.

In November 1843 Pownall decided to sell the works, and the following ad appeared:

Chester Chronicle November 1843 – To be sold by private treaty. The unexpired term of 20 years in the old established firebrick and tile manufactory situate on Buckley Mountain connected by a tramroad with the wharf on the Dee. Also the dwelling house etc etc containing about seven acres. And also all the kilns, six in number now enclosed thereon capable of burning about 8000 bricks each. This manufactory which is simple in its nature and easily understood requires only the necessities of clay, coal and labour, has been carried on for many years by Messrs Smalley & Co, possesses many privileges from the superior quality of the fireclay and may well be said to present a favourable opportunity for investment. The stock on hand with the wagons for the tram road can be taken as may be agreed.

The reference to Smalley & Co in 1843 raises an interesting question. I believe that even though Pownall was working it, the factory was perhaps still commonly referred to as Smalley & Co, simply because it had been known as such for so many years previously. John Pownall had probably been Smalley's works manager on the site for some time – the earlier 1839 tithe map lists this site as in the occupation of Pownall, even though the leasehold was clearly in Smalley & Williamson's hands.

Pownall held the works until an agreement of 28th June, 1844, part of which reads "I Walter Pownall have agreed to sell and I Charles Davison to buy for £900 the Old Ewloe Fire Brick & Tile Works". From this date Charles Davison occupied the works until the company passed into the hands of General Refractories Ltd.

I should mention the horse drawn tramroad referred to in the above Chronicle article of 1843. It was owned by Rigby & Hancock of the Lane End Brickworks, and royalties were paid to them on the bricks transported down to the quay on the River Dee at Sandycroft.

In July 1866 Davisons leased a further four acres of land just south of the works, then known as the Cock Pit, to work as an extra clay source.

I include at this point an interesting record of casual workers' payments for "day work" at the Old Ewloe Works. Dated 1872, it gives an insight into

Old Ewloe Works in the 1930s. Photo: FRO.

the many and varied forms of work which had to be carried out as part of the day-to-day running of such works:

J Gitten's donkey and cart to Mold
    to get some bags 2s 6d
J & S Jones bricklayer, half day
    repairing No 4 kiln...................................6s 9d
Thomas & Sam Ellis, half day each
    for turning the roller.............................3s each
JD, JF, WB, quarter day
    each breaking rock...................................2s 7d
JD, WB, quarter day each
preparing road in clay hole...........................1s 9d
J Lewis and R Reynolds
    half day each for loading 3s

By the end of the work's life, the then owners G R Stein were manufacturing concrete building blocks here; the production of clay building bricks having ceased decades before. The works closed in 1979, and the local council acquired the large clayhole as a rubbish tip. The factory itself stood at OS 2870 6503, and is now the site of Buckley's football ground.

SITE 39: CATHERALLS EWLOE PLACE BRICKWORKS

Trap Brickworks was the Catherall family's only concern until 1793, when Jonathan Catherall II set up business on his own at this site adjacent to the house where his family had been living. On his death 40 years later his son William, whom he had taken into partnership at his coming of age in 1819, took over the Ewloe Place works.

Chester Chronicle 17th November, 1860 – An inquest was held on Monday on the body of Ann Davies, wife of James Davies brick maker, which had been found on Sunday in Mr Catherall's fire brick claypit, having fallen a depth of twenty feet. The deceased was well known in the neighbourhood for her intemperate habits and although the mother of eleven children, would frequently leave her house for three or four days. The house was but four or five yards from the brink of the precipice and without any protection. The reason assigned by Davies for living in such a place was that it was near his work and that it was necessary that he should frequently visit the house owing to the dissolute conduct of his wife.

The position of James Davies house is shown on a detailed railway map of 1866. There were at that time many scattered little hovels near the brickworks on this part of the Common, but they have long since vanished.

Little documented evidence seems to remain concerning this site, but it stayed in the hands of the Catherall family's descendants until its closure, which was supposed to have been at the start of the Great War in 1914. With the scarcity of manpower at this time, the firm probably decided to concentrate all production at their larger Trap Works. On 15th December, 1917 George Lewis wrote

"The double chimney at Catheralls was blown down by James Boswell. It was built in the shape of an egg, was about 38 yards high and became one chimney 8 yards from its top. It had stood over 100 years".

The works stood at OS 2801 6487 and the site was redeveloped many years ago, but the flooded clayhole still remains and is used as a fishing pond. Catherall's original house still exists alongside the pond and is now the Hope and Anchor public house.

SITE 40: BUCKLEY BRICK & TILE CO – BELMONT BRICKWORKS

The Belmont, or Belmount, brickworks was developed from a drain – pipe works which was already present on the site just immediately to the south of Catherall's Ewloe Place works. A trade directory of 1850 lists the Draining Tile Company with George Powell as its manager. By June 1863 the works was being styled as the Buckley Draining Pipe Works, and George Powell began discussions with John Palin and his son Francis with regard to it being acquired by them. John

The clayhole tramways and inclines at Belmont Works, 1894. Photo: FRO.

Palin then followed this up with negotiations with the landlord Mr Davies Cooke, but there were initial hurdles to be cleared, and as Palin described:

"There is a very large quantity of slop brick clay now lying upon the ground, and this must be removed either by carting it away or making it into bricks before we can work the fireclay".

On Saturday 8th August Palin went to the works and met with the owner Mr Powell and Davies Cooke's land agent, whereby a deal was struck that when Palin took over the place he could get rid of the slop clay by turning it into drain pipes for a small nominal royalty of one shilling per thousand. On 17th November, 1864 the lease on the factory and its clay land was officially transferred to Francis Palin and his partner William Gaman.

Palin and Gaman were the principal shareholders in the Buckley Brick & Tile Co, incorporated on 20th February, 1865, at which time the drain pipe works became one of the company's holdings together with the Brookhill works, which was still then in the planning stages. The drain pipe works at this time only consisted of a shed and two kilns, but by mid-1866 the new company had spent £4,284 on enlarging the newly named Belmont Works by three extra kilns.

Wrexham Advertiser 15th December, 1866 – Among the catastrophes occasioned by the storm that was raging on the night of Thursday week was the fall of a chimney 105 ft high at the works of Buckley Brick & Tile. It fell about 1 o'clock on Friday morning, completely destroying the office and the stabling adjoining. There were two horses in the stable at the time, which after excavating for about two hours were brought out alive – one of them unscathed; the other much crushed and now under treatment of a veterinary surgeon who thinks it will recover. There was a house under the same roof as the office, where a carter and his wife and three children lived. No harm befell the house beyond the bending of the bedroom wall. It is rumoured that the breadth of the chimney's foundation was not adequate to its height, some 10 or 12 yards having been added to it some years after its first erection and hence the accident.

In May the following year a new chimney was completed and production could proceed unheeded; the Wrexham Advertiser reporting that

"a flag gaily flaunting on the summit served as a signal for a general rejoicing on the occasion".

1867 also saw the start of a bad depression in the brick trade, and two years later, following poor sales, the company's bankers urged them to offload Belmont works, but the company declined. Unlike Brookhill Works, which had been purposefully erected alongside the railway to Connah's Quay Docks, Belmont was only approachable by the poor roads of the day. All the factory's output was having to be carted by waggons to the company's sidings at Brookhill, and this had always proved the one significant problem which had dogged Belmont's competitiveness. The building of a tramway had been considered in late 1868, but the idea was shelved due to the financial climate, so in October 1870 the Buckley Co proposed that the tramway at the adjacent Catheralls works should be extended into Belmont's property. Unfortunately Catheralls wanted to charge them too high a rental for using their line, but by this time the market had upturned sufficiently for the Buckley Co to seriously consider laying down their own line, and by March 1871 a horse drawn tramway was in operation. This line was called Meakin's Tramway, named after its designer and constructor John Meakin, and it ran westwards in a semi circular arc from the kilns at Belmont, via the Willow Colliery at OS 2763 6510 to the sidings at Brookhill. Meakin financed its construction himself and charged the company 3d per ton of bricks sent along it. The line also came

in useful during the very hot summer of 1884, when water had to be sent in casks from Belmont to Brookhill, where shortages were jeopardising production.

Belmont's future was again in the balance by January 1888, when the company was looking at ways to cut costs. It was suggested that the works could be closed if the machinery at Brookhill could cope with taking on the extra production load, but things stayed the same until March 1894, when a new lease agreement was drawn up to work the Belmont site on a year by year basis; obviously anticipating a possible closure in the near future.

1912 saw the eventual closure of the works, and demolition of the chimney and buildings began in the June. The remaining clayhole to the west of the factory existed for many years later:

Chester Chronicle 23rd March, 1940 – A horse was drowned in the Belmont clayhole on the Common which is used as a tip for refuse. Two men were with the horse and cart tipping a load of refuse. Something frightened the animal and it careered down the embankment with the loaded cart. The horse kicked itself free and swam many yards across to the other side where it made a gallant attempt to climb up the steep embankment. The exhausted horse fell into the water and was drowned.

In due course the clayhole was filled in and the whole site is now scrubland. The factory stood at OS 2798 6477, and immediately to the south is a row of houses named Belmont Crescent.

SITE 41: STANDARD BRICKWORKS
For such a large and long lived works, there is very little documentation left in existence concerning its earlier history.

One thing we do know is that it was absent from the 1871 OS map, but was present by 1900 as a large factory adjacent to, and connected by tramway with its sister works, the Mount Pleasant Colliery. The consensus amongst local historians is that the brickworks was constructed in the year 1886, and indeed both the colliery and brickworks were founded by John Bates Gregory, who took the

Standard Works in 1933. Photo: FRO.

site on a lease which states that his workings had begun in March 1886. However, the Standard company's letterheads confusingly names 1880 as the year the company started, and perhaps this is the year when the company had changed its name to Standard.

In the brickworks' earlier years it was noted for its production of a hard fireclay buff coloured brick. In catalogues for that period the company announced

"If you are likely to use buff bricks, have the best in the market. Write for a sample and judge for yourself".

The rates book for 1906 lists the company as being styled the Standard Buff & Glazed Brick Co, but the next available list in 1910 registers a name change to the Standard Brick & Terracotta Co.

The works were still under the ownership of the Mount Pleasant Colliery Co until they let the Standard Brickworks to the Herbert Heaton Co of Halifax for a 20 years term from 1st January 1922. As to the colliery, the Mount Pleasant company renewed its lease on 19th May 1922, and their new agreement confirmed the colliery's dissolution from the brickworks by included the stipulation "no part of the surface land which is being used by Mr

Herbert Heaton". By this time the brickworks was fairly large with ten round and four oblong kilns. Production of bricks eventually ceased and the manufacture of stoneware sanitary pipes became the works speciality. In 1947 Standard goods were displayed at the Welsh Industries Fair, and the Chronicle reported that they were "showing their wide range of earthenware goods with special emphasis on glazed and vitrified electrical conduits".

Wrexham Leader December 1957 – Flintshire is noted for its variety of mineral deposits and there is a large deposit of stoneware clay which is worked by Standard Buckley Ltd, the largest of its kind in North Wales. It has been modernised in recent years and is now equipped with the latest pipe making machinery. The company's salt glazed drainage pipes are extensively used and considerable quantities are also exported to the Middle East, East Africa and elsewhere.

At the end of its life the company was trading as the North Western Ceramic Pipe Co. In 1966 there were 90 employees at the works, but only 65 remained at its closure in September 1969; brought about apparently by labour shortages which were making it difficult for the company to meet its orders.

The factory stood at OS 2894 6492 and the area is now the site of the Spencer Industrial Estate.

SITE 42: CHARLES JONES BRICKWORKS

This small brickworks lay alongside the larger Sandycroft Brickworks, and the only concrete evidence for its location here was found in the Land Valuation Map of 1912, at which time it was recorded as being the "site of an old brickworks" in the occupation and ownership of Charles Jones. From the descriptions in the rates books and the evidence of the OS maps we learn that Charles had lived in the adjacent house for some years before deciding to establish a brickworks some time around 1879. The works was listed as a going concern until 1905, after which time it ceased to be

registered as such, but the two defunct kilns continued to exist certainly until 1914.

Charles was unusual for his time in that he owned the brickworks, together with the land and his adjacent house.

We do have one interesting thought to play with. A Charles Jones was listed as being the manager of the Sandycroft Brickworks in 1889, and there is always the possibility that as he became more experienced he may himself have taken on managership at Sandycroft, not only by virtue of his capabilities and entrepreneurial spirit, but also because he literally lived next door. His own brickworks could easily have been left in the charge of a foreman.

And does the following evidence relate to Charles's brickworks? From the diary of the labourer Joseph Ellis we find an entry of 26th June, 1890 which reads "Charles Jones had the first kiln he was burning fall down". The OS map shows this works with two round objects, presumably permanent kilns, but that remark confirms the use of clamp kilns. Did Charles also build clamps to supplement his main kiln supplies?

If the works finished in 1905 (the last rates listing for it as a brickworks) Charles would have then been 58 years old.

The site of the factory is now a small field and wooded copse centred at OS 2895 6472.

SITE 43: SANDYCROFT – DRURY BRICKWORKS

This works is named after the old farm which was in this district, and has nothing to do with the village of Sandycroft near Queensferry. I have read of a Sandycroft New Main coal pit at work in 1756, and a Sandicrofts Coalworks in 1760, but have not confirmed any exact location for these early enterprises. What is certain though, is that the landowner of this site, Charles Lloyd, had "his farm of Main Colliery Coal" at Sandycroft in Ewloe, and on his death in 1807 he left the estate to his family, who remained the landlords of this site until 1906.

In 1856 the Chronicle mentions the coalfields under Sandycroft Farm being up for let, mentioning 320,000 tons of coal being still unworked "in addition to the coal left in former workings".

The first evidence for brickmaking comes in 1863 when John Charles Lloyd let some surface lands to Joseph Catherall and the brick-burner John Lewis "for the sum of £10 of lawful English money for every kiln that may be erected". The rates books from 1866-70 show Lewis & Co's Colliery, but no brickworks were mentioned – perhaps because such activity was on a very small scale, or practised very sporadically. In the pages of the Chester Chronicle however, more detailed information becomes apparent. On 22nd April, 1867 Sandycroft Colliery and Brickworks was for sale under a distress for rent and "a large quantity of fire and other bricks" were included in the inventory. Perhaps the sale did not transpire, as the same advertisement appeared again for a sale on 27th January, 1868. Whatever actually happened, a lease of 19th June, 1868 again let the colliery to Catherall and Lewis; condition seven of the agreement stipulating "that the royalty on the clay obtained from the mine for manufacturing bricks shall be not less than one shilling per thousand bricks, should the same be manufactured of underground clay, or eight pence per thousand should such be of surface clay".

The whole affair of leases and re-leases, sales brought about by non-payment of rents, company liquidations and re-registrations, were in Victorian days quite a common occurrence. It is sometimes a difficult task to keep track of who owned what and when, especially as so much documentation has been lost over the years.

The first mapping of any clay workings on site appear with the 1871 OS map, which shows a small square plot attached to a claypit directly on the site of the later and much larger brickworks. For this same year we have some evidence from a court case which proves that John Lewis was the manager of the Sandycroft Colliery and Brickworks, and that, yet again, just as in 1867, he was having financial difficulties and found himself unable to pay some of his men. One witness at the trial said that he "would not say that there was a man in Buckley who would trust Lewis to the extent of £5". By July 1872 the works had almost ground to a halt – the rates books in that year also show the company's brickworks as not delivering any revenue – and a saviour was urgently needed for

the enterprise. In due course Mr S P Ward, one of the company's major shareholders, came up from London and assumed managership. This co-report from the Chester Chronicle and Wrexham Advertiser of 7th September, 1872 sums up the situation very well:

"The Sandycroft Brick Coal and Iron works have recently become the property of English gentlemen, under the management of S P Ward Esquire. The estate is extensive and exceedingly valuable, promising as we understand, to turn out pottery equal to anything produced in Staffordshire, as well as an abundance of coal and ironstone. The directors were down the works during last week, and they generously resolved to commemorate the auspicious occasion by treating all their numerous workmen, as well as their wives and children, to a most hospitable festivity provided at the work shed. Some 150 persons sat down to enjoy the variety of good things. The honours of the table were excellently performed by one of the proprietors Mr R Sinclair of London. Beef, ham etc were supplied in abundance, and tea, cake etc went round most amply. Mr Sinclair was followed by Mr Ward and congratulations on the happy occasion conductive to the success of all concerned in this most fortunate undertaking – fortunate as well for the enterprising proprietors who have followed an almost forlorn hope to a most extra ordinarily successful issue. Mr Ward's sincere good advice and most practical suggestions for the common welfare of his workmen were received with loud applause. Mr Ward appears to enjoy the unqualified attachment of his men, and we think we can foresee a bright future for this end of Buckley in the enterprise".

From 1873 Mr Ward had taken managership of the company from John Lewis, and in May of that year the company was styling itself as Sandycroft Colliery Brick Tile & Pottery Co. The brickworks itself had by now increased in size from the small clay pit to a large three acre site, shown in the rates from 1872 onwards. Tenders had been invited from contractors to work on bricking the colliery shafts with the company providing the bricks needed for the job, and by September 1874 they were left with a massive surplus of materials – two million red firebricks were advertised for sale from the works. It would have taken more than a small claypit site to have made enough bricks to leave that amount surplus to requirements! The first documentation to verify the exact position of the works can be found in the trade directory of 1874, with P Samuel Ward & Co Sandycroft Firebrick Works being described as adjacent to Buckley railway station, which was literally just across the road. Four years later their advertisements for sales of bricks show that their output had grown to include blue and white firebricks and buff facing bricks.

Ward eventually installed Mr A McAllister as manager in 1879. Here is a rather "sobering" event from his life:

Wrexham Advertiser 14th February, 1880 – The Buckley Assault Case. The complainant Mr A McAllister was manager of the Sandycroft Brick & Tile Works, and William Evans, a labourer, and John Lewis, a collier at Buckley, appeared with having assaulted him. On the day in question the complainant arrived at Padeswood station by the last train in the evening a little the worse for drink. He called at The Bridge, Padeswood, and asked for somebody to accompany him home. The two defendants agreed to go with him. They called at The Rose and Thistle but it was closed. They then went to the Cross Keys where they were refused by Mrs Nixon. The defendants, seeing they could get no drink, asked him for money. He said that if they would call at the brickworks in the morning, he would pay them what was reasonable. Upon that, Evans, a powerful man, aimed a blow at his head. The complainant seeing the blow coming, put up his left arm, the blow falling upon it, breaking it and felling the complainant down. There they kicked him violently.

His assailants were fined £2 each, and would have been sent to jail had it not been partly Mr McAllister's fault, because of, as the judge put it, the "disgraceful state" he was in.

Wrexham Advertiser 10th November, 1888 – On Guy Fawkes evening a young man named Ebenezer Peers was in the act of firing a cannon, and being afraid that it would burst, was running to a place of safety when he fell down the Sandycroft Brick Company's clayhole and sustained serious injuries.

Poor Ebenezer was not the only misfortunate to end up in the deep hole. In 1883 two little boys fell into it, and a year earlier one of the landlord Mr Lloyd's horses fell 20 yards to the bottom and was disabled.

Wrexham Advertiser 26th January, 1889 – A social gathering of the employees of the Sandycroft Brick Tile and Colliery Co was held on Friday at the Black Horse Hotel. The workmen and their wives to the number of 120 sat down to a supper, Mr and Mrs Gittens sparing themselves no trouble in their anxiety to please. The Sick Fund in connection with these works having accumulated during the past three years, the men thought it a good way of spending the surplus and at the same time of honouring their master Mr McAllister and the managers Messrs John Newton and Charles Jones, by inviting them to spend the evening with them. The sight of the men and wives all in holiday attire was a very pleasing one. The usual toasts having been given, Mr McAllister said it was the interest of men and master to pull together. He had been among them 10 years and he hoped the mutual good feeling would increase.

Some time around late 1889 the company changed hands. The new owners were John and Charles Wycherley and Samuel Higginbottom, but by the turn of the century a dispute had arisen between the partners as to the role Mr Higginbottom had been playing. The company was liquidated on 19th June, 1901, and Charles Wycherley took sole control, closing the colliery workings, but continuing the brickworks under the separate clay

Making a special order of sand faced bricks by hand at Drury Works in the 1950s. Photo: Danny McLeod / FRO.

lease. The rates books for that year confirm his ownership and also the fact that the brickworks' take had trebled in size to 9.5 acres. By 1904 Wycherley had, despite his efforts, sustained further losses and he closed the brickworks. A year later he was negotiating the transfer of the property to the Lloyd family and Mrs Newton, the widow of the former manager of the colliery, but this never materialised.

For the next few years we only have the rates books and the land valuation maps with which to follow the development of the works. In 1906 Messrs Williams & Wilson bought the 9.5 acre site and continued working Sandycroft Brickworks, as it was still being called, until circa 1914 when Mr Williams left the partnership. Wilson, who lived just down the road, continued the works alone.

The trade directory for 1913 lists the works as the Drury Lane Brick & Tile Co; the first time that the lane off which it stands became associated with the company name. What happened in the next few years is a mystery, but in 1921 Sandycroft

Works reappeared in the rates lists as owned by Calcinators Ltd. The newspapers reported a serious fire here on 7th February of that year, and the diarist George Lewis also records the event by writing "a fire at Drury Silica Brickworks". Evidence suggests that Calcinators had concentrated on the production of silica goods instead of fireclay bricks.

Calcinators Ltd Drury Works was put up for sale in October 1923 and was taken over by Drury Brickworks Ltd, who officially registered their name on 25th February, 1924.

The last chapter in the brickworks history occurred in the late 1940s when the Shone family took over the works. In 1955 they built a new continuous kiln on the eastern side of the factory, and on 14th March George Lewis reported that the first filling of it had begun. The eight round kilns which had served the works for many decades were demolished shortly after. I talked in the year 2000 with Danny, a man who had worked there in those days, and he explained that the next step in modernising the works was to install an oil-fired heater, which was intended to dry the bricks in the drying shed located in the centre of the factory, but the fumes from the oil left a residue on the bricks. "That turned out to be a bit of a white elephant" he said, so a gantry of overhead pipes were then laid from the new kiln to the drying shed to utilise the kiln's waste heat – a principle of Victorian technology which they should not have overlooked in the first place!

The factory still exists today at OS 2906 6453, and on its western side can still be seen the bricked-up doors leading onto a platform from which the bricks were loaded into the kilns which were once lined alongside the works. Today the factory is used for other industrial purposes. The adjacent colliery buildings were centred at OS 2908 6460 and have long since disappeared; all the old spoil dumps now being overgrown with gorse bushes.

SITE 44: MOUNT PLEASANT BRICKWORKS

There seems to be little in the way of historical documentation for this works. From the 1839 tithe map we see it began life in a small way as a "brickground and buildings" in the occupation of Honoratus Leigh Rigby. Rigby was the business partner of William Hancock, the owner of the prestigious Lane End works. In 1931 the diarist George Lewis wrote that it was Hancock who built the Mount Pleasant works in 1842, so perhaps that was the year in which the small brickground was developed into a more substantial factory.

Wrexham Advertiser 8th February, 1868 – Some serious destruction to property at Buckley was caused by the storm raging on Friday night. The most important was the blowing down of a high chimney stack, recently erected, at Mount Pleasant Works.

In 1872 a sale document for part of the Hawarden Estate confirms the works in the holding of "W Hancock and another".

Wrexham Advertiser 14th December, 1878 – On Monday a serious breakdown of machinery took place at Mount Pleasant, one of Messrs Hancock's works. From what can be judged the engine -beam must have fallen on the piston rod while in action, whereby the cylinder burst causing great damage to the connecting gearing. The estimated damage is about £700 at least and while the machinery undergoes these repairs a great number of men (Chester Chronicle says 60) will be out of employment.

In February 1890 the Mount Pleasant works opened a distribution office in Chester, and it's worth a note that all the bricks, tiles and glazed pipes advertised were buff coloured. Perhaps the works specialised in this range of goods.

The rates book of 1912 shows the works designated as an "old brickworks", but this must have only been a temporary state of affairs, as George Lewis wrote that the Mount finished making bricks on 22nd May 1931. On 30th April, 1938 he remarked that "they threw the chimney down about 25 yards high at the Mount brickworks".

It stood at OS 2877 6456.

SITE 45: KNOWLE LANE BRICKWORKS

This was one of the very earliest of Buckley's established brickworks and it was supposedly begun circa 1792-4 by William Leach, who had inherited the freehold land from his uncle Thomas Jones. The Hawarden Parish Survey of 1815 shows that a Messrs Jones were working six brick kilns here, probably under lease from Mr Leach. By 1822 it is known that Messrs Mather Parkes & Co had possession of the works, and the tithe map clearly shows the works still occupied by them seventeen years later. For a very short period thereafter, the company was restyled as Messrs Parkes Ashton & Co, and in March 1841 the landlord Mr Leach, overburdened with heavy mortgages which he had originally outlayed on the works, sold it to Mr Ashton for £1,725.

Richard Ashton was a Liverpool merchant whose name was thereafter associated with the site until well after its closure, and the Indenture of sale to him explained how he "now uses part of the said premises as a brick and tile manufactory, called or known as the Nowland End Brickworks, otherwise the Buckley Brickworks".

Ashton immediately secured a mortgage for £1,000 from the Chester spinsters Martha, Mary and Sarah Whalley and set about improving the works' already respectable position in the market. Another two loans of £1,500 total were taken out in 1853 and 1860, when, in that latter year, 10 kilns were recorded being at work – a respectable number for that period.

In 1862 the main line Buckley Railway was opened to the Dee and the opportunity for increasing output even further was hastily taken. Ashton had a branch siding laid into the site and applied for yet another mortgage to take advantage of the expected increase in sales, but the loan was refused. Despite Knowle Lane's manufacturing capacity, the mortgage assessors pointed out that the clay extracted from the available take had quadrupled in only three years, leaving the works with a projected life expectancy of only 25 years. From the amount of clay already extracted the surveyor John Palin estimated that work must have been going on at the site for the previous 66 years.

Wrexham Advertiser 3rd January, 1863 – The Wesleyan annual tea party was held on Christmas Day by the kind permission of F Prince Esquire in one of their large bricksheds where a large number of persons partook of the "cup that cheers", the supply being abundant and very good. After tea, a public meeting took place.

Ashton died in March 1867 and his widow Louisa leased the works to the brothers Frederick and Richard Prince. Richard was a Liverpool businessman, but Frederick was resident in Buckley, and as the previous newspaper report intimates, had been Mr Ashton's manager at the works for some years. A condition of the Prince's lease, obviously included to ensure Louisa's long-term financial security, was that the new proprietors should not work more than eight kilns at any one time to help prolong the clay supply. The company also retained the name of Ashton:

Evidence from Mr Bignold, Inspector of Factories 1875 – There were a large number of children employed in the Buckley Fire Brickworks of Ashton & Co which were of a very extensive character, and he regretted to say that the school attendance regulations had been entirely disregarded.

Richard Prince died in Feb 1894, and a year later the managing partner Frederick took out a huge loan of £3,957-17-8 against the security on the Knowle Lane Works and the Etna Brickworks, which had been acquired by Prince back in 1890. Trade however was starting to take a down turn, and on 7th May, 1900 Frederick took a gamble and secured a further mortgage of £3,000 from the Watkinson firm of colliery proprietors, but by 1902 the backlog of mortgage arrears could not be met – the brick trade was in serious depression and Knowle Lane could only manage to keep four kilns in operation. There were no salvable options left open, and the works fell into the hands of Watkinson's.

This development came to the attention of Henry Hurlbutt of Davison's & Co Brickworks, who must have been aware that the financial clout which Watkinsons wielded could damage them badly if the brickmaking operations were re financed at Knowle Lane, so Davisons negotiated a compensation package to Watkinsons for their agreement not to work the site. The following solicitor's statement, written in April 1904, highlights what a sad decline the once great works had suffered since its closure in March 1902:

"The owners of the brickworks, Messrs Watkinson, in March 1902 entered into an agreement with Mr Hurlbutt to cease for 10 years to use the Knowle Lane Works and not to work the clay bed on condition that Hurlbutt paid them £260 p.a. From the time of that agreement the building had been wholly disused and in point of fact had fallen into a state of considerable disrepair. To bring the works up to date an expenditure of £2-3000 would be required. There was about an acre of clay land still left – the value of it if made into bricks being £1,500, while the cost of equipping

Site 43

Site 43

Site 43

Site 45

Site 48

Site 50

Site 50

Site 50

the works would be double that sum".

By early 1903 the shed roofs and even some of the chimneys had fallen – Prince had been forced to ignore basic maintenance on these ancient buildings for quite some time. Watkinsons managed to earn a little revenue from the site by renting out the office, stable and carpenter's shop to a James Hurst for £18 p.a. (after having to repair the office roof beforehand) whilst the house at the works was let to his brother Herbert. The kilns, sheds and engine house were still left to rack and ruin.

The brickworks never went into production again. In 1912 there was a serious national colliery strike which led to great deprivation amongst the labouring classes, and Watkinsons Co charitably allowed coal-pickers into the clayhole. The Flintshire News of 21st March recorded

"It is a wonderful sight to watch the coal – getting operations taking place in what is known as Princes Clayhole near to the Mountain Colliery, where coal belongs to Messrs Watkinson. The thanks of the whole neighbourhood are due to them for their kindness in allowing the mineral to be taken away, and thereby relieving the distress which otherwise would have been most acute".

In July 1914 the clayhole was used as a firing range for the Territorial Army, and by 1915 a plan of Buckley drawn by J K Gregory marked the factory as being used as a railway wagon works – perhaps Watkinsons repaired their coal trucks here. On 19th August, 1959 George Lewis remarked in his diary that thousands of tons of clay had been brought from Port Sunlight to fill the clayhole. The factory site at OS 2855 6444 is now housing.

SITE 46: JOHN LEWIS BRICKWORKS

In those far off days of hard living and cheap drink, the brickmen and colliers of the industrial towns could be said to have at times been very "colourful". What we might expect from the class of men who had the fortune to be their masters could perhaps have been of a more temperate and

responsible nature. Not so in the case of brickyard owner John Lewis – of all the Buckley men certainly one of the most colourful of them all.

To begin his story we should first consider John Shone, who in 1851 was the publican at the Horse and Jockey in Church Road, and was also a brickmaker employing two men and a boy. By 1861 his wife Margaret, originally from Mold, had become his widow and had taken over the pub, but the rates lists from 1862-4 show that she was also occupying a half acre site at Ewloe Town as a brickworks on land leased from Davies Cooke; probably the same site which her husband had used. This then is clearly an established brickworks, albeit a small one, and in the Wrexham Advertiser of October 1863 we can see that she was intending to offload it. The ad reads:

"To be sold or let. A good brick and draining pipe Work with all the plant consisting of an excellent pipe machine, moulds, brick benches, barrows, planks etc. The kiln and hot shed are all in good working order. The Work is situated near the Buckley terminus of the Buckley Railway. Apply to Mrs Shone, Horse and Jockey, Buckley".

In 1865 our friend John Lewis is shown from the rates listings as having taken over Margarets brickworks, and whilst she continued at the public house, he ran the works until June 1868, from when on it looks to have become unproductive, and from 1870 it was listed as being void.

So who was John Lewis? If we scan all the census records for Buckley district between 1851 to 1891 there is only one man who fits the bill – all the other characters named John Lewis are either too young, too old, or are in the wrong occupation. John was a Hawarden born man living in 1851 at Burntwood in Buckley with his wife Hannah. He was then a 25 year old "brickmaker journeyman ", and ten years later he was classed as a " brick burner".

And where was the brickworks which he took over from Mrs Shone? We are lucky to have a railway map of 1866 at the time when the rates book states that he had the works. The map shows that he had two sites in the Ewloe Town district;

both on land owned by Davies Cooke. The one which most fits the newspaper description of October 1863, and is also shown on the 1871 OS map at about the right size and with a kiln, claypit and single shed, is at OS 2820 6442 and is recorded as being occupied by John Lewis and William Griffith. This site still exists today in part – the old clayhole is the pond on Buckley Common, where children fish on Sundays and feed the ducks.

The smaller site, in sole occupancy of John, was very close by at OS 2832 6430, and in later years it became part of the site of Watkinson's Mountain Colliery. The colliery was apparently dismantled in 1930 and is now the site of more modern industrial activity.

And what of the man himself? There is a possibility that he may have been the brick-burner John Lewis who was in partnership with Joseph Catherall at the Sandycroft site in the 1860s. The rather scathing remark made in court that nobody in Buckley would trust him to the extent of £5 seems to be indicative of a character trait which would fit later reports about him, and I get the uncanny feeling that he was the same John Lewis as the one at this site. In the census records I can find no other John Lewis to indicate that we might be looking at two separate persons. And I think this following report also concern the same man:

Wrexham Advertiser 8th November, 1873 – John Lewis, a well known man at Buckley was charged by Mr John Edwards, builder, with threatening to kill him. On the 4th the complainant was removing the material of a condemned house, he having bought the materials, when a man came to him and said he was a bailiff and he was not to remove any more. Complainant asked for his warrant and the man sent for Lewis, who came with two or three men, telling them to pitch the cart and the complainant into the clayhole, at the same time saying he would kill him, grind him into clay and make bricks of him.

That John Lewis was clearly a brickmaker! And in July 1875 a Buckley brickmaker, also enticingly named John Lewis, was up in court after being locked up for drunkenness. To much laughter from the onlookers he pleaded

"I deny that I was drunk, but I acknowledge that I was affected with intoxicating drinks".

In an attempt to convince the magistrates of his sober character, he continued

"Didn't I tell you that I was going that day to Chester to get some tracts published about the magistrates, the policeman, and Johnny Lewis of Buckley, the reformed drunkard?"

This engendered still further mirth from the crowd. The magistrate asked him what he did at Buckley, to which he replied

"I am a brickmaker and take contracts".

Lewis locally became known as Sound Doctrine, seemingly because of his predilection for public preaching, and during the 1880s he was frequently in court answering charges of drunkenness, and even on one occasion for having interfered at a funeral.

Wrexham Advertiser 1875 – The renowned John Lewis, better known under his nickname of Sound Doctrine, was charged by his wife Hannah with threatening to kill her and throwing her out of the house into the garden. She said he had been in the public houses until ten and then had gone round the village "lecturing" as he called it.

In the Chronicle of 1877 there is mention of a John Lewis, described as "an aged brickmaker of Buckley". Could this be our John? If so, he would have been only 51 years old and hardly aged, although his alcoholic lifestyle may have weathered his appearance. Of his brickmaking the newspaper reported "he had not made a single thing but what he had spoiled, and had even made two kilns so jerry that they had fallen down".

From our vantage in the 21st century it has become difficult to ascertain if these reports all concerned the same man, and if indeed that man was the John Lewis who held the brickworks on Buckley Common, but on continued revision of what facts we have, they appear to be more than mere coincidence. I believe we have the right man – John Lewis – the most colourful of the Buckley brickmen.

SITE 47: HANCOCKS NEW MOUNT BRICKWORKS

There is relatively little documentation concerning this works which also went by the name of Knowle Hill Works. It was the property of Hancock Co, who had an older established brickworks at Lane End just to the south, and the best information on its history is contained in this article from the Chronicle of 22nd June, 1895 –

"The new works began to be put up some 30 years ago. Some 33 years ago a suggestion was made by the lessor Sir Stephen Glynne that it was desirable for Mr Hancock to erect new works where they were now put, and unless Mr Hancock was prepared to do so, Sir Stephen would have to consider letting the land for the purpose to some other firm. Mr Hancock therefore found it imperative to take the land, and the new works were erected,and at the time it was hoped they would be able to find full scope for both the old and the new. Hancock admitted that he erected the new works to stifle competition. The speculation however turned out to be a bad one, and for 25 years those new works were not worked at all. In 1889, in the summer of that year, a tramway was being constructed up to the new works which had got into a bad condition through being idle for 25 years, and which were put into proper repair so that a new light clay could be worked. At that time Mr Hancock's intention was to develop this very clay".

By that reckoning, the works were originally begun circa 1865 and soon after closed for a period of 25 years, which would have meant it being unused until at least 1890. Perhaps that may well have been the case. The 1871 OS map shows the factory with six kilns, and the rates book for 1869 lists the works with six kilns, but the entry suggests it was unused.

In 1885 the New Mount Brickworks was the venue for the workmen's festivities on the celebration of the marriage of Mr F Leigh Hancock. "The population was aroused early by the sound of cannon fired from the Knowle Hill and firing was kept up all morning" said the Chronicle. The report tells of the workmen marching to New Mount from the Lane End Works, and perhaps this new works was chosen as the venue, precisely because it was empty and the bricksheds at Lane End need not have had their routine affected.

As to when the works was actually established, perhaps the rates lists hold the answer. There were previously two long established Hancocks works at Lane End and Mount Pleasant, and the first listing of a new Hancocks works on Sir Stephen's lands appears in July 1867.

On both the 1900 and 1912 OS maps the works is marked as "disused". During the long coal strike of 1912, Messrs Hancock did for the local populace what Watkinson's did at the Knowle Lane site:

Through the kindness of Messrs W H Hancock & Co many houses in Buckley have been replenished with an abundant supply of coal gratuitously. During the whole of the week over a thousand men, women and children have been busily engaged excavating in the disused clay hole known as the New Mount, under which lies a seam of coal about a yard in thickness. Much difficulty is experienced in getting away the dirt, but when this is overcome the miner is well recompensed for his trouble. Many tons of coal are being daily removed.

After its closure the sheds and kilns were used by a local farmer as stabling for his animals. The factory itself was during its lifetime nicknamed the Sugar Stick, because of the four white spirals built into the brickwork of the chimney and twisting their way up to the top, upon which was a large coping overhanging by 2 ft 10 inches (86 centimetres):

Chester Chronicle 15th March, 1941 – The New Mount Brickworks chimney, which for 75 years has been one of the most conspicuous landmarks in the county, was felled on Thursday. The chimney was the highest in the district, being 75 yards high, it was built by Buckley craftsmen, members of the Humphreys family, who were noted for this class of work. Many amusing stories have been related concerning this chimney – one was that to celebrate its completion, members of the Buckley Royal Town Band were hoisted to the top and sat around the brim to play their instruments.

The works stood at OS 2881 6437 and was eradicated by the clayhole of the Lane End works as it was extended northwards.

SITE 48: HANCOCKS LANE END BRICKWORKS

This was certainly one of the largest of all of Flintshire's brickworks and had the distinction of being not only one of the earliest, but of being the last to close. The original William Hancock, believed to have been a Liverpool carpenter, arrived in the Buckley district circa 1750, and may well have gained employment with the Catherall family of brickmakers. He himself was not responsible for founding the Lane End works. It was his son William II, the child of his marriage with Jonathan Catherall's daughter, who started the works in 1792. Almost immediately, he went into partnership with John Rigby, the son of William Rigby, the surveyor in charge of district highways maintenance.

William II died in 1832, leaving his son William III to continue the partnership with Rigby, which probably ended in the 1850s, as the Chronicle in 1858 mentions that the partnership had ended some time before that year.

Chester Chronicle 24th April, 1852 – Messrs William Hancock & Co having recently removed to a more extensive works in the immediate vicinity of those so long held by them, embrace the opportunity of expressing their gratitude for the great favours so many years bestowed upon them, and feel desirous of acquainting the public generally that with the increased space

and facilities which they now possess, they can supply much larger quantities than heretofore of all bricks, tiles, etc.

That "more extensive works" must have been an expansion of the same original site, as the tithe map of 1839 shows the factory in much the same position as it appears on all subsequent mappings. By the time the lease of the property was up for renewal from Sir Stephen Richard Glynne in April 1866, the works had 15 kilns in operation – well in excess of any other major Buckley manufacturer at that time. The plan of the works on page 24 shows a large ruined building on the opposite side of the tramway to the kilns, and this might have been one of the original sheds, prior to the 1852 enlargement.

William Hancock III was certainly the most productive brickmaster of his family's line, and it was he who had been principally responsible for ensuring the growth of the company's holdings. It must be said though that he was not alone in the venture – the company's other major shareholders were Horatio Lloyd, a wealthy gentleman of Middlesex; John Nunns, a Dublin merchant and Wiliam Hignett of Sealand.

So as not to fall behind the competition, Hancocks also built a fleet of schooners based at Connah's Quay to service their overseas markets. In 1866 they launched the "Padeswood", and a year later:

Chester Chronicle 13th July, 1867 – On Thursday two fine vessels, the "Mary and Gertrude" and the "Glynne" belonging to Mr W Hancock were successfully launched from the building yard of Messrs Ferguson & Baird. The day was beautifully fine and a large concourse of people assembled to witness the unusual event of launching two vessels built by the same builders for the same party. The ceremony of christening was ably and graciously performed by the Misses Glynne and Sir Stephen Glynne, landlord of the extensive works of W Hancock & Co, after whom the vessels were called. This part of the proceedings having been accomplished a large party numbering 200 sat down in a spacious marquee erected on the grounds of the Ship Inn to a substantial dinner liberally given by Mr Hancock and served up in Capt. Coppack's best style.

The company's records show that goods were sent as far as Canada, British Guiana, Newfoundland, Las Palmas, Manilla, Australia, Palestine, Peru, Brazil, India, China and Japan, and in 1941 the directors of the then company were pleased to relate that they had customers on their books with whom they had been dealing since the company's founding 150 years before.

In the earlier days of Buckley's history the Lane End district had been the main hub of the town, and it was only in later years that Buckley's centre became established further westwards, where it is today. By 1884 the Chronicle described Lane End by saying "The number of rough noisy lads abound here in scores and are allowed to run about the street yelling and shouting every night". With so many children in the streets, and in immediate contact with so busy a factory as Lane End at the height of its powers, it's not surprising that we come across such reports as the following:

Wrexham Advertiser 23rd July, 1887 – On Friday morning about 11 o'clock a son three years of age of Mr Enoch Hughes met with a shocking accident which terminated fatally. It appears that the engine driver of Messrs Hancock brick and tile works had tapped his boiler and the hot water was running down a ditch by the road side near to the works, and the child while playing near accidentally fell into the scalding hot water. A neighbour hearing the child screaming ran to the spot and at once pulled the poor little thing out. It lingered in great agony up to 11 o'clock in the evening, when it succumbed to its injuries. On Wednesday the coroner held an inquest at the Glynne Arms, when the jury returned a verdict of accidental death with a recommendation that Messrs Hancock cover over the open portion of the drain or turn its course some other way.

Wrexham Advertiser 8th October, 1887 – A wild unkempt boy named Isaac Jones, and who looked half-witted, was brought up in custody charged by Mr Piercy, foreman at Mr Hancocks brickworks, with being on the premises stealing coal, filling a bag out of a wagon. Sergeant Jones said the boy was incorrigible. The boy said that if he did not go to steal, his stepfather used to thrash him. He was ordered to have six strokes of the birch rod.

There was, for a short time at least, another industrial concern at Lane End, which ended up causing Hancocks much annoyance, and which, if it had been left unchecked, might have irreparably damaged the brickwork's financial position. In 1889 Mr Mayhew, the trusted land agent to the brickworks landlord Mr Gladstone (Sir Stephen's successor), formed a small company to search for coal on the western side of the take leased by Hancocks. This was legally possible as Hancocks only leased the surface clay lands, whereas Mayhew took a lease on the subterranean coal measures. Mayhew had sent Hancock a plan of his proposed workings, explaining "We are going to sink a small shaft here". Hancock had abandoned working the clay face in that sector since before 1856, but there was always the possibility that it may be opened again, and Hancock was rightfully apprehensive about the venture. And there were other considerations. He wrote to Mayhew *"With reference to the pit which you are about to sink adjoining our works, you will certainly take our water away, and even supposing you don't, the water remaining will be useless to us"*. But on Monday 28th October the sinking operations at Mayhew's new Lane End Colliery began. By 1891 1,500 square yards of surface land had been utilised – not too large an area – but Mr Gladstone died soon after, leaving the influential Mayhew to do as he pleased. His "small shaft" soon developed into a full sized colliery with two pit heads, and 10,074 square yards of Hancocks surface land had been engulfed by its surface workings.

By 1895 Hancock had taken Mayhew's company to court for blocking the brickworks ' access to its rightful clay source, and Mayhew suffered a humiliating defeat. Lane End Colliery (also called Dumpling Colliery) closed in 1903, and its entire plant was auctioned off on 23rd July.

The Hancock family's connection with the brickworks came to an end in 1933 when the works was sold to Mr Fred Jones, who had also purchased the Wepre Hall works at Shotton. In June 1956 it became the property of Castle Firebrick Co, who set about expanding its output. In October of that year the clayworkings were extended and six years later Castle spent £120,000 on modernising the works. An enormous crushing plant was installed and the ten clayhole workers were replaced by a mechanical excavator. The tramway and tubs which took the clay to the factory were scrapped in favour of an eight ton diesel truck, and new oil fired kilns were built to replace the coal fired originals. Natural gas fuelled the kilns during their last decades.

The great Castle Firebrick themselves succumbed to market forces in 1971, passing on the Lane End Works to the Butterly Building Co. The last owners were the giant Hanson Company, who themselves had to announce the impending closure of the works in February 2003, citing the competitive prices of foreign bricks and the cheaper products produced by more modern works as the eventual reason for the closure. The end of the works heralded the cessation of over two centuries of Buckley's once most famed history. The works was centred at OS 2879 6394.

SITE 49: PENTROBIN COLLIERY

This relatively minor colliery site was situated at OS 2902 6398, a little way to the east of Hancock's Lane End Works. From the proceedings of a Victorian court case we learn that Pentrobin was established circa 1860 as H Fenton & Co, with Wiliam Tudor having been the engineer who supervised its running. The available rates listings show Fenton & Co here from 1865 to June 1868, after which the colliery was acquired by the Aston Hall Colliery Co from May 1869. Some say that the Aston Hall Co worked Pentrobin from 1866, but I cannot confirm this, but when the Aston Hall Co was put up for sale in 1883 Pentrobin was indeed included as one of its assets.

As for its brickmaking operations, I could only find one reference from the Chronicle of 5th July, 1884. Reporting on a theft from the colliery, the text reads

"Joseph Connor, a brickmaker employed in the works, stated that he was at his work at the kiln and at twenty minutes to ten o'clock at night he saw a person coming up".

Brickmaking would have been a necessary requisite during the colliery's initial establishment, but for it to have been an activity by 1884 strongly suggests that it was an ongoing concern, operating from a permanent or semi-permanent brickyard.

The works had gone by the time of the 1899 OS survey. Today the extensive spoil heaps still exist covered by woodland with pathways running throughout, and a concrete cap marks the position of the pit shaft.

SITE 50: SOUTH BUCKLEY COLLIERY & BRICKWORKS

The most westerly of Buckley's brickworks also became one of its largest. In the February of 1866 the South Buckley Coal & Firebrick Co was registered by colliery owners and engineers from the Manchester and Rochdale districts, to open a new pit and brickworks on virgin Buckley land. During the earlier years of this enterprise its main appearance was that of a colliery only – the 1871 OS map shows no recognisable brickmaking plant at all.

By the late 1870s the coal industry was undergoing a serious slump, and according to a newspaper report of the time, the works was taken over by the Main Coal & Cannel Co at some time around July 1877, but the new company was soon falling behind with its mortgage repayments. After having been closed for a while, it was restarted in November 1878.

The South Buckley company was finally dissolved in 1880 and was taken over by David Evans, a Liverpool brickmaker and builder. He simultaneously acquired the works of the North Buckley Colliery & Firebrick Co, which had been registered back in August 1875 to work the minerals in the Alltami district until its dissolution two years later. In July 1881 David Evans sold the two sites to the newly incorporated North & South Buckley Colliery, Brick & Tile Co Ltd; the north works netting him £2,280 and the larger south works £4,280, and Evans himself was retained as a director of the new venture.

Wrexham Advertiser 6th May 1882 – On Friday afternoon a fatal accident occurred at the N &S Buckley Colliery Brick and Tile Co to Mr John Lewis, smith. It is supposed that he had gone too near the machinery and that he must have been drawn into the cog wheels, between which he was crushed and his body frightfully mutilated, his head and arm being completely severed from his body. The manager Mr Rosborough on hearing of the accident was at once on the spot and immediately dispatched a messenger with his own conveyance to Mold for Dr Edwards. The deceased was about 40 years of age and leaves a wife and eight children.

The new North & South Company set about improving the brickworks site, spending £3,200 on four new kilns, machinery and new rail links. In 1882 the mining engineer J J Williams made a report of the improvements for the benefit of the company's directors, and he observed:

"I shall not be overstepping the bounds of my discretionary powers if I draw your attention to the money expended since your possession, as it will be no doubt interesting to know that the amount has not been frittered away (as in many instances) upon worthless experiments, instead of being spent on permanent improvements that will bear their value to you in the future".

The following year he made a further report and remarked:

"That the manufacture of bricks continues a profitable source of returns is apparent at a glance at your sale and order books. The additions of surface plant during the year has been necessary and judicious. I took note of a large stock of clay on the bank – a very valuable contingent in case of unforeseen stoppage of the works".

The colliery and the brickworks were structured to be two independently managed parts of the company, which meant that when the mine workers went on strike in August 1884 the brickworks did not have to follow suit; large stocks of clay and coal having been stockpiled at the brickworks in case of just such an eventuality.

In Jan 1886 a further report was drafted for the benefit of the company directors, and the plans accompanying the report show us just how small the colliery sites were in comparison with the south site brickworks. The north colliery was not in production at this time and little evidence of its existence was apparent at ground level. The south site however was much more developed, but was still only very modest in appearance, and only one pit was being worked.

By the early 1890s the brickworks side of the business was given a completely new name; its success having managed to eclipse that of the colliery by virtue of its reputation as well as its size. In 1892 the brickworks exhibited its wares at the London Building Exhibition, and the British Clayworker journal said of it: "The South Buckley Rock Brick Co has just introduced a new manufacture. They now produce coloured glazed bricks of all tints which have been very successful. The glaze is so thoroughly burnt that it becomes part of the brick itself. Specimens of these glazed bricks were the chief feature of their exhibit".

The Rock Brick Co prospered greatly, and by 1899 there were 17 round kilns in use, which by 1912 had increased to an amazing 28.

Chester Chronicle 26th March, 1904 – On Tuesday morning about 2 o'clock a fire broke out in one of the large drying sheds of the South Buckley Rock Brick Co. There was only one man in the works at the time; his attention was first drawn to the smell of wood burning, and he went round the works to see for the cause of it. The doors and window shutters of the shed were closed but he saw light inside through the crevices in the shutters. He at once raised the alarm by setting the hooter going, which he kept on from 2 till 4. In a very short time there was a large body of helpers on the scene who at once set to work protecting other parts of the buildings. Before long the fire brigade from Mold came to the rescue and a little later the brigade from Connah's Quay. The damage is estimated at between £1,000 and £1,500 which is covered by insurance.

All the fireclay for the company's exceptionally hard bricks was mined at the adjacent colliery from the same seam which yielded the Brassey Coal, a good fuel for brick burning, but the colliery had to cease operations in 1909, after which time the clay was obtained from the north site, which by then had been renamed the West Buckley Colliery at OS 2669 6534. A purpose built tramway was constructed between the two sites to cater for that function, and this arrangement continued satisfactorily for the next few years.

Wrexham Advertiser 3rd January,1914 – A somewhat serious accident befell Mr Dinfold, manager of the South Rock Brickworks on Wednesday afternoon. It appears that he was about to leave for Liverpool and when preparing tea, slipped with the cream jug in hand which unfortunately broke and cut one of the arteries in his wrist. No one being in the house at the time, Mr Dinfold managed to knock the wall on the next door neighbour who came in and found him in a fainting condition and lying in a pool of blood. Dr Fraser and Dr Maclean were hurriedly sent for and after preventing further loss of blood, ordered his removal with all possible speed to Chester Infirmary. He is progressing towards recovery.

Closure of the South Buckley – Rock works came in 1914 and everything was dismantled soon after. Perhaps the clay source from the West Buckley Colliery had dried up, or perhaps the start of the war had something to do with it. The works proved to be one of the most prolific producers of glazed bricks throughout the locality.

The brickworks was centred at OS 2741 6437 with the colliery alongside it to the north west. The site of the factory is now new housing.

SITE 51: SPON GREEN COLLIERY

This modestly sized colliery with a large brickfield attached is shown on the 1871 OS map. Back in 1858 William Shepherd of Catheralls brickworks went into partnership with the great brickmaster William Hancock, to take a 21 year lease on what was by then the deserted Spon Green Colliery. A report written for the landlord Lord Mostyn in December of that year says of Messrs Hancock & Shepherd's Spon Green Colliery "The coal field comprises three pits situate about 100 yards apart of each other. A small pumping engine is applied to shaft No. 1; scarcely powerful enough to contend with the water". This sounds to me like the new proprietors were only just beginning to get the site into any workable order.

Apart from the brickyard's presence on the OS map, we are lucky to have Mr Shepherd's own testimony as to its existence. In 1862 a parliamentary hearing was instigated to weigh the opposing merits of the G W R and W M &C Q railway schemes, as to which company should construct a railway through Buckley. Shepherd was supporting the latter's proposals. As he explained,

"The G W R line will not serve the Spon Green Colliery. Your line – W M & C Q – will afford me the means of competing with others in coal and bricks. We could make a large quantity of sanitary pipes if we had direct railway accommodation. We have fireclay sufficient to make any quantity. We make 250 tons of earthenware annually. My brickworks are connected by a tramway to Connah's Quay Wharf. There was an arrangement with the Buckley Railway to make a branch to my brickworks, but it is not made".

The tramway which he mentioned was a branch from the Hancocks Lane End Works, a spur of which led directly southwards into the Spon Green brickyard.

Shepherd died in 1866 leaving Messrs Hancocks to run the site, and from the 1871 map onwards all evidence concerning brickmaking at this site is absent, save for one tantalising puzzle. The rates books from 1868-75 list a John Williams as owning and occupying a one quarter acre brickyard and shed at Spon Green, although scrutiny of the large 25 inch maps has drawn a blank as to where it might have been. Could it perhaps have been the brickyard at the colliery, in which case Hancocks must have sold the land to Williams .

The colliery and brickyard were at OS 2882 6360 in the Lane End district.

SITE 52: BUCKLEY JUNCTION BRICKWORKS

This was a fairly recent brickworks by the industry's standards, as it was begun ten years after the death of Queen Victoria.

The works was built on a field, originally named in the 1839 tithe as Top Gorsey Field.

The first reference to it appears in the rent ledger for the Hawarden Estate, in which is listed a lease of brickearth and clay granted to Jones & Lamb Brickworks from 2nd August, 1911. John Jones and Henry Lamb were local men, both of Daisy Hill at Buckley. Their next move in assuring the future success of the venture was to make an agreement with the Great Central Railway – the successors to the Wrexham Mold & Connah's Quay Railway – for a junction and siding to be built from the adjacent line into the works. This work was agreed to in November 1912, and cost £103 plus an annual line rental of five shillings.

For some indiscernible reason, the local legend has it that up to the time of the Great War the works was referred to as "Jack Cheshire's brickworks", and the most logical assumption is that he was probably the works manager.

In 1919 the company passed into the hands of Frederick Phelp Jones, and acquired the style of the Buckley Junction Metallic Brick Co Ltd, with Walter Jones and C W Earde as co-directors. The name Junction derived from its situation immediately alongside the railway junction where the line forked to Connah's Quay and Hawardwen Bridge.

Our next evidence comes from the diarist George Lewis, who wrote on 3rd February, 1956 that the brickyard had closed down in a state of bankruptcy, but only days later the Castle Firebrick Co came to the rescue and bought it. However, three years later to the exact month, the decision was taken to close the site:

Chester Chronicle 21st February 1959 – There will be no redundancies as a result of a decision of Castle Firebrick Co to close their Buckley Junction works. Mr G E Tregoning, managing director, said manufacture of the celebrated "Jacobean" and "City" facing bricks is to be transferred from Buckley Junction to the neighbouring Lane End works. The decision to move has been prompted by the need for urgent and extensive repairs to the kilns and buildings. The Lane End works has more modern buildings and more room for expansion necessary to meet growing demand. About 40 men are affected. The Junction works have been in operation about 40 years, but there was a small works of two round kilns on the site previously. The works will be closed in the course of the next few months.

The " small works of two kilns" was a reference to the Jones & Lamb concern prior to 1919. Probably the factory's last major contract was to manufacture the Jacobean trade mark bricks and architectural mouldings for the new Financial Times offices at Bracken House, St Paul's, London, which were made, according to the Chronicle "in the required shade of pink".

The factory stood at OS 2935 6350 – the present site of an industrial maintenance depot.

I must also mention an earlier brickmaking site very near to the Junction works. At OS 2959 6331 there was a Brickfield marked on the 1839 tithe map in the occupation of Robert and John Jones, and this site is now occupied by the housing on Meadow View, off Little Mountain Road.

SITE 53: PADESWOOD HALL COLLIERY & BRICKWORKS

The investigation of the history of this enterprise is dogged by sketchy evidence, and the possibility that what evidence is available might just refer to two separate collieries.

It seems that the original Padeswood Hall Colliery Co was registered in April 1875 on a lease from W Hancock, to work the coal seams beneath his Padeswood Hall Estate. The colliery, if my source is correct, soon earned the nickname of the Scotch Jump, and in later years, the Skip Colliery.

The Chronicle in 1876 mentions a reference to the Padeswood United Cannel Coal & Iron Co "who were sinking a shaft to commence colliery operations at Buckley". In December that year the company was offering for sale "a large quantity of good red bricks", which could be delivered to any railway station. Was this company the same as that working Padeswood Hall Colliery? And does this following report of nearly twenty years later also refer to the same site?

Chester Chronicle 18th May 1895 – On Tuesday the Skip Colliery belonging to the Padeswood Coal & Cannel Co was finally closed. This has been a very valuable mine and a large quantity of cannel has been raised. The exhaustion of the seams is the cause of stoppage.

In September 1897 we find a prospectus issued for the setting up of a new company called the Padeswood Buckley Brick & Coal Co, which announced its intention of acquiring the Padeswood Hall Colliery and working the slack coal, which was much in demand for the local brickworks. The company was formed by Cheshire businessmen, with John H Billington of Tarporley as its managing director and B B Glover of Manchester as its principal surveying engineer. A report for the benefit of prospective investors was commissioned, making particular reference to the seam of fireclay on the site:

"The establishment of brickworks would be a valuable addition to the colliery. The Vendors have had a careful estimate made of the cost of erecting four kilns with a total capacity of 80,000, brick making machinery, drying sheds etc, and it is considered that the whole brickworks can be erected for about £2,000. In addition, the fireclay has been specially excavated and reported upon by B B Glover & Sons, mining engineers, who say – Immediately underneath the coal is a very fine bed of fireclay. A bore hole has been put down 6 ft in this without passing through it, and from sample bricks made therefrom, it is capable of producing the best buff bricks and tiles which will take a beautiful glaze and be sure to command very high prices. The price to be paid to the Vendors – Mr Edward Wheldon of Mold and Mr John Green of Buckley, for the whole property has been fixed at the low sum of £10,000. This sum does not repay them for the actual expenditure on the property, but the Vendors confidently expect that the introduction of fresh capital to properly develop the resources of the property, will result in large dividends to all shareholders".

Were Messrs Wheldon & Green the owners of the defunct Padeswood Coal & Cannel Co?

The Padeswood Buckley Co was officially registered in October 1897, and Mr Wheldon stayed on as one of the principal directors, but the new management failed to turn around the colliery's failing fortunes. By August 1898 the company was in the hands of the Official Receiver, and on 27th January 1902 all the plant and machinery at the works was auctioned off. No brickmaking plant was included in the sale however, and it is unlikely that any grand brickworks was ever constructed. No kilns are evident on any of the OS maps. The works stood at OS 2926 6244 and is now part of the Padeswood Cement Works land.

Hope Area

SITE 54: HIGHER KINNERTON BRICK & TILE WORKS

The many little brickworks which served the rural communities around Hope and Penymynydd were a complete contrast to the large and noisy works not so far away at Buckley. The landscape surrounding the Higher Kinnerton Works remains for the most part much as it must have been when the works was operational, and it was here in July 1859 that Messrs John & Edward Davison & Co were selling off 74,000 bricks and pipes. John was the principal partner in the company; a Hawarden born man who was 42 years old at that time, and the rates books show him in the early 1860s at this one acre brickyard leased from Mrs Massey.

By 1866 it seems that his company was in trouble. In September of that year the Higher Kinnerton Brick & Tile Works was offered for sale, all inquiries to be sent to the Massey family, who were resident at Cornelyn in Beaumaris, Anglesey. The stock consisting of 300,000 bricks, 50,000 firebricks and various pipes, tiles and pig troughs was to be sold separately, whilst the works itself with its kilns, drying sheds and stables were to be let: "There are beds of excellent firebrick and other clays and every convenience for carrying on an extensive and profitable trade" ran the advertisement.

By April 1867 no takers for the lease had been forthcoming, and the works was again advertised to be let. By August the company was being sued by the coal merchants Dunn & Catherall for an unpaid £33-3-8 worth of coal supplied to the brickworks, and from the report of the case in the Wrexham Advertiser of 31st August we learn more about the structure of the company. John and his brother Edward had originally commenced the works in 1855, but circa 1860 Edward left the partnership, and he crops up in the Hope district census for 1861 where he was working as a publican and brickmaker at the Cross Keys at Llanfynydd, not far from Coed Talon.

The works is shown on the 1871 OS map with three kilns, and three years later the next available rates book shows that the brickyard, still leased from the Massey family, was now being run by William Gibbons. It had increased in size from the one acre site of Davison's day to being just over 2.75 acres. By 1876 Charles Gibbons had acquired it, but the works was now being listed as simply "land with an old brickyard", but two years later Charles had redeveloped it into a "pottery with new shed and kiln".

By 1910 however, it had become defunct. The land valuation map for that year shows it as still in the occupation of Charles Gibbons, although the site is not accredited with any industrial usage whatsoever. This state of affairs is confirmed by the 1912 OS map, which has it marked as a "worked out clayhole".

Flintshire News 2nd January, 1913 – In consequence of Mr Joseph Davies, licensee of the Crown Inn, Penymynydd, having disappeared on Thursday evening, his relatives on Friday instituted a search for him. The body was found in the Brick Kiln Pond between Penyffordd and Black Wood on the Chester road. Deceased was in money trouble. He was a sober man but did drink a little, but never to excess. Inquest jury returned a verdict of suicide.

The local residents have told me that Black Wood is the old name for what is now designated on modern maps as Rough Piece Wood.

The works stood at OS 3120 6245, and looking at it today, it requires a lot of imagination to believe that a fair sized country brickyard once thrived here. The pond has now been filled in, and the site is thick with brambles and nettles.

SITE 55: PENYFFORDD BRICKYARD AND HOPE OIL WORKS

Half a mile SSW of Higher Kinnerton Works was a small brickyard, of which very little information can be found. It is shown on the 1871 OS map and listed in the Hope rates ledger for the same year as an old brickyard of area 1 acre,3 rood, 19 perch (just over 1.75 acres) at Penyffordd. The old yard was then occupied by George Hollins on land owned by Mrs

Hamilton.

During the first half of the 19th century the whole of this district was bristling with little clayholes and brickmaking sites which over the years have been eradicated and forgotten about. The rates listings between 1865-6 show that a Messrs Millington & Co had a one acre brickyard at Bramley Lane, Kinnerton and a newspaper advertisement for that company mentioned that their works was near Hope Station, which was only one third of a mile away from the Penyffordd Brickyard. Where exactly it was though is a mystery.

The little Penyffordd Brickyard stood at OS 3075 6159 and we don't even know who actually worked it, but we can be fairly sure that it was defunct from the early 1870s. The site was later used as a horticultural nursery, and today is home to a riding stables.

Hope Station is shown on the maps at OS 3027 6152, and was in later years renamed Penyffordd station.

There were two small oilworks which were situated just eastwards of Hope Station; the first, on the south of the railway line, being that of Peter Wilcock & Co, which was certainly there in 1871 and still operational in 1883. But the works which we are interested in was called Hope Oil Works and stood at OS 3058 6143 adjacent to site 55 on the northern side of the railway. It belonged to the Leeswood Main Coal Cannel & Oil Co and there is a possibility that it may also have had its own brickmaking facilities. The lease on this works was taken in February 1866, and in January 1869 it was up for sale by auction; "a large quantity of bricks" being included in the catalogue. The original company lease also contained the stipulation that "the land contains clay which the lessees have the right of getting without paying any royalty for such as may be used for the purposes of the buildings on the land, but all bricks sold from the premises are liable to pay royalty of 1s. 6d. per thousand." By August 1869 the Hope Oil Works of Messrs Buttery Dyson & Bain – perhaps the directors of the Leeswood Coal Oil Company – was in bankruptcy, and the rates book of 1871 confirms that Hope Oil Works had by then become dilapidated.

There is one last proposition to consider. The later 1872 rates book lists the occupiers of both the brickyard at site 55 and the adjacent dilapidated oil works as the Leeswood Coal Oil Company. Did the Leeswood Co acquire and run site 55 at some point? Perhaps they made their bricks at site 55 instead of at the oilworks itself.

Whatever the case, all traces of the oilworks have now gone and the site is overgrown with trees.

SITE 56: HOPE TILERY

Between October and September 1855, what was called the Hope Tilery on the Caergwrle to Kinnerton road was for sale due to Mr G Colquitt Goodwin "having suspended his drainage operations". Perhaps Mr Goodwin was a local drainage contractor and the tilery the place where he manufactured the necessary pipes, or more likely he was the local estate owner and the tilery was his property. The inventory of the sale lists a quarter of a million drain pipes together with some bricks, sheds and kilns. The works is shown marked as a brickworks on the 1871 OS, and it stood along the aforementioned road at OS 3124 5934 – half a mile outside Hope village. The works is also shown on a plan accompanying the prospectus for the sale of the Rhyddyn Hall Estate on 23rd September, 1875. How long after 1875 it survived is not known, but it was not there by the turn of the century. The site is now occupied by a private house.

SITE 57: HOPE HALL ESTATE BRICKYARD

Just to the south of the present day Hope Hall Farm lay a small brickyard which was used to make bricks for the maintenance of the Hope Hall Estate buildings. According to local knowledge the hall itself was built of these bricks, and unusually for such a small country works, the bricks were name – stamped and made by machine – not by the use of a wooden hand mould, which might be expected of such a small rural works. The hall was demolished by the council despite much local objection, it having been a listed building.

The old road alongside Hope church, leading eastwards out of the village, is called Kiln Lane, and it leads directly to the site.

We cannot be sure at what period the brickworks was operational. The 1871 map shows nothing, but the works is shown as a shed and small claypit on a sale plan of Hope Hall in July 1912, although by that time the site was described as being used as pasture land. The works stood at OS 3155 5842.

SITE 58: CAER ESTYN BRICKWORKS

In 1864 a map for a proposed branch railway was prepared, which shows that the line would have run right past this site. No brickworks was here in that year, but by the time the 1872 OS was surveyed a small brickworks was present – gone by the turn of the century. Who ran the works in those early days is not known, but it was later resurrected, and the following text from the British Clayworker of May 1909 refers to the event: "A new brickworks is being constructed at Caer Estyn, Caergwrle, to deal with about 25,000 common wire cut bricks per day. Mr J Cotgrave of Water Tower St., Chester is secretary". It was an unusual time to have considered opening a new brickyard, as the industry was in a dire state of depression in 1909. The land valuation survey of 1910 shows no brickworks on this site whatsoever, although it might have been surveyed some time previously. Perhaps the works was established slightly later, as an OS map published in 1912 shows a works had reappeared here consisting of a small shed, chimney, one round kiln and a small clayhole to the west.

Flintshire Observer 16th October 1913 – The news that the Caer Estyn brickworks are to be restarted by a gentleman from Wallasey has been received with much satisfaction in the neighbourhood. These works have been stopped for some time, but the present proprietor believes that a very successful business can be built up there. The plant is being overhauled with a view to an early start.

The Wrexham Advertiser of September 1914 announced that the Caergwrle Plastic Brick & Tile Co at Caer Estyn, which had been lately constructed by Mr George Brick, had been purchased by William Hughes & Son. Common wire cut bricks were to be had from here.

It can only be conjecture that the last paragraph refers to this site, but in all honesty it is difficult to find any other location which would suit. It seems that the works changed hands quite frequently during this period, and for how long the William Hughes company survived is a mystery, but the works had been demolished not long afterwards. I spoke with a local man in his eighties, and he remembers playing as a child on the site in the 1930s when the only remains were the underfloor heating flues and a ruined engine foundation. That engine bed still remains today, standing alone in a field, which may be the reason why many years ago it was referred to by the locals as "the donkey". The works stood at OS 3211 5762.

SITE 59: RICHARD WILLIAMS BRICKYARD – CAER ESTYN

A few hundred yards west of site 58 was an older brickyard which had vanished from the landscape many years earlier than its neighbour.

The 1864 railway proposal map shows this small "brick and tile yard" occupied by Richard Williams on land owned by himself. How old it was at that point is unknown. The Hope district rates listings show Mr Williams as still owning the 3a. 2r. 28p. site in the years 1871 to 1875, but by this time it was being described only as an "old brickyard" and the following advertisement is strongly suggestive that it had been long defunct by the late 1870s:

Wrexham Advertiser 18th October 1879 – Sale by public auction at Bridge End Inn, Caergwrle. All that piece or parcel of land known as the Estyn or Brickyard Field, abutting on public roads leading from Hope to Gresford and Caergwrle to Rossett, containing an area of 3a. 2r. or thereabouts, about half a mile from Caergwrle.

The site, shown as still present on the 1879 map (but not necessarily functional) had gone by the turn of the century, but there are still visible signs of its past usage. The works itself was sited on level ground and the clay was dug from the base of a hill slope. This excavated hollow still remains today with trees and bushes growing in it. The site is at OS 3187 5751.

SITE 60: NERCWYS CAMBRIAN FIRECLAY WORKS

This small works was probably constructed some short time before the date of the following article. The building of a tramway to a colliery would surely have been an early priority to the survival of any country brickyard situated in so rural a setting as the Cambrian was:

Wrexham Advertiser 12th September, 1874 – Last week a vestry was convened at Nercwys to consider the application of the Cambrian Brick & Tile Co to construct a tramway on the side of the highway leading from their works at Plas Onn towards Nercwys Colliery. It was put to the meeting and carried. Subsequently Messrs Thornton, Wheldon and a large number of those present adjourned to the White Lion, where an excellent repast was provided by Mr and Mrs Bythell, to which the company did full justice, the toast of "Success to the Cambrian Brick & Tile Co" being received with much enthusiasm.

The works stood at OS 2271 6164 and seems not to have lasted very long. The 1878 OS shows it with a clayhole just to the west, but it had gone by 1900. Perhaps the following advertisement might have marked its final demise, although it may have been purchased and carried on for a few years later:

Wrexham Advertiser 26th August, 1876 – The liquidators of the Cambrian Fireclay Works Co Ltd invites tenders to be sent to him for the purchase in one lot of the company's interest in the works known as the Nercwys Works. The property comprises an area of about eight acres and is held for an unexpired term of about 32 years at a rent of £35 p.a. subject to an increase of £10 for every additional kiln, and upon it there is now erected a substantial moulding and drying shed 120 ft. by 30 ft., with stock, two kilns etc furnished with an engine, pug mill, rollers, press and other plant with tramway.

The Geology of Flint, published in 1924, makes reference to the old workings by saying "at Pentre Bach 300 yards north-west of Plas Onn, some old brick works expose white shales and fireclays".

Nothing is left either of the brickworks or the tramway, and a modern house and gardens now occupy the site. The Nercwys Colliery was exactly one mile away at OS 2352 6024, and again there is absolutely nothing remaining, not even any spoil heaps. Whether there was any company connections between the brickworks and the colliery is not known, but it is always a possibility that the directors of both were one and the same. One thing I do know is that the colliery was later the property of the Tyn Twll Co of site 19.

Leeswood Area

SITE 61: ERITH BRICKWORKS

The Leeswood district was one of Victorian Flintshire's industrial hot spots, with a degree of activity far in excess of anything to be witnessed in the district today.

Wrexham Advertiser 5th Jan 1867 – The London Leeswood and Erith Oil Mineral Co treated their workmen at the Pontblyddyn Oil & Coal Works to a substantial dinner on Saturday last when between 60 and 70 assembled in the brick-shed near the Miner's Arms, which was well warmed and decorated for the occasion. The providing of the repast was entrusted to Mrs Jones, landlady. Mr W M Williams, the general manager, presided, and gave the health of "The Chairman and directors of the company". When the workmen enjoyed their treat twelve months ago, there were two companies, one of which gave a treat to the men, but now they were under one board of directors. The oil trade being bad just now, they might have excused themselves and said they could not give the men the treat this year, but such was not the case (cheers). The vice chairman then proposed "Success to the London Leeswood and Erith Oil Mineral Co". He had no doubt all present would wish them a large dividend. Let them hope there were better times in store for the oil trade. He knew Mr Williams lived in Hope (laughter).

The brickworks at site 61 was at Pontybodkin, and existed well into the 20th century, but from that report of 1867 we can see from whence it derived the name Erith, which stuck to it from beginning to end. Erith is actually a town in the south of England. The Miner's Arms pub is now a private house and stood at OS 2710 5934 with the company's little brickworks just to the north at OS 2708 5940. A railway map of 1867 shows the oil company's works very close to their brickyard, which can be seen on the accompanying map.

The oil company liquidated and sold off their assets in April 1870, and the brickworks is shown on the OS map for that year with a single shed described as an "old clay pit", so perhaps the works had ceased a short time before. The OS edition of 1879 shows nothing in this area, and the next progression in its history comes with a lease granted in February 1884 from the Gwysanney Estate to Edward Wheldon of Mold. It was he who built the works which became properly known as Erith Brickworks – probably so named after the previous company to occupy the site. The lease granted him the coal, shale and clay

"within and under all those several fields of land... and liberty to convert and manufacture the said clay into bricks or other articles and to sell and dispose of the bricks so manufactured, and to build, erect and set up all such kilns, sheds and other erections for more effectually working the clay and converting the same into bricks to the greatest advantage".

His new works were built near the NW corner of the earlier oil company's brickyard, and were at first very modest in size compared to the large factory complex of later years. The fuel for the kilns was available on site… a mineral surveyor's report shows that a 2 ft. coal seam was worked at the brickyard, probably from a pit shaft.

From a court case in June 1899 we learn that Wheldon was trading at that time as the Erith Brick Tile & Terracotta Co, and one of the witnesses, the mining engineer Owen Price, gave evidence that Wheldon had owned the works for three years. Another report from July 1904 mentions his trading as the Erith Blue Brick Co Ltd, whilst it is a known fact that he formed a new company circa October 1904 under the same style as he was using in 1899.

Putting aside the intrigues of the boardroom and the subsequent name changes, what seems to be true is that the works' principal product of this period was blue bricks. The court case in 1899 was all to do with Mr Wheldon's problems in achieving the right colour, and the company were also supplying the G W R Rly. Co. with blue bricks for their railway bridges etc.

The Erith company may have been in difficulty by

the beginning of the new century, as the works was sold on 10th January, 1905, and by 1910 the rates record it as being owned by the Gweedore Quarry Company, a fact also verified by the 1912 valuation survey. By 1925 however, Messrs Benjamin Brooke & Co were the proprietors, and the site was called the Erith Silica Calcining and Milling Works, but on 25th February of that year they sold the works and transferred their operations to a more modern plant in England. By then the Erith works consisted of a grinding plant, electric generating house, engine house, crushing and milling plant, five brick kilns and a private railway siding.

The next proprietors were Messrs Heaton & Heaton, whose partnership later dissolved leaving one of them to form Messrs Herbert Heaton (Clayware) Ltd. This was purely a family affair – Herbert was chairman and managing director, his wife and daughter were co-directors, and his son in law John Sadler Oakes was secretary and sales director. The Chronicle in 1956 ran an article on the works and mentions that "at least 20 per cent of the firm's employees have been at the works since the early 30s." Another article in 1959 mentions the works having started 27 years earlier, which would mean that the Heaton family acquired Erith circa 1932. By now the speciality of the company was salt glaze sanitary pipes; the only other factory in North Wales producing such a product being Standard of Buckley, also owned by Heatons.

Chester Chronicle 9th June, 1956 – This works is indeed extremely busy and there are eight kilns, and one is drawn each day and one set. This time it was a case of a kiln being drawn, and Messrs T Foster and J Jones were literally rushing around with loaded wheelbarrows containing large and hefty looking pipes. This works has built up a sound reputation over the last few years and all those in connection with it have every reason to be confident in its future.

The works closed some time in the 1970s and the site's last usage was as a stock yard for a builder's merchants. This function ceased in the late 1990s, since which time it has been derelict. Only a few buildings remain, and the kilns and chimney stacks were demolished years ago. The site is centred at OS 2700 5942.

SITE 62: GEM-ALYN BRICKWORKS

This works was at Coed Talon, half a mile from Erith, and being of a similar size, these two were the biggest brickworks for miles around. The works was established quite later than most. The man behind the business was Mr Joseph Hetherington of the Ruby Brickworks (site 27), who registered the Gem Brick Tile & Terracotta Co on 9th March, 1896. This period in history was one of unprecedented growth in the building trade, and new brickworks were sprouting up all over the country – in London at this time, old bricks which would formerly have been used as road aggregate were being sold for large profits because of the then brick shortage. By August that year the British Clayworker said of the Gem that:

"the works are being proceeded with as rapidly as possible under the guidance of Mr Hetherington, and the works are being connected with the L N W Rly. We have perused some testimonials from leading architects of Chester and district who pronounce the bricks to be first class and almost impervious to moisture".

By November 1896 the works was in production and the Wrexham Advertiser could report:

"It is a pleasing sign to note the revival of trade in the neighbourhood of Coed Talon, which has so long been desolate, the fires from the brick kilns being a most encouraging sight".

By January 1901 however, the Gem Works was up for sale as a going concern, due to the company having by that time gone into liquidation. On 11th June the Alyn Brick Tile & Terracotta Co was registered to take over the business. Their capital was only £2,000, a pathetically small sum even for those days, probably due to the fact that the works was at that time very small – the Tryddyn rates books show that in 1898 the site was just over 0.75 acres in size.

Chester Chronicle 21st March 1903 – After nearly

forty hours continuous downpour of rain a heavy flood took place in the low lying districts of the Alyn, in many parts from four to five feet deep. At Coed Talon the mountain stream was so overcharged with water that the storage bank at the Gem brickworks was undermined by the river and a store stack of 12,000 bricks was completely washed away, as well as a stack of coals used for engine purposes. Several of the coal tubs at the Pontybodkin Colliery were carried away and found nearly a mile away. The clay pit was flooded at the Erith brickworks and work will be suspended for several days until the water is pumped out.

Note how the old name of Gem was still being used. By 1905 the Alyn Co had opened out the works to over four acres in size, and great improvements had been achieved since the days of the Gem company. In fact, the products from the Alyn works were almost of as fine a quality as the Ruabon types and certainly of a better class than the red bricks produced just down the road at Erith.

I could find no intermediate historical evidence on the site until November 1960, when British Industrial Sands of Surrey took over what had by then become the Alyn Silica Works of Colin Stewart Minerals Ltd. In April 1961 B. I. S. transferred part of the works' business to a new factory in England, and sixteen of Alyn's workforce were made redundant. By 1965 the factory was used as a processing plant for felspar imported from Norway, and by this time the production of clay building bricks had probably ceased some decades before. Today the works is still used, but in a totally different field, and most of the original buildings, including the imposing chimney stack, still exist. The site is at OS 2672 5868.

SITE 63: PLAS YN MHOWYS BRICKWORKS
By today's standards the entire district between Padeswood and Coed Talon could be said to be a rather sleepy backwater, and what industries existed in the latter part of the 20th century have now mostly died. But in Victorian days this area could tell a totally different story and was alive with a plethora of industrial activities. Brickworks , collieries, foundries,

ironworks and oilworks dotted this landscape – all serviced by an impressive network of railways and mineral tramways.

Now that we have looked at the Erith and the Alyn, the two major brickworks of this district, we can concentrate on the smaller ones which were to be found in Leeswood Vale, the thickly wooded countryside running westwards from Pontybodkin, through which the Mold and Treuddyn Branch Railway wound its way from Brymbo to Mold.

A composite map of part of the Vale itself is illustrated in this book and site 63 is just NW of Cae -bleiddyn Colliery. So let's begin with the earliest reference to the site – the 1839 tithe map, at which time it was nothing more than a field owned by one of the local landowners, Charles James Trevor Roper of the Plas Teg Estate. By 1864, when the railway companies were planning to open up the district to the outside world, the proposal maps show a "field brickyard" at the position where the later brickworks clayhole was to be. It was leased by a Wiliam Griffiths who had a "brickshed, machinery and old pit" at the site – the pit may have been the remnants of an earlier coal working, or perhaps it refers to a clayhole. By 1867 the proposal map for the L.N.W. Rly shows that a larger works had been constructed on the site at OS 2635 5965, looking exactly as it is shown on the enclosed map with what appears to be four kilns between two sheds. The works was now in the holding of John Thompson, John Clark Barrett and Thomas Whaley – John Thompson being the major player in their undertaking. An undated surveyor's report lists him as being connected with mine workings at Plas yn Mhowys, and a reference to him appears in the Chronicle of 1870 as having oil works at the same place, and the map shows a tramway from his brickworks leading up to a colliery and oil works.

By 1884 the rates books listed him as still operating the oilworks, but by this time the brickworks were held by Mason & Son, and this continued until two years later, after which the relevant columns showing brickworks ownership and rates charges were left blank. From 1898 the rates books did not list the works at all, and the 1900 OS showed it as having been engulfed by the workings of the colliery to the south. Interestingly, all the rates books show that the land was in the ownership of a

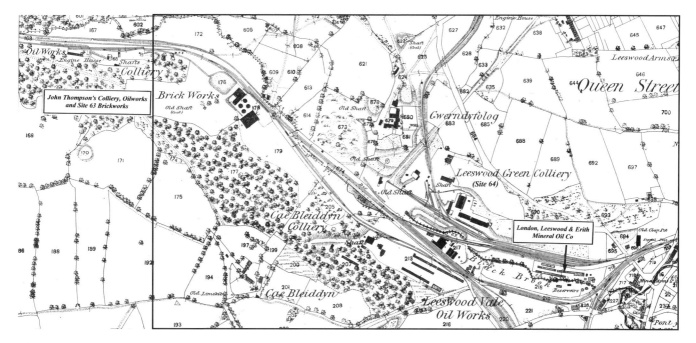

The intense Victorian industrial activity of the eastern side of Leeswood Vale. Pontybodkin village lies at the bottom right, with the works of the London Leeswood and Erith Mineral Oil Co identified from a railway map of 1867. Their little brickworks may well be the site marked on this 1871 map as the Old Clay Pit on the far right, close to where the larger Erith Brickworks would later be established. The Pontybodkin Brickworks of the New North Leeswood Colliery (Leeswood Green Colliery) is numbered on this map as 217 on the opposite side of the railway from Marston's Leeswood Vale Oil Works. The old railway line is today a footpath.

Mrs Twiston, whereas on the earlier documentation it was part of Trevor Roper's estate. I can only suggest that Mrs Twiston either bought or inherited this particular piece of land from the Plas Teg estate.

John Thompson and his partners should be due a small mention at this point, as they owned many industrial undertakings in the Vale, and the railway maps show a string of their coal, brick, oil and branch line workings around almost every bend of the railway. At OS 2435 6008 they also had some colliery buildings and brick kilns, but these kilns were not actually shown as a brickworks proper, and may have been only temporary clamps.

I mentioned earlier the numerous industries which once flourished in the Leeswood Vale, and I think I should highlight the importance which the local oil industry played during this period. Apart from the oil works owned by John Thompson, the Vale was also home to those works of William Marston, the Canneline Oil Co, Flintshire Oil & Cannel Co, Williams Patent Mineral Oil Co and the British Oil & Cannel Co, and there were also numerous other such works elsewhere around Leeswood, Pontybodkin and Padeswood. In the 1860s there were at least 21 oil works in this general district, and the reason for their existence was the presence of the "curly cannel". Cannel, also called Gas Coal, is a bituminous coal which burns very fiercely due to its high oil content, and curly cannel is the best of its type to be found. Mineral oil could be extracted from this cannel and an oil company prospectus for 1864 mentioned that *"the curly cannel of a small district of Flintshire yields a larger percentage of crude mineral oil than any cannel yet discovered"*, whereas the prestigious Colliery Guardian said of the Leeswood product that *"its quality is not surpassed by that of any cannel in the kingdom"*.

The process of distilling oil from oil bearing rocks had been discovered by the Scotsman James Young, and when his patent expired in 1850 the floodgates of opportunity opened for hundreds of would-be oil barons all over the country. Shale, another common rock in the district, was also a major yielder of oil.

One ton of shale could yield between 20-40 gallons of oil, and during the 1860s Britain could produce oil at one third the cost of the imported American product. In 1865 a newspaper correspondent, familiar with the vast American oil fields, visited the Coppa company (O S 276 615) and submitted this report:

Chester Chronicle 18th November 1865 – I pushed for Padeswood, a small station about two miles from Mold, and I landed in the very heart of the mineral oil region.'Twas as if I had fallen asleep in the train and woke up among the oil wells at Pennsylvania. There was the identical mud, the same run of land, the same rough people, the same sort of fires and furnaces, cauldrons, retorts, kettles, stew pans for oil, and distilleries – the same heaps of lime and the same carboys of sulphuric acid – everything the same, but the primeval forest, for the trees are all fast disappearing. The Coppa company's works cover seven acres of ground. They are like gasworks on a small scale, only the tanks are underground. They have 198 retorts each of 15 hundredweight capacity, and 16 stills, so that they possess a capacity of producing 170 tons of oil weekly.

As well as lamp oil and paraffin, these works helped keep our flourishing industries running with their supplies of lubrication oil and several types of grease.

By the end of the decade however, maritime transportation from America had improved so much that the British oil industry found itself severely undercut by the lower costs of transporting American oil by sea, and most of the smaller works in Flintshire came and went within 15 years. The Coppa works, probably the largest in our area, survived until 1893.

SITE 64: LEESWOOD GREEN COLLIERY – PONTYBODKIN BRICKWORKS

The map of Leeswood Vale shows Leeswood Green Colliery at a time when it was already one of the principal mine workings in the Vale, but its story began many years previously. In June 1852 the mineral agent Henry Beckett, working for Townsend Ince Esq, one of the landowners of this area, reported to his employer that "from information gained at the spot I find that some coals were worked on this estate many years back, but the operations were probably confined to thin coals near the surface". At this time Mr Ince was granting to Messrs Jones a lease to work the coals on his land at OS 6000 2652, where Jones sank two pits, shown on an estate map of 1859 and called the Leeswood Green Colliery, and which were officially referred to as pits 1 and 2. The lease mentions that Jones "be allowed brick earth and shale which may be found on the estate and required for the usual erections, and also slack for converting the same into bricks".

In May 1858 the estate granted a further lease to Jones's son, William Charles Hussey Jones, to work another site which was called the North Leeswood colliery, which he had actually been working since July 1857. This colliery may well have been site 64 itself, marked on the map as Leeswood Green, as an Indenture granted from Wynne Eyton for the building of a tramway in 1857 refers to William Charles Hussey Jones as "proprietor of Leeswood Green Colliery".

We have, even in these early stages, hit on one of the great problems when trying to compile a history of this place – we seem to have two sites which used exactly the same name! In fact, it was certainly not uncommon in those days for such anomalies to occur, but it does make the task of determining the truth a very hard one, as companies not only changed their names sometimes very frequently but also sub-let part of their takes to other companies. To further confuse matters there is a newspaper article of 1861 which makes a passing reference to Messrs Battersby operating at Leeswood Green colliery. Could they perhaps have taken over at pits 1 and 2, or is it more likely that they had a completely separate coal working in a different part of the Leeswood Green area.

In 1860 Henry Beckett submitted a further report to Mr Ince, stating:

"At the time I made my Jan 1858 report, little had been done beyond sinking a pair of pits down to the Main Coal. Since that period the colliery plant of satisfactory character has been completed, a

weighbridge for land sales with office has been erected and a tramway and wharf connected with the Treuddyn Branch Railway has been laid down".

Whichever member of the Jones clan was working pits 1 and 2, by April 1861 they had not managed to locate the more valuable coal seams and they subsequently transferred their operations to site 64 and resumed operations under the style of the Leeswood Green Coal Co. By August 1862 the Jones lease was transferred to George Haworth and his partners, who had registered their Leeswood Cannel & Gas Coal Co to take over the operations. Their new lease granted them way "to make Smithies, Cabins, Kilns, Furnaces..... also for burning bricks to be used solely for pit linings or buildings erected". As time passed, the new company extended into making bricks for sale to the general public, and the following letter written in August 1866 is from a customer explaining the state of the brickmaking operations at the colliery:

"I enquired about the bricks as I promised. He have sold a great many thousands of them. There is 20,000 and put down close to our land to build a house with. The man that is making them told me they was selling them to any one that liked to buy and give from a pound to twenty two shillings a thousand".

For further evidence of brickmaking here we have a letter of 1868 from Henry Beckett to Haworth's company, referring to the site as Leeswood Green Colliery, and complaining of irregularities in the royalty returns. Beckett says "I have no check on your brick returns, as they are made without notice, but of course you have to pay royalties for all bricks which were not absolutely used on Mr Ince's estate".

The company responded with a tally of bricks made: "bricks used in mines 40,850 – used in other properties 19,000 – sold 179,200 – now in stock 5000".

From those figures it is clear to see that the bricks sold off site far exceeded the number used at the colliery itself.

The company was also at the centre of one of Mold's most notorious historical events – the Mold Riots. In 1869 they had found it necessary to reduce the colliers' rates of pay after a slump which had closed the pit for weeks. It was the job of a Mr Young, the underground manager, to enforce the company's new orders, and he became the focus of bitter resentment. Young was assaulted at the pit, which resulted in the ringleaders being arrested and tried at Mold Courthouse. After being sentenced to prison a mass demonstration of colliers turned out to support their cause. Expecting trouble, the authorities had the prisoners escorted the short distance to the railway station by an armed guard of police and army, but they came under fierce attack from hundreds of colliers and their sympathisers, which resulted in four of the crowd being shot dead.

By December 1877 the company was in liquidation, and the lease was sold at auction for £850 to Urias Bromley, Edward Wheldon and Robert Wright, who continued the works under their new company name of the North Leeswood Cannel Co. It is not recorded what fortunes may or may not have befallen the new venture, but it appears that it was not as profitable as they had hoped. By October 1889 Robert Wright was writing to his solicitor saying "I have no income from any source – Leeswood has been my ruin". The industrialist John Howard then began negotiations for acquisition of the colliery's lease – the latest in the site's long line of proprietors. On 20th November 1890 John Howard and his partners registered the New North Leeswood Colliery Co Ltd, and it is from this time that I believe that the brickmaking operations took a new turn. From 1891 the rates ledgers lists John Howard & Co as owner and occupier of Pontybodkin Brickworks – a completely separate operation from the colliery itself – and it is important to establish its exact position. Pontybodkin Brickworks became the New North Leeswood Co's brickmaking site, but tracking it down proved difficult at first, as it is not identified on any maps. The solution to the problem came courtesy of Richard Williams, who in 1936 wrote a small booklet entitled "The Oil Works of Leeswood in the Old Days"; two of the sites he listed being:

*Maxwell Davies (the manager) which was the name popular of the Oil Works which stood where the Leeswood Green Brickworks now stand.

Marston's Meadow Vale Oil Works situated opposite the Leeswood Green Brickworks between the sidings and the main line.

From those descriptions I could locate the new brickworks site and I also managed to confirm its position by talking with locals who remember it's ruins. The brickworks stood opposite Marston's Meadow Vale Oil Works (marked on the map as Leeswood Vale Oil Works), and from the railway maps we can also learn something of its earlier history. The future brickworks began life in 1867 as "Marston's oil refinery, offices and sheds", and remained as such for many years.

Wiliam Beale Marston had originally come into the district after having made his fortune on the London property market, and established this site as part of his Meadow Vale Oil Works, which had been working since circa 1863. His interests in the oilworks were eventually sold to his son Frank in 1888, and William died later the same year. Frank must have sold the site to the Leeswood Green Colliery shortly afterwards, keeping hold of the main Meadow Vale Oil Works on the opposite side of the railway. And as with the colliery, the brickworks was also known under a number of guises – Pontybodkin, Leeswood Green, or Leeswood Vale Brickworks:

Wrexham Advertiser 13th August, 1892 – One of the largest, if not the largest excursion to the seaside from Padeswood was run off on Saturday. Mr John Howard gave all his workmen at the New North Leeswood Colliery and the Leeswood Vale Brickworks free passes. Mr Alderman Parry performed a similar favour to his workmen at Coed y Celyn Colliery. Upwards of a thousand persons travelled to Rhyl or Llandudno, and nearly 13 hours were spent at the seaside in glorious sunshine.

In September 1893 many of the collieries in the district were closed due to the workmen striking over pay, but industrial relations at Mr Howard's pit could not have been more of a contrast from those earlier days of the Mold Riots. The Wrexham Advertiser for that month recorded: "Leeswood and the surrounding neighbourhood was thrown into a state of wild excitement on Friday 22nd at the news of the arrival of a body of Buckley strikers about 300 strong, who had come for the purpose of compelling the men in the New North Leeswood Colliery to come out. Their efforts were unavailing, as the men are determined not to strike as they have received an increase in wages and have an excellent employer in Mr John Howard".

Mr Howard's agent Thomas Jones, enthusiastically backed by his men, faced the Buckley strikers and read a statement, part of which said "Our colliery is the only means of sustenance we have in our neighbourhood with the exception of one small colliery. Our employer has sunk a vast amount of capital in the concern which we know he will never get back – that is a certainty. Our output is but small, which he uses himself, being a ship owner".

John Howard, a local JP, was the ex mayor of Bootle in Liverpool, and for the first two years of his association with Leeswood Green Colliery he had funded most of the operations himself. But by August 1895 the company was insolvent with debts of over £33,000, and Howard found himself personally out of pocket to the tune of over £23,000. After being closed for nearly a year the colliery finally reopened on Tuesday 7th July, 1896 under the new ownership of Mr Thomas Parry, who had other works in the district. Parry was a director of the nearby Phoenix Colliery, and had reformed it under the style of the Phoenix Coal & Cannel Co in order to raise the capital needed to acquire the Leeswood Green site. As for John Howard, he took on the position of manager at another colliery in the district.

During this takeover, Parry's solicitor wrote to him advising " As regards the brickworks in mortgage to Mr Shoobridge, it seems to us to be a practical question as to what value there is in these properties. It would appear to be clear that Mr Shoobridge must make up his mind to accept a very much less sum for his mortgage than the amount stated in the deed".

This suggests that the brickworks must have earlier been acquired by Howard under a mortgage to Mr Shoobridge.

Interestingly, it appears that Howard may have kept hold of the Pontybodkin Brickworks, as the rates for 1898 show him as owning the site but that it was run by Edward Wheldon – probably the same man who had co-owned the colliery from 1877 until Howard took it over, and perhaps Mr Wheldon had been retained to run the brickworks thereafter. He certainly had the experience, as a trade directory from as far back as 1868 shows him advertising his services as an independent brickmaker.

By 1905 the colliery had been acquired by Messrs Higginbottom of Liverpool, and the fate of it and the brickworks becomes a mystery until June 1925, when the British Clayworker ran a small ad which stated that the Leeswood Green Colliery & Brickworks was to be sold in order to close an estate.

Today at OS 2675 5939 there exists an old wall, behind which lies much brick rubble overgrown by trees. This is the site of the Pontybodkin Brickworks, which is situated immediately alongside the old railway track bed, which is now a public footpath. Locals in the district can remember the ruins of the kilns, demolished decades ago because of their dilapidated state. On the opposite side of the line, cut into the gently sloping hillside, are the terraces on which Marston's Meadow Vale Oilworks once stood, and higher up the hillside is a ruined building, which was once one of the oilworks offices. The Leeswood Green Colliery was just NNW of the brickworks.

SITE 65: LLANFYNYDD BRICK & TILE WORKS

I am afraid that firm and positive evidence for the positioning of this works are sadly lacking, and we must rely on supposition as our only guidelines. What we do know is that the brickworks was established in 1898 by the brothers Arthur George and Alexander Payne together with Mr H. P. Bennitt under the style of the Llanfynydd Terracotta, Tile & Brickworks.

British Clayworker September 1898 – New brickworks are in progress of construction at Llanfynydd which are expected to be completed in a few months, promoted by Messrs Payne Brothers of the St Albans district.

On 17th October 1900 however, Arthur George Payne declared himself a bankrupt, and explained at his official hearing a month later that he had for the last six months been forced to live on a houseboat on the River Dart. "It seems it was a happy-go-lucky sort of affair" remarked the Receiver; critical of the way in which the company had been set up. "We simply opened up the works and went ahead" replied a somewhat naive Mr Payne. He had invested £900 in the venture, together with whatever monies his two partners could afford, and it was clearly a woefully underfunded enterprise. Although they had managed to make and sell some bricks, they had not enough capital to fund the necessary branch connection to the main line railway, despite the fact that it was frustratingly close by; this consequently resulting in their not being able to honour brick orders large enough to ensure their survival.

The company in the meantime managed to struggle on until November 1901, at which point the remaining partnership was itself dissolved. The works however is listed in the rates as being run by Payne & Bennitt in 1902, but it may well be that they still technically co-owned the works at that time, but by 1905 a Thomas Kendrick had taken it over, the works itself being listed as a " 2a. 1r. 13p. brickyard at Penuel"; Penuel being the name of the chapel close by. Perhaps Mr Kendrick acquired this works in October 1903 – the British Clayworker for that date told of a Hafod Abley Brick Co Ltd being formed to acquire clay and mines in the area, and Hafod Abley was being described in Mr Payne's evidence as the area of Llanfynydd in which they had their works. The connection between the Hafod Abley Brick Co and Mr Kendrick must however be purely one of conjecture.

So where was the works actually sited? Information forthcoming from the local landowners proved inconclusive, but the local belief is that it may have existed at the site of some ruins in the woodlands at OS 2751 5658. These ruins are very well overgrown, but are clearly large enough to have constituted a small brickworks. They are situated alongside a stream, part of which has been walled off to form some sort of reservoir. A little to the west is the walled up entrance to a driftmine into the hillside, and what can still be recognised as an opencast quarryworking lies just to the south east; a feature which appears marked on the 1914 OS map as a claypit.

It seems today to be a strange place to have put

an industrial works, as the surrounding land is now extremely waterlogged, and any traces of what roads or tracks that may have existed to the works have completely disappeared, but nevertheless, what physical evidence still remains does seem to be very persuasive. There is a claypit, there is a driftmine, there is a substantial ruin together with clear evidence of industrial usage of the stream – so all in all, I am fairly confident in naming this site as our brickworks. As to when it closed, we can only guess. The 1914 map shows a building where the ruin now stands, but does not list it as a brickworks.

SITE 66: THE FORD ARTIFICIAL STONE WORKS, FFRITH

Although not a clay brickworks, this factory is nevertheless worthy of a small mention because of its unusual status as being the only one of its kind in the district. It was founded by Mr L P Ford, who was himself a remarkable man. He was a lawyer by profession who had become the Government's attorney general in the South African Transvaal in 1877. He had established and owned new suburbs of the city of Johannesburg, and had founded the city's waterworks, as well as the Pretoria Electric Light Co, and had other interests in ventures all over the world.

He came to the Ffrith district to take over a silica stone quarry in which he had a financial stake. Artificial stone was becoming a popular architectural material by the end of the 19th century, and circa 1899 he decided to build a factory alongside the quarry to produce this new material. The new factory is shown on maps as the Cambrian Stone Works, but is also referred to in newspaper reports of 1901 as the Crown Dale Works, and although still very small at the beginning of the century, it soon grew into quite a large place. By early 1908 it was in liquidation, but by 1912 the company was still owned by the Ford Stone Co, although being run under the style of the Crown Dale Stone Co. By September 1916 it was again in liquidation and probably closed around this time.

The manufacturing process involved the moulding of large blocks of the material from a mixture principally made from silicate of lime which would then be hardened in a drying kiln for eight hours. This kiln is shown on the 1914 OS map alongside the factory which stood at OS 2810 5614; its large quarry lying to the south. The ruins of the factory still exist today, and blocks of the artificial stone lie scattered around, but the most interesting feature to have survived is a domed portico made from the material and dated 1901, and which was once the gateway to the original works manager's house, now replaced by a more modern building.

Site 52

Site 62

Site 64

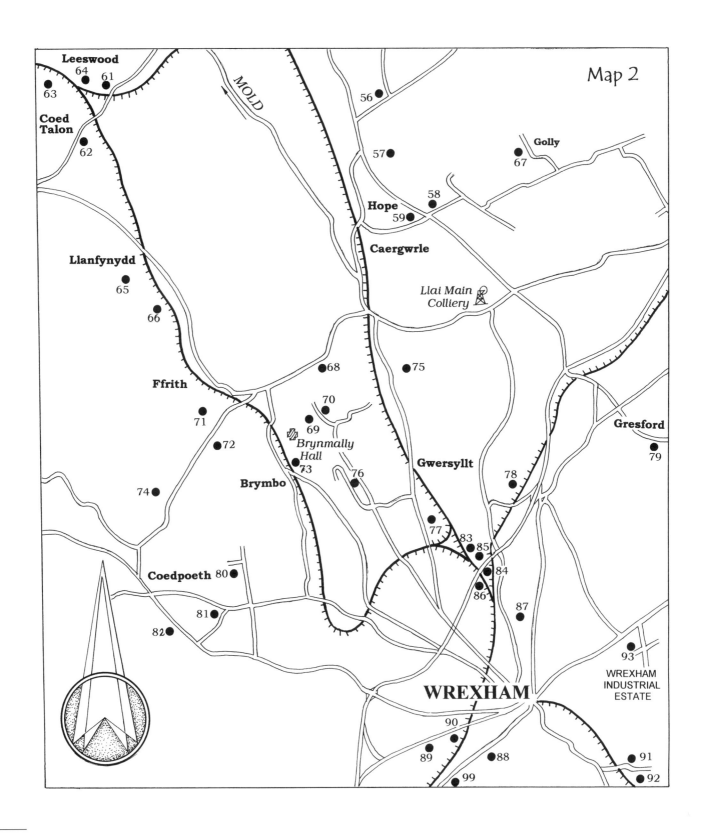

Map 2

Leeswood
64 61
63
Coed
Talon
62
Llanfynydd
65
66
Ffrith
71
72
74
Brymbo
Coedpoeth 80
81
82

MOLD

56
57
Golly
67
58
Hope
59
Caergwrle
Llai Main
Colliery
68 75
70
69
Brynmally
Hall
73 76
Gwersyllt
77 83 85
84
86
87

Gresford
79
78

WREXHAM
90
89 88
99
93
WREXHAM
INDUSTRIAL
ESTATE
91
92

DENBIGHSHIRE WORKS

Hope Area

SITE 67: GOLLEY BRICKWORKS

The northernmost of our Denbighshire area's brickworks was a tiny country brickyard near the present day Golly Farm, 1½ miles east of Hope village, shown on the 1871 OS map at ref 3360 5842. The census roll for the same year shows Wiliam Davies working here as a builder and brickmaker, employing eight men and two boys. By 1881 the site was listed as being a Brickworks with Cottage in the holding of William Kendrick, who worked there as a brick and pipe maker with his son and two men and three boy labourers. By 1891 the brickyard had gone, and the Kendrick family had become farmers. The site is still a small farm today.

Brymbo Area

SITE 68: FFRWD IRON, COAL & BRICK WORKS

The district of Ffrwd, closeted in the steeply sided valley between Cefnybedd and Brymbo, has for many decades remained a quiet and verdant backwater, but hidden within its woodlands is the evidence of a past which could not be more of a contrast to the present.

Chester Chronicle 16th May, 1891 – The Ffrwd Colliery, owned by the Messrs Sparrow, gentlemen who are known throughout the colliery districts for the kindly consideration with which they treat their men. Standing on Hope Mountain one looks down upon a country dotted over with coal and iron works, the dense sulphurous smoke ascending heavenwards and blackening the sky in every direction, making it appear like a slice carved out of the dismal Black Country and planted bodily amid the glades and vales of Wales. A colliery, iron works, brickworks and coke works all in one – a human ant hill on which hundreds of strong men daily dig and delve. Such is the Ffrwd Colliery and Ironworks.

The site originated as a small colliery, which had existed for many years prior to the above report – Richard Kyrke having occupied it certainly between 1796 and 1815. The works expanded its function when John Thompson took it over, and we know this from the evidence of the landlord's mineral agent Mr Kelly, who recalled:

"In 1824 he entered upon the Frood Works and in that year it was that he built the present iron works. From 1824 to 1842 the works were kept in blast".

Thompson ran the coal and iron works until his death in 1852; the "Frood Works" – note the more anglicised spelling for the benefit of English businessmen – being put up for letting in August of that year. The lease was taken over by John's son Richard, and from this date the proprietorship of the site begins to get a little more complicated. In late 1853 the Chronicle mentioned Messrs Johnson & Edwards at the Frood Iron & Coal Works, whilst in May 1855 it was quoted as being held by Messrs Sparrow, Pearson & Co. It appears that there may have been a good deal of sub-letting going on – a common practice within the structure of early Victorian industry. What we do know is that Richard Thompson at some point must have bought the works and let it to the Westminster Coal & Coke Co, a large concern whose main works were at Gwersyllt, and it was in 1855 that Mr James Sparrow sub-let most of it from the Westminster Co; proof of this having come to light from a parliamentary railway examination of 1862. This situation existed for some years until Mr Sparrow became wealthy enough to acquire the works in its entirety.

James Sparrow is the one figure who eventually became synonymous with the Ffrwd, becoming in time one of the best loved and respected gentleman throughout N.E. Wales; most of the people of Flintshire and Denbighshire having had at least known his name. James was born in Staffordshire in 1824; the same year in which the Ffrwd acquired its ironworks. He was the son of a family already involved with industrial ownerships, particularly in collieries. After being educated in Ireland he became fascinated with ships and began his working life as a seaman, eventually becoming the Chief Officer on Brunel's Great Western, on which he participated in its maiden voyage in becoming the first steamship to cross the Atlantic. Returning to a life on land in 1849 he worked in his uncle's ironworks at Wolverhampton until 1855 – the year in which he moved to Denbighshire to take on the Ffrwd.

The details of his involvement in the partnership of Messrs Sparrow, Pearson & Co of 1855 are unknown to me, but it certainly was a short-lived affair. Other members of his family quickly joined him in his new venture, and in mid-1858 they were joined by Samuel Poole; the company changing its name from Sparrow & Sons to Sparrows & Poole. Samuel Poole was a 29 year old Lancashire ironmaster who was probably taken into partnership with the intention of his running the blast furnace, and to commemorate his arrival, as well as the opening of a new coal shaft at the colliery, the workmen were treated to a dinner in a large marquee erected at the works.

But what of the Ffrwd's brickmaking operations? There is no recorded evidence that there was any purpose built brickworks at the Ffrwd during this period in its history, but it is unquestionably the case that bricks were made on site, and undoubtedly had been for many years, although this might well have been done by contract makers and only when such bricks were required. We have evidence of a court case in November 1861 in which Mr Gallagher, a brickmaker, sued the company for non-payment on a batch of bricks made for 15 shillings per thousand. "I am a brickmaker. I made a bargain with Messrs Sparrows & Poole to make some bricks. The contract was in writing" explained the plaintiff. He won the case and we find his lawyer making some damning remarks about the company: "The conduct of the defendants is extremely shabby to meet the case in this way when a poor man has worked for his money. I apprise all working men to be careful how they make contracts with Messrs Sparrows & Poole". Considering the respect in which Mr Sparrow would later be held, that comment seems uncharacteristically harsh towards the company, but in truth we might query as to whether Mr Sparrow even knew of the details of the case, as the brickmaker's contract would most certainly have been handled by his site managers.

The year 1862 saw the first objective description of the works' operations. James Sparrow himself gave testimony at a railway hearing in which he said: "I am the lessee of Frood, Windy Hill and Plasmain collieries. I do not raise a large quantity of coals at present. In the first place my works, properly speaking, are not a colliery. My property is principally iron works. The Windy Hill Colliery I sub – lease from the Westminster Co".

We also have the following comment from Colin Napier, the manager of the Westminster Colliery: "The Frood is a small colliery compared with others in the district. It may be 70 or 100 acres and a great portion of it is sub-let to Mr Sparrow by the Westminster Co".

On 18th April 1867 John William Sparrow left the company and a subtle change took place to its name – Sparrows & Poole becoming Sparrow & Poole.

In May of that same year we find the first evidence of bricks being sold off the site, but whether they were left over from earlier makings is not known. Its interesting that the advertisement specifies the bricks as originating from the Iron Works and no attempt was made to publicise any specialist brickworks at the site:

"Bricks of excellent quality for building, particularly adapted for engine foundations and any work requiring a strong hard brick, can be obtained at moderate prices from Sparrows and Poole Ffrwd Iron Works".

Note also the continued use of the plural of Sparrow – probably accidentally or from force of habit.

During this period in its history the ironworks dominated the operations at the Ffrwd:

Wrexham Advertiser 18th March, 1871 – New blast furnace at the Ffrwd Iron Works. Mr Sparrow kindly and ably performed the duties of a cicerone and conducted us to the new furnace which is 60 ft high. The internal lining of the furnace is of Stourbridge firebricks and the external case of bricks made on the premises.

Sparrow's partner Mr Poole sadly died aged only 43 years old. He had had an operation for some "rare condition", but had paid more attention to his duties at the works than to his convalescence. After catching a bad cold whilst still weakened he took himself to the Isle of Wight in order to recuperate, but died there on 5th October 1872.

By 1879 we see the first real evidence of a purpose built brickworks on site. The ordnance map shows the brickworks with two kilns at OS 3048 5526 – a little way from the main works itself – and this was also the year in which the company began purposefully advertising their *" first class common brick for building purposes".* We also know who the brickmakers were during the 1880s. The census of 1881 lists the 25 year-old brickmaker John Pomford living at Frood Cottages, and February 1891 saw the death of William Pomford, the foreman brickmaker at the Ffrwd and presumably John's brother, who died at the early age of 30. His funeral was recorded as being "one of the largest ever held in the district".

Wrexham Advertiser 17th August, 1889 – Ffrwd Colliery and Ironworks are working full time. A handsome bridge is being built over the turnpike road to carry the slag from the furnaces; an engine is being fixed to do the work of horses. The supporting walls of the bridge are faced up with the firm's buff pressed bricks and their appearance should be a good guarantee of their sale.

One of the walls of that bridge still stands today at OS 3040 5538, close to the Ffrwd public house, and the line of the slag railway is now a public footpath from the pub to Cefnybedd and still has some of the original platforms along its route.

If there is one thing which my research has proved to be undeniable it is that the Ffrwd works was signal in commanding the greatest of respect, and the name of the Ffrwd became legendary amongst the Denbighshire industries. The admiration for Mr Sparrow's works can be sensed in this next report:

Wrexham Advertiser 25th May 1889 – At the Ffrwd Ironworks and Collieries they put up all their own erections and do all their own repairs. They have their own boiler and locomotive works, and in fact they do nearly all the engineering work themselves. They have also blast furnaces, a large slack washing and coking plant and a brickyard for fire and common bricks.

That report however, despite its historical interest, falls somewhat short of the literary mark when compared with the following gem – an account of a journey into the subterranean workings of the Ffrwd Colliery itself:

Chester Chronicle 16th May 1891 – " Ffrwd Colliery. No more vivid representation of industrial life can be seen anywhere than in the composite works. I do not propose to detain you with a description of the art of casting tubes or making bricks which I saw proceeding, nor describe the powerful machinery for winding coal up shafts and pumping fresh air to men in the pit five hundred foot below. In the lamp room we were handed lamps and a short stick, the purpose of which I could not comprehend at the time. Twenty yards from the manager's office stands the shaft. A short flight of steps brings us to the pit mouth. Overhead the rapid whir of the wire ropes; the crash of the cage as it came with great force to the surface; the displacement from it of two trolleys full of coal; the throb of the gigantic fan forcing air down to miles of workings; the noise of escaping steam and rotating machinery all around is confusing to a man bred to a newspaper office. "In you go" exclaims the sub-manager. "Seize that upper bar and grip it tight", and before you have time to analyse your sensations, the crust of the earth appears to glide away from beneath your feet and you are hurled down into black darkness at a fearful speed. Thirty seconds or so and the cage stops with a thud over the spot colliers call "the sump". Before us extending right away into the darkness is a long bricked passage. Six or eight trolleys of coal are awaiting transportation to the pit's mouth. We walk along the main cutting. All pleasant here if you dodge wire ropes and tramlines. For perhaps two hundred yards there is space for two horses to pass abreast, but at the point where we debouched, the cutting goes down at a stiff angle for several hundred feet. We turned into No 10, a long low vault-like cutting extending a third of a mile. Before you have time to appreciate the novelty, you hear a roar as of thunder. Your guide shouts "Look out", and as you bolt to one side, a horse's head emerges out of the Cimmerian blackness, followed by four trolleys full of coal and then disappears in a like manner. "Here is a nasty bit" cries our pilot as we push forward, and I stoop my shoulders after my head has come into violent contact with the roof. Feet constantly slip into slush and mud knee deep. "Walk on the tramline", and then the short stick used as a balancing pole is of inestimable value. We eventually reached the spot where the men are working. Three are engaged in digging the coal, while one has charge of the horse which drags it off. A sinewy fellow bare to the hips has crawled into a hole, and lying on his side guided by the light of his lamp, is using his short pick with great effect. The temperature all around drenched me with perspiration. And there he digged and delved into the bowels of the Earth, literally carrying his life in his hands, for over him were many tons of solid coal.

We got safely through, examined the air workings, watched a train of cars disappearing into the deep and eventually reached the upcast shaft. Going up the shaft is an experience worse than going down. You hold on like grim death, for a head outside that cage would be reduced to pulp in a moment of time. You go whirling up as rapidly as you go down; you pass a veritable Cave of the Winds – a spot where all the breezes of heaven appear to meet in one terrific gale – it is the air for the toilers below – and presto, you are in bright daylight".

In July 1890 Mr Sparrow was experiencing severe difficulties with his men, as there had not been a single day that year in which all his workforce had reported for work. It was a time when the iron trade had become very sluggish and the irregularity of his workmen was telling seriously on the company's ability to meet urgent production targets; so much so that in August he had to announce the closure of the blast furnace department as a desperately needed cost cutting measure. Had the men been more responsible perhaps the company could have managed to weather the slump and avoid the closure, but for once, with circumstances conspiring against him, Sparrow was left a bitterly disappointed man, and had to wait nine years until the economy had improved enough to bring the iron plant back on line:

Wrexham Advertiser 12th August, 1899 – It was with intense satisfaction that the neighbourhood heard that Mr Sparrow and Sons intended to re – light their extensive furnaces which have been stopped for the past nine years, and on Saturday last the blast furnace was lighted with some show of ceremony. Mrs Sparrow was conducted to the scene of action and having been handed a torch specially made for the purpose, spoke with clear and sweet enunciation: "I have much pleasure in applying this torch to this furnace which has been for some time idle, and I wish her and those connected with her proprietors, managers and workmen, Good Luck, and now I proceed to light the fire". Three ringing cheers were then given, for the surrounding cinder banks were crowded with workmen, their wives and children, and as the flames roared and crackled and the smoke filled the air, these were lustily renewed. On Wednesday afternoon at 3pm, the fire having worked itself through the materials in the furnace, Mrs Sparrow again appeared on the scene and by opening a valve, a favourable start was effected. In about a week the furnace is expected to be in full work and one of the sights of the district for our summer visitors will be the blasts.

I love that description of how Mrs Sparrow "appeared on the scene" – like some ghostly apparition! The furnace itself was called The Old Lady, and produced a basic form of iron called in those days *mine iron*, and the cinder banks on which the workmen crowded are still there today in the form of steep hillocks covered by trees. The furnaces by night must have been quite a sight and did indeed attract tourists, and must have appeared a little like those at Coalbrookdale, of which Thomas Carlyle said in 1824: "At night the whole region burns like a volcano, spitting fire from a thousand tubes of brick".

James Sparrow died on 21st March 1902 and was thus spared the sadness of witnessing the final demise of the enterprise he had run for 47 years. A great depression hit the coal trade in 1904 and the Ffrwd was not the only company to collapse because of it. Unable to produce at a profit, the entire plant of both the colliery and the ironworks was dismantled and sold; the entire property taking four days to dispose of between 4th and 7th July, 1904.

As for the brickworks, its destiny may have taken a slightly different turn. I believe that it may well have been renamed the Windy Hill Brickworks, which we find was up for sale by private treaty in June 1902, not long after Mr Sparrow's death, and there is every probability that the company was trying to offload it at this time. Windy Hill Brickworks was again for sale during 1904, this time described as being at Ffrwd with the contact name as Mr Edward Jones at the Red Lion Inn, the same public house which is now called the Ffrwd Inn – just a stone's throw away from the brickworks. No sale went ahead, so it was put up for auction on 29th May, 1905, and interestingly, it was included in the same auction as was being held to dispose of the old Ffrwd Coke Ovens land. The advertisement listed the brickworks as being around one mile from Cefnybedd station on the Ffrwd branch of the GWR, and this distance also tallies with the Windy Hill Brickworks having being the old Ffrwd Co brickworks. It was also in hand at this time, as it was on 13th May, 1907, when it was up for auction

again.

Apart from the cinder banks and a few ruined buildings hidden amongst the undergrowth, there is little left to show that this area was once the thriving hub of the Ffrwd industrial complex. As for the brickworks, it had disappeared by the time of the 1914 OS survey and the site today is occupied by a more modern building, part of whose walls are clearly more ancient than the rest, and I think it likely that these were part of the original brickworks itself.

SITE 69: BRYNMALLY COLLIERY

This once extensive colliery site has now vanished completely – even more so than its near-neighbour at the Ffrwd, and its history also goes back well into the 18th century. Opinions concerning it's establishment seem to vary. George Lerry, the great colliery historian, wrote in 1946 that it was started by Charles Roe and James Venables in 1770. In a sense this may well be true – perhaps a Brynmally Co was indeed founded in that year, but there exist account books from earlier in 1761 which list brickmakers working at Brynmally Colliery, probably in the capacity of making bricks to line the first pits sunk there. The following are excerpts from the books:

1761 – To John Gittins for bricking the head of a new pit..................................4 shillings.
1762 – To Thomas Barclay for making 2300 bricks......................................£17-17-6.
1763 – To John Price for 1300 bricks......................................£5-17-0.

The most important transposition of Brynmally's ownership occurred in 1849. Around this time Richard Kyrke, the same gentleman who had earlier involvements at the Ffrwd, had a major share in the running of Brynmally along with others of his family. His uncle George Kyrke became bankrupt in that year, and the decision was taken in March to offload the colliery, including the one quarter share owned by another family member, James. At this point Thomas Clayton stepped into the scene. Here was another of our district's remarkable men. He was born in Chorley,

Lancashire on 14th May 1826, and by the time he arrived in Wales in October 1849, aged only 23, he must have already been a decidedly wealthy man. He purchased Brynmally Colliery together with the estate's extensive mansion and grounds, as well as Gwersyllt Colliery, the New Broughton estate and the lands of the future Ffos-y-go Colliery. He was a churchman "of decided evangelical views" and both he and his wife were the consummate Victorian philanthropists who were "most generous friends to the poor and always had them in mind".

Chester Chronicle 18th September 1858 – On Thursday the children of the Brymbo National Schools were treated to tea at Brynmally Hall by Thomas Clayton Esq. The children to the number of 300 assembled in their respective schools at 2 o'clock and marched in procession to Brynmally preceded by the Poolmouth band. Tables were arranged for tea in front of the mansion and the little juveniles were kindly waited upon by the ladies and gentlemen present. After tea the boys and girls sang a number of hymns and songs in a very effective manner. Archdeacon Wickham and Mr Clayton addressed the children on the advantages of learning to read the Word of God. In the evening a variety of amusements took place in a field belonging to Mr Clayton.

In the early 1850s Thomas was the first of the district's works proprietors to donate 10 tons of coal to the poor of Chester city, an act which was speedily imitated by others of his peers, and "by which means nearly one hundred tons have been distributed for the last three winters" remarked a clergyman in 1856. He also donated the grounds upon which St Paul's Church at Broughton was built, and in July 1890 he assisted the building of a public hall at Summerhill by donating £20 worth of bricks, as well as providing a man to act as superintendent in the construction of the building.

Wrexham Advertiser 29th December, 1894 – Mr and Mrs Clayton as usual at this festive season were very busy on Friday and Saturday in sending out presents of beef to their employees and the poor in the neighbourhood. Two fine

Thomas Clayton. Colliery and Brick Master.
Photo : DRO.

beasts were slaughtered for the purpose. The officials of Brynmally Colliery each received a fat goose in accordance with a custom extending over forty years.

The Clayton family also actively ran the Brymbo Sunday School every week for over 40 years until their deaths, and Thomas also found time to be a regular lecturer on religious and moral issues at meetings and dinners throughout the district.

Three years after his acquiring the colliery, Thomas employed a rather ingenious scheme to clear the pits of the dangerous fire damp, or methane gas:

Chester Chronicle 2nd October, 1852 – At the Bryn Mally Colliery, Thomas Clayton Esq the proprietor, by means of pipes, has conveyed from the bottom of his coal pits, the gas or fire damp contained in the workings. The pipe on the surface which is about three inches in diameter is raised about eight feet from the ground, and when the fire is put to the gas, the blaze lights the country around for some distance and a person may see to read on the darkest night at a distance of ten or twelve yards. This scheme has tended materially to clear the pits of fire damp and to answer the purpose intended admirably.

The official style of the company at this time was Messrs Clayton & Darlington, but it is not quite clear as to who Mr Darlington was, or to what degree he was involved. He may have been a principal sleeping partner or perhaps the manager of the site, as such persons were often included in company names during that period in history.

The greatest calamity to befall the company during its heydays occurred in 1856, when for some months the entire site was brought to a standstill when water engulfed the workings. It had broken into Brynmally's tunnels from old workings at the nearby Ffrwd Colliery, resulting in the death of 14 miners, and 21 million gallons of water had to be pumped out of the workings before operations could be resumed. But once the pits were up and running again business boomed, and by 1858 the press could report that "the Brynmally company is scarcely able to supply its demands". This was also the period in which the company's brickworks was set to producing goods which could appeal to the general building trade, and from November 1857 and throughout 1858 the Chronicle ran a continuous advertisement reading

"The Bryn Mally Works. Best white firebricks, tiles, chimney tops and all other kinds of fireclay and terracotta ware manufactured at the above works. At the depots at Saltney and Cow Lane Bridge, Chester".

Those depots were the company's principal land sale outlets for Brynmally coal into Chester, and alongside the canal at Cow Lane Bridge (the canal bridge at Frodsham Street) the company had a yard and weighbridge for the sale of coal, which is marked as " WB " on the first edition OS map of Chester.

The colliery brickworks was shown on a railway map of 1861 with three kilns, but the OS map of ten years later shows only two brick kilns, as does a sale map of 1897, so perhaps we may surmise that brick production was greater during the earlier years of Clayton's involvement.

At Wrexham County Magistrates' Court, 22nd February 1869 – John Boyker was brought up on remand charged with stealing two wheelbarrow trundles, the property of Mr Thomas Clayton of Brynmally. Only one of the trundle wheels had been recovered. Mr Hutchinson said that on 20th November a wheelbarrow trundle was missed from the brickyard in connection with the Brynmally Works. About a month ago another trundle was missed from the brickyard. He identified the one produced as belonging to Mr Clayton – the initials T.C. had been rasped off it. John O'Brian in the employ of Mr Clayton as joiner and model maker also identified the trundle, the woodwork of which he had made himself. The prisoner was sent to jail for two months with hard labour.

Note the employment of a model maker at the works – this indicates the manufacture of products which were a little more sophisticated than simple bricks.

Thomas Clayton died on 28th February, 1896 after contracting a chill four days previously; the cause of death being attributed to pleurisy and inflammation of the lungs. He was buried at St Paul's Church in Pentre Broughton near Brymbo, the same church he had helped to build, and with him was placed his personal Bible which he had used ever since he left school.

By the time his executors got round to disposing of the colliery in 1897 the works were only producing on a two-day week. It was taken over by Mr T B Barton of Wrexham, and from this time onwards there is no evidence at all of any further brick production taking place, although that's not to say that bricks might not have been produced for the upkeep of the colliery workings themselves. By 1903, when a Mr Harris was taken on as the new manager, he was advised that due to the economic climate the works was expected to have only 12 months left to survive, but that prediction proved in the end to be wildly pessimistic. The company was, however, registered as being in liquidation in May 1907, after which time Messrs Dutton, Massey & Co of Liverpool purchased it and took possession by the end of June that year. The colliery continued producing until the depression years, and in March 1935 its Liverpool owners sold it to a business syndicate based in Wrexham, but following a crisis meeting held on 4th September that same year the raw new owners decided that the colliery must close, throwing 300 men out of work. The dismantling and winding down of the works took place gradually, until production finally ceased with the last shift on Saturday, 12th October, 1935 – the date on which the last Brynmally coal ever reached the light of day.

During the following year the tall chimneys were blown down and the site's buildings dismantled by Edward Tudor of the Pentresaesson Foundry. The colliery site lay wasted and unused until a few years of opencast mining was begun during World War Two.

The site has today been totally re landscaped and now forms the northernmost reaches of a municipal golf course, and the position of the colliery buildings and brick kilns can be recognised by the copse of trees at OS 3045 5440.

SITE 70: FFOS-Y-GO BRICKWORKS

This little works, nestled in the countryside very near to the Brynmally site, was close to a small colliery just to the south called Pendwll or Ffos-y-go Colliery. The brickworks was first registered as the Ffos-y-go Salt Glazed Brick Co Ltd on 16th January 1896 by a firm of Lancashire makers based in Southport, and the principle manufactures of the new works were intended to be glazed bricks, pipes and sanitary ware. The works was nearing completion by the end of that year, but it seems that they had a little trouble in eventually getting themselves established in the market place; the Wrexham Advertiser in October 1897 remarking that "the new brickworks at Ffos-y-go are doing very little".

Apart from these initial facts we know little else of its short history, save that it was owned by a Mr Corkling, who retired circa 1901, giving possession

of it to his daughter Miss Yates Corkling.

The works was built on a narrow strip of land which had formerly held the trackbed of an earlier railway to the Pendwll Colliery. There was however, another line of railway running parallel to the old line, and this features in the next report. It says little of the works other than that it was still going by the end of 1901, but I have included it here as a document of just how some of our social values have changed since those days. It may seem quite a bizarre piece of evidence to include in a history book on brickmaking, but it does highlight the human interaction which these works were witness to, and I regard this aspect as important a factor as any commercial considerations. As an aid to understanding the legalities of the case, you should bear in mind that during this period, the age of consent for girls was 13 years old:

Wrexham Advertiser 7th December, 1901 – Wrexham County Court – John Williams, Ffos-y-go, was charged by Inspector Dyson of the NSPCC for assaulting Clara Blackwell, a girl under the age of 13, on 27th October and on divers other dates. Clara Blackwell said she had known defendant for about twelve months. She saw him on 26th October. He asked her to go down to the brickworks on Sunday. She did so instead of going to Sunday School. When she got inside she saw defendant sitting on a table. Defendant took her upstairs and afterwards gave her a shilling. He told her not to let anyone see her leave the premises. Instead of going home along the main road she went along the line. When she saw defendant on 26th he told her to bring some more girls with her, but she went alone. She had been to the works on Sundays before with the defendant and received money from him. On one of those occasions a girl named Edith Hughes accompanied her, and on another occasion a girl named Charlotte Edwards. She knew what he intended doing to her on each of her visits. Edith Hughes, 15, had been to the brickworks with the previous witness. Defendant took hold of her around the waist, but she screamed and got away from him. She saw him assault Clara Blackwell and give her sixpence. Charlotte Edwards, 12, said she had once been to the works with Blackwell. When they left, defendant gave them sixpence each.

A. Edwards, collier, Ffos-y-go, said he saw Clara Blackwell going in the direction of the brickworks on 27th and watched her until she went through the engine house door. Police Constable Phoenix deposed to going to the brickworks where defendant was employed as a watchman and serving him with the summons. Defendant said "Which is the best way out of this? Do you think I had better get any help? I shall be like a dummy there unless I get some help". The officer had known him for some time. He was a respectable man and he had never heard a word against him before. Mr Wynn Evans for the defence said the whole case depended absolutely on the statement of the girl Blackwell and whatever else one might say for her, she was a wicked little madam on her own admission. An indecent assault must be committed against the will of the person who was assaulted. Prosecuting counsel said this was no defence to an assault upon a child under the age of 13. John Cyffin, manager of the brickworks, said defendant was trustworthy as far as workmanship was concerned.

As to the fortunes of the adjacent colliery, the Wrexham Advertiser of 1887 says that it was Thomas Clayton who had sunk the first pits in 1858. Its main coal seam was only 2ft. 3in. in hight, and was therefore "mainly worked by lads". Miss Corkling purchased the colliery from the Brynmally Co on 16th October, 1901 on the assurance from the landowner that 800 tons could be raised monthly. The landowner, Frederick Hutchinson, also owned the land on which the brickworks stood, and he had previously been its manager in its early days. The fortunes of the brickworks were now directly linked by ownership to those of the colliery, but the colliery outlived it. The 1912 map shows the brickworks as disused, as does a lease map of adjacent lands in 1926. The colliery itself finally closed in 1917.

All that remains of the brickworks is the concrete floor at OS 3068 5455 – all now well hidden amongst trees. The clay was extracted from a perpendicular quarry face hewn into the hillside along the eastern side of the works, and this still remains, atop of which runs a little backroad high above the site.

SITE 71: FFRITH FIRECLAY CO.

Most of the older locals of the district still remember the Ffrith Fireclay Co, but only in its mid-20th century reincarnation , which had nothing to do with the earlier Victorian brickworks. The original works was sited on the floor of the steeply sided Glascoed Valley, which is accessed by an extremely overgrown public footpath.

The earliest industry in this small valley was the little Ffrith Colliery, centred at OS 2860 5474. The colliery is shown on the 1871 OS map, and we know that it was worked by Charlewood & Co certainly between 1874 – 6. In May 1876 it was sold to Dinsdale & Co, and the sale prospectus advised that *"There are some very valuable beds of fireclay and the surface clay in some places being about 20 ft. thick. The auctioneers have great pleasure in recommending this property as particularly well situated for a good brickworks"*. Dinsdale & Co did not themselves take advantage of this option, and their tenure didn't last long; the works being dismantled and disposed of at auction on 5th and 11th March, 1878; one of the lots being 2000 tons of fireclay. The colliery must have seen a later resurrection, as the historian George Lerry says that by 1901 the pit was owned by Ffrith Coal & Fireclay Co, and a reference in the newspaper of 1900 refers to the firm of Messrs Taylor & Carter being the owners of this company. Lerry says that it was later owned by the Brynmally Co, and eventually closed in December 1922.

But what of the brickworks? The separate colliery company was obviously producing large amounts of fireclay from its workings, but there is no evidence that they were transforming it into bricks, and the Glascoed Valley had to wait for yet another group of English entrepreneurs to bring that about:

Wrexham Advertiser 27th July, 1889 – On the London North Western Joint Railway which runs from Mold to Brymbo, near the iron viaduct that crosses the Glascoed Valley, preparations are being made for a branch line. This is to run from the main line to a place where a company from Bolton have found an immense bed of fireclay, which for quality cannot be surpassed in this district. The company's intentions are now to commence a large brickworks. Several men are now engaged felling trees to make way for the railway. On top of the bed of clay is a bed of coal about 4ft. thick, while in the middle of the clay is another bed of coal.

The main line of railway across the valley originally opened in 1872 as a mineral only line, and is the same line which served the collieries and brickworks at Coed Talon, Pontybodkin and the Leeswood Vale. The last train ever to work this section ran on 24th April, 1952. The line had also for a time been used to work passenger trains – the first running on 2nd May, 1898 and the last on 24th March, 1950. On that first passenger run a reporter from the Wrexham Advertiser saw the brickworks from the viaduct and recorded "It was very curious to see a clay works nestling in a lovely little valley".

The new brick company was styled the Ffrith Fireclay Co; a modestly sized works positioned at OS 2868 5462 – a little further to the south and on the opposite side of a stream to the site of the earlier colliery. The branch railway from the main line ran through the woods from a spur on the eastern side of the viaduct – its path is still discernible today.

By March 1891 the works were advertising its wares as *"Red and Buff bricks and tiles, facing bricks, firebricks and salt glazed bricks"*, and the early years of the 1890s were recorded as being a heyday for it, as well as for the other brickworks in the district.

Some open clayworkings are still visible in the valley today, showing beautiful striations of red and yellow clays, but I believe that most of the clays used at the works came from a driftmine which ran into the steep hillside behind the factory, the blocked entrance to which is still there today. Unfortunately, nothing is recorded regarding the final demise of the works. It was still functional in April 1901, when Brymbo Parish Council wrote to the then Ffrith Brick Co concerning damage they

had caused to a footpath, but by the time of the 1914 OS survey it had disappeared, obviously having been demolished.

With the colliery having closed in 1922, we have to wait until 1925 before we find any new activity in the valley. In December that year the owner of the old colliery site granted a lease on that land to a new company styling themselves the Valley Brick & Tile Co. This new enterprise was formed by four local men, and the lease agreement shows royalties to be paid on any bricks made and brickearth mined. In 1928 the company restyled itself as the Ffrith Fireclay Co (using the same style as the earlier brickworks) and struck a deal with the Brymbo Steel Co, the owners of the old brickworks land, to use the concrete floor of the old demolished brickworks as a stockpiling area for fireclay. In 1936 the company sold the works to Thomas Marshall of Sheffield for £2,750, but no brickmaking plant was listed in the sale – only winding machinery and grinding plant, and this strongly suggests that the site was used exclusively for fireclay mining. If brickmaking was ever undertaken here it was probably not for long, and this may be the reason why the company changed its name to the Ffrith Fireclay Co – excluding any reference to bricks – after only three years in existence.

A plan of this fireclay works, sadly undated, does show a clayhole alongside two round kilns, but we don't know if those kilns actually made bricks – they could even have been limekilns, or perhaps used to dry the newly mined fireclay.

The fireclay works did have one thing in common with the earlier brickworks in that both used the driftmine into the hillside. The fireclay company constructed an elevated tramway to breach the stream and connect the mine to the factory, and the mine became the principal source for their clay. The plan of the works shows that the network of underground roadways became quite extensive; the main access tunnel being 330 yards long at a gradient of 1 in 7. By July 1973 however, the mines had become worked out, and negotiations to acquire adjacent property broke down, resulting in the closure of the works and the loss of the 15 jobs still left.

SITE 72: THE BRYMBO CO'S CAELLO BRICKWORKS

The mighty steelworks which once loomed over Brymbo village like some Welsh industrial parthenon, is now but a memory. Its history began in 1792 when John Wilkinson (Iron Mad Wilkinson, as he was nicknamed) bought Brymbo Hall with its estate and lead smelting factory, and three years later he established the first Brymbo blast furnace and iron foundry. In March 1846 William Henry Darby, building on his family's successes at Coalbrookdale, became a partner in the ironworks, and in January 1850 he bought the land on which the works was built, and also secured his position as principal shareholder.

Bricks had been a part of Brymbo's operations since its beginning, and a sale document for Brymbo Hall in 1829 included not only the "well known Iron Works", but several beds of fireclay "which has been used for making firebricks for the works". Brymbo Hall itself stood at OS 295 532 – now long gone. The sale plan also showed a Cae Bricks (Brickfield) close by to the north of the Hall, and perhaps this may have been where the ironworks made their first crude bricks. As the works grew in importance, the Brymbo company sought out a more profitable base for their brickmaking department, and a new greenfield site well away from the ironworks was chosen:

Wrexham Advertiser 25th September, 1869 – The proprietors of the Brymbo Works are embarking further and at considerable expense in the brickmaking trade. One of Hoffmann's patent kilns with engines and the best class of machinery is now being erected at Caello adjoining the Minera branch of railway, where there appears to be an almost inexhaustible supply of clay of very excellent quality. We learn that it is the intention of the proprietors to offer a most excellent well pressed brick at such a figure as to ensure a good demand.

The newspaper followed up on 2nd July 1870 by announcing that the works had commenced production within the last few days, with a projected output of 15,000 bricks per day, a figure which would be trebled in later years. Apart from common bricks for public sale, the works' principal manufacture was furnace bricks for the company's ironworks, which were taken up the hill to Brymbo via the Minera branch line.

Wrexham Advertiser 21st August, 1875 – The men with their wives and all the hands employed at the Caello brickworks, Brymbo Co, were on Monday treated to a trip to Llangollen. The party numbered over sixty and were conveyed by Mr Ion Green's "brake", Mr Wright's "wagonette" and three stage carts. Arriving timely at Llangollen, they dispersed according to their inclination, and amused themselves thoroughly in running over the hills, some indulging in foot races, while others were burking on the ennobled quadruped of the East. After enjoying a splendid holiday, the party arrived home safe and in good humour, for furthering the interest of their employers, singled out from among the Brymbo workmen for a treat. We learn that a month's make of bricks amounts to 375,000 in addition to pots, tiles etc – the large make being the reason for giving the trip in acknowledgement for past endeavours and encouragement in future efforts.

That strange word "burking" was a Victorian reference to riding, and the " ennobled quadruped of the East" – a camel. There was probably a travelling circus in Llangollen at that time, and we know that Mander's Menagerie had visited the town in April 1867, which included camels amongst its exhibits – as did Myer's Great Hippodrome and Circus, which had 20 of the creatures travelling as part of their tour of the Wrexham districts in 1879.

In 1882 the Brymbo Co's great mentor Mr W H Darby died. His brother, Charles Edward Darby, who was the manager of the ironworks and had been in partnership with his brother since its early days, never got over the loss. Two years later, having suffered from long term depression, he hung himself.

By late 1884 the Caello Works was in the throw of major extensions. New plant was being installed in order to satisfy the particular requirements for a new specification of brick for the lucrative Mersey

Rail Tunnel contract, as well as for supplying the expanding Brymbo company itself. Silica brick production was begun in the late 1880s after unsuccessful trials at Caello were followed up by a bit of industrial espionage at another company's works in Yorkshire; the manager of Caello posing as a potential customer in order to discover the secrets of successful silica brick production. Silica brick was required as the ironworks moved over into steel production; a move which resulted in the fortunes of the brickworks flourishing during the first two decades of the 20th century, unlike those of so many other local works. As its production of common brick diminished Caello found itself relying heavily on supplying the needs of the steelworks, and when the nationwide steel recession hit Brymbo in 1930, it hit hard. By December the Brymbo blast furnaces had shut down, resulting in Caello working on reduced time. In June 1931 the entire company ceased all operations and appointed the Receivers, and the long wait began until an upturn in the market might bring the huge plant back on line again. This occurred in October 1933. The company's directors registered the new Brymbo Steel Successors Ltd, and by January 1935 they could report that all the departments were back on full production. Strangely enough however, the brickworks had actually made efforts to restart before the new steelworks company had been formed. In July 1933 a number of men were taken on for the purpose of preparing the brickworks prior to reinstating the making of common bricks for the newly revitalised building trade, and the resurgence of the steelworks was just the catalyst Caello needed to herald the total renaissance of the works.

Caello brickworks parted company with Brymbo Steel when it was acquired by Castle Firebrick Co of Buckley. Castle's parent company was the British Steel Corporation, and it could be debated that the brickworks had as much a chance of survival with either of the two steel giants. Unfortunately for Caello, it was British Steel which hit on hard times in 1971. By July that year Caello had been scheduled to close down by the end of December; Castle Firebrick having decided to focus all its silica production at its Buckley works, and despite the intervention of the local MP, nothing could be done to save the brickworks in the wake of the financial devastation brought about by British Steel's troubles.

I should lastly mention the Smelt Fireclay Mine. Caello Works was situated in a district which was dotted by over one hundred small coal shafts, most of which were remnants from the early days of intensive coal speculation. The Smelt Pit was one of the Brymbo Co's better established coal pits and was first opened in 1849. In its heyday it was worked around the clock by 400 men raising coal for the ironworks, and was situated not far from Caello at OS 2835 5390. In 1876 a seam of fireclay was discovered, and the separate Smelt Fireclay Mine was established with a tramway laid up to the Caello Works. This 51 centimetre narrow gauge line was horse drawn, even until 1963, when its operations were replaced by road haulage. " The Smelt" became the brickworks' principal source of clay and coal, and up until the beginning of 1952

Miners going "down the slip" into the Smelt Driftmine in August 1953. 170 tons of fireclay were mined to every 10 tons of coal.
Photo: Wrexham Leader / British Library.

the miners were still using candles as underground lighting. By 1953 only 18 men were left working the Smelt, and for this reason the National Coal Board never saw any purpose in nationalising it. By that time however, the pit had become a very small affair, producing exclusively for the brickworks.

Wrexham Leader 28th August, 1953 – To the passer – by on Brymbo back roads there is little to indicate a colliery. An overgrown slag heap, a gutted cart track, little more. No boiler houses, no pit head derricks. A country colliery for a country setting.

The mine was abandoned on 31st May 1968, and today the area has been totally obliterated by more recent opencast excavation. The site of the Caello factory at OS 2870 5424 is now just an open field, everything having been eradicated, but the trackbed of the railway to Brymbo steelworks is still just discernible to the north of the site.

SITE 73: BRYMBO BRICK TILE & POT WORKS

To the north of Brymbo village was a small works which was shown on the 1860 North Wales Mineral Rly proposal map as a Brickworks, Kiln and Yard owned by David Hughes and worked by Samuel Johnson. It stood centred at OS 2975 5391 on the junction of four roads where The Queen's Head public house used to stand.

Wrexham Advertiser – To be sold by auction on the premises of the brick and pot works near the Queen's Head, Brymbo on 7th May 1860, the area of which contains about half an acre and now or late in the holding of Messrs Griffiths & Co. Also the three newly erected sheds and kiln upon the works, one of which sheds being 40ft long and 22ft wide, and at a trifling cost might be converted into three substantial cottages. Together with the machinery, pug mill, rollers for grinding clay, horse wheel, wheel for pot making, brick moulds, brick and tile makers tools, square moulds for chimney tops etc. The clay at this works is of very superior quality, being well adapted for firebricks and all kind of earthenware.

We notice one immediate problem – a discrepancy in the occupancy of the site, yet no other brickworks were shown on the highly detailed railway map of the same year. However, the ad did say that it may have been "late" in the holding of Messrs Griffiths, so it might suggest that a transference of ownership had recently taken place.

Another proposal map for the W.M. &C.Q. Rly of 1863 shows that the above works had gone by that year, but had been replaced by a new Brickyard with Kiln and Drying Shed on the opposite side of the road at OS 2974 5398, owned and occupied by the same David Hughes.

This later site had also disappeared by the time of the 1871 OS survey. Modern housing has today replaced both sites.

SITE 74: PENTRE SAESON COLLIERY & BRICKWORKS

This site was principally a small colliery with brickmaking facilities. When it was established is uncertain, but on 16th January 1863 the Pentre Saeson Colliery partnership was dissolved when Joseph Gibson left the company, leaving it to be carried on by William and George Clark Pattinson. Thomas Walmsley then took Gibson's place, and on 7th April, 1864 the Pattinson brothers also left the partnership. During these periods no evidence of any brickmaking activity was mentioned, although it must surely have occurred to provide the pit linings etc.

The works' demise probably came with the auction by order of its liquidators on 13th December, 1871 of all the plant, machinery and stocks. By this date the company had been trading as the Pentre Saeson Colliery & Brickworks, and amongst the lots we find a brick pressing machine, 80,000 bricks and 200 floor tiles.

The little colliery is named on the 1871 OS but does not appear on any other maps after that date. Pentre Saeson is roughly translated as Englishmen's Hamlet – a name which it is believed referred to the Staffordshire miners who supposedly sank and worked the pit; the Pattinson brothers themselves also being from Staffordshire. The colliery buildings stood at OS 2784 5340 and nothing exists above ground, but just to the north sits a large spoil hill, now overgrown by gorse bushes.

It is important not to confuse the colliery site with the existing ruins of the Pentre Saeson Foundry. This stone building and chimney is not far away at OS 2773 5325 and is being converted into a private dwelling. The foundry saw the nearby colliery come and go, and it celebrated its centenary well before it finally closed. It had been run by the Taylor family since its establishment in the 1850s, and produced castings and ironwork for local collieries and brickworks.

Site 72

Site 75

Site 76

Site 77

Gwersyllt Area

SITE 75: LLAY HALL COLLIERY & BRICKWORKS

This was one of the most extensive coal and brick concerns in N.E. Wales, and it's difficult not to find examples of the pale red Llay Hall brick in walls and on waste sites anywhere throughout the district.

Going back to the early Victorian period we originally find that the Llay Hall area was home to the following three small separately run companies – a wire mill, a colliery and a brickworks; all within close proximity to each other:

* Gwersyllt Wire Mill, sometimes called Gwersyllt Forge, appears on the 1843 tithe map at OS 3145 5525, and was the earliest of the three industries. It passed through various ownerships, the last as an independent concern being in 1865, when it was acquired by a firm of Staffordshire ironworkers:

Chester Chronicle 5th August, 1865 – On Tuesday morning last a band of music with about 150 men and boys carrying flags and banners arrived in Wrexham from the Regent Ironworks, Bilston, Staffordshire. After marching down from the railway station, the procession went on to the Gwersyllt Iron and Wire Works, which were formally opened. A dinner was provided for the men at the work.

* Llay Hall Colliery was only recently opened out by March 1845, when the landlord put it up for lease affording "a most eligible opportunity for investment of capital". One of its earliest shareholders was the father of its later owner, Mr E S Clark.
* The brickworks seems to have been established sometime in the 1850s. The following advertisement ran in the Wrexham Advertiser throughout April and May 1859:

"Gwersyllt Fireclay Works. J Dodd & Co beg respectfully to inform the Nobility, Gentry, Farmers and Builders and the public generally that they have now on sale a quantity of first class bricks, tiles, ridge tiles, chimney tops etc which they recommend with great confidence; considerable improvements having been effected by them in the manufacture."

Throughout 1865 – 6 the Gwersyllt Brick & Tile Works, as it was then called, were offering an increased stock including drain pipes, cow feeders, glazed stoneware and firedoors, yet any inquiries had to be addressed to the Llay Forge Iron Co – the forge works having taken over the brickworks by this time.

The year 1866 saw the formation of a new company composed of gentlemen from the south of England, their intention being to incorporate all the three concerns under one name – the North Wales Coal Iron & Firebrick Co Ltd. From their prospectus published in the Advertiser on 12th May the following text paints a picture of the situation at that time:

The Directors have entered into arrangements to secure or lease the valuable property known as the Llay Forge Iron and Brickworks with about 80 acres of valuable minerals. The estate on which these works is erected is at Llay, and is intersected by the river Alyn which affords great facilities for water power. A new line of railway passes the works connecting Wrexham and the GWR with the port of Connah's Quay, affording cheap and easy facilities for shipment of goods and receiving pig – iron from the Hermatite and Scotch districts. This property and the right to work the estate have been purchased for the sum of £12,000. The brickworks are situated on a clay field of unusual extent. The blue brick clay has been proved to a depth of 60 – 80 ft and the firebrick clay to the depth of 12 ft. The firebricks have been used in the works and proved to be little, if any, inferior to the celebrated Stourbridge bricks. The works comprises a steam engine with machinery, a large drying shed and kilns. There is one important feature to this property, viz that the Iron and Brick Works when extended will consume from 2000 – 3000 tons of coal per month, which being supplied from the Colliery will materially increase the profits.

Despite their obvious optimism and a significant outlay of capital the venture quickly foundered, and by order of the Sheriff of Denbighshire a great sale of plant and stock took place on 3rd June 1867. At the brickworks the stock list was considerable – 50,000 firebricks,

3,000 white floor tiles, 10,000 dark tiles, 4,000 roof tiles, 1,200 ridge tiles, 1,500 garden ridges, 200 chimney pots, and much more besides. Despite this setback the brickworks pushed on with production; advertising in August that the works was again functional, but by the following month the company's directors decided to wind up the venture entirely, and a petition to this effect was presented to the Court of Chancery on 3rd March, 1868.

All operations probably ceased completely during the hiatus which followed, and the site was eventually offered for sale by private treaty in October 1871.

By 1873 a new company under the style of the Llay Hall Coal Iron & Firebrick Co had been formed. They took possession of the site in April that year and set about repairing the forge. On 11th June the company's agent and chief engineer Mr Edward Stanley Clark reported "a new tunnel has been driven into the fireclay. The machinery and kilns have been put into working order at a trifling cost of £115. I shall be able in addition to supplying our own wants, to put into the market a considerable quantity of firebricks and other clay goods. We start brickmaking on Wednesday next".

The new proprietors clearly had all the financial clout to develop the site extensively, and it was by their intervention that the previously insignificant colliery grew to become one of the most prestigious in the district. They also constructed a new road to the works, plus a branch railway link from near Cefnybedd station, as well as purchasing three-and a-half acres of land on which they built many cottages, allowing the workers to live nearby. As the Earl of Airlie, probably one of their major shareholders, pointed out: "All wise men must feel that to walk two or three miles to and from his work must exhaust much of a man's power and strength for labour".

1874 saw new kilns and sheds put up at the brickworks. The new railway connection was completed in March 1875, and the separate running of the ironworks was let on a seven year term to Messrs Bridge & McDonald. The two following inclusions show how well the brickworks was progressing by the mid-1870s; the first being extracted from a shareholder's report:

Wrexham Advertiser 13th March 1875 – They had trebled the size of their brickshed. It was now 190 ft by 45 ft so as to enable them to enter into further operations. Their clay was not only eminently suitable for tiles etc but of even greater importance, the company would be able to come into competition for the production of firebricks as used by gas companies. The greater advantage they possessed over other works was that they could produce cheaper than any other, for this reason their clay was at the surface, and instead of being obliged to pump to keep it dry, the fact of it lying on the side of a hill did away with that necessity.

Wrexham Advertiser 21st April 1877 – The Fire Brick Works is a very large concern and of the most complete character. First of all at the top of the ravine formed by the river, is the clay pit. The clay is raised by a small engine and then conveyed down the embankment to the crushing mills. These mills are attached to the brickshed, and there is a powerful engine with boilers. The clay is again raised by means of elevators placed in an endless band. These elevators empty into a kind of trough through which the dust clay is conveyed to another mill where water is introduced and converted into paste. Thence it is conveyed to a shaft where it is thoroughly mixed and conveyed in handbarrows to the brickmaking machines. Underneath the shed are a number of flues which keep the flooring at a temperature sufficiently high to enable the men to stack the bricks in 24 hours. They are then taken to the kilns, of which there are five, and two of which are always burning. In connection with these works Mr E S Clark the manager showed me a series of vases etc manufactured out of the same clay, and among other things, tea and coffee pots nicely glazed, which had been made out of the Llay Hall clay, proving that the quality is sufficiently good to justify the company in attempting the manufacture of domestic articles.

I should mention at this point the important figure of Mr E S Clark himself. A local man born on 2nd August 1848 he trained in civil engineering, and it wasn't long after his involvement with the company that he was appointed its general manager – his quick rise being a clear indication of his abilities. He became a well travelled man abroad, and apparently had a very humorous disposition:

Wrexham Advertiser 21st January, 1893 – A capital two hours enjoyment was given on Tuesday evening in the Cross Street School by Mr E Stanley Clark. The school was thoroughly packed and the incessant roars of laughter from the juveniles was plain proof of their delight. Many of the comic slides were indescribably ludicrous and were much enhanced by the witty observations of the "showman". To the elder portions of the audience, the photographic views of places on the continent were very interesting, especially as described by Mr Clark from his own personal knowledge.

Mr Clark unfortunately suffered from acute rheumatism, and he died from sudden heart failure on 10th February, 1900, aged only 51 years old.

The 1880s saw a period of insecurity and change. In 1881 the company liquidated, and again in 1883, after which it reorganised itself as the Llay Hall Coal & Clay Co Ltd. That incarnation lasted until further liquidation in June 1885, when Mr Clark purchased the whole concern himself; running it until his death in 1900. Thereafter it was his son Mr E Stuart Clark who took on his responsibilities. The less important ironworks had by this time probably closed, and at some point into the 20th century the brickworks followed suit – the 1914 OS (surveyed a few years previously) listing it as disused with its railway connection removed.

It was a completely separate colliery company which gave the brickworks a new lease of life. Just before the start of the Great War the newly formed Llay Main Colliery was sinking a vast new pit near Llay village itself, and they negotiated with Mr E Stuart Clark that his Llay Hall Brickworks should supply them with the necessary bricks; there not being any clay in Llay for them to make their own. In April 1914 Mr Clark reformed his defunct brickworks into a separate concern from his colliery and the Llay Hall Brick Co Ltd was born; £6,000 being spent on new mills, chimney, railway siding and an 18 chamber continuous kiln to replace the older plant. It happened however that due to the outbreak of war the contract with the Llay Main Colliery was cancelled, but salvation for the works came from the Ministry of Munitions, who ordered that the brickworks' entire output be channelled for the war effort. Mr Clark's testimony at a court hearing informs us that the works actually came back into production

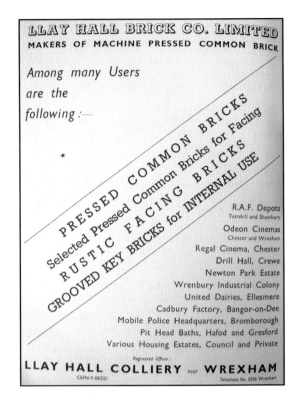

circa February 1915, and from that time forward the Llay Hall Brick Co became probably the most productive of all our local works in the manufacture of common building bricks.

As to the fortunes of the colliery it eventually passed into the control of the National Coal Board, who took the woefull and bitterly opposed decision to close it, despite its meeting its output quotas. The 450 colliers were dispersed to other pits, and the last Llay Hall coal was wound up on 25th November 1949.

The Llay Hall Brickworks closed in June 1975 following a bad recession in the building industry and 20 employees lost their jobs. "The past year has been a very grim time" remarked Mr Lloyd, the sales manager.

The brickworks stood at OS 3172 5509 and has been completely replaced by modern industry. On the opposite side of the River Alyn there still remain many architectural features of the old colliery, including the tall chimney stack, and it is these old buildings which form part of the present day Llay Hall Industrial Estate.

As regarding the fortunes of the Llay Main Colliery, the initial sinking was resumed in 1919 after the wartime stoppage, and with a shaft 18 ft in diameter and 3096 ft deep it became Britain's deepest coal pit.

It ceased production in 1966 and is now the site of the Llay Industrial Estate.

SITE 76: WESTMINSTER COLLIERY BRICKWORKS

Much could be said of the Westminster Colliery – it was once a massive complex of buildings, shafts, inclines and railways spread over the valley and hillsides just west of Summerhill, Gwersyllt. Extremely little is known of its brickworks however, so I see no point in chronologising the colliery's history, save to say that it was supposedly opened by John Thompson (he of the Ffrwd) circa 1813.

After scrutinising the 1843 tithe map for the whole of the district, I could find no brickworks present at that time, and the first evidence of any brickworks in the district is a mention in 1852 of a brick and tile works at Summerhill. The Chronicle also mentioned the Summer Hill Tile Works near Gwersyllt, which was for sale on 8th February 1858:

> "All that field now or lately used as a brick croft or pot work being near to Summerhill together with new steam engine with boiler 21ft long, tile machine, rollers with pan for grinding clay, kiln etc etc".

Where this works could have been is a mystery, but as its name suggests, it is unlikely to have been associated with the Westminster Colliery. It will have to remain as one of the few works I have not managed to locate.

As for any brickworks at the colliery, there is no documentation to locate any such before 1872, at which time it was recorded that the company moved a steam engine onto a flattened hilltop to haul coal trucks up a newly constructed incline, which is still present today, and it was here at OS 3096 5360 that the company's new brickworks was built. It is not shown on the 1871 map, but is clearly marked on the 1899 edition. However, Westminster Colliery was extremely large and must surely have had an established brickworks since its earliest days. The brickworks must have been fairly well established by the turn of the century, as we find that the company was listing itself as being a brick manufacturer in the Trade Directories for 1898, a factor which must surely indicate that their products were intended for general public sale.

The colliery closed on 20th February, 1925 following continuous losses due to a serious trade depression. Nothing exists of the brickworks today, but a shallow clayhole, now very overgrown, is still recognisable to the east of the site. A nearby industrial unit stands where some original colliery buildings once were.

SITE 77: GWERSYLLT SILICA BRICKWORKS

Little is known of this works' early history other than it was believed to have been established by Thomas Clayton of Brynmally Colliery and named the Wheatsheaf Brickworks. It is not shown on the 1875 OS, and the first documented record of it appears in the sale prospectus for the July 1897 disposal of Clayton's assets following his death. It was probably manufacturing building bricks at that time and was fairly modest in size, as the following description shows:

> Freehold brickworks of 6a. 3r. 19p. Large brick drying shed with double pitched slated roof 33 yards by 22 yards. Engine shed with double pitched boarded roof with a chimney stack 60ft high. Two brick burning kilns capable of 42,000 and 18,000 bricks respectively. Small office. Large iron water tank 36 ft by 6 ft. Nearly new brickmaking machine. Hand brickmaking machine. Self-contained double brickpress. 300 yards of tram rails. Barrows. Three clay wagons with endless chain pulleys.GWR and WMCQ have sidings into the works.

The factory stood at OS 3210 5295 with its opencast clayhole adjacent to the S.E. alongside the main line of railway. The sale was withdrawn when the bidding failed to reach the reserve price, and further attempts to sell it in October also failed. It was finally purchased on 4th April 1898 by John Harrop, who paid £400 for the works – the least amount offered during all the sale attempts.

> Wrexham Advertiser 24th June, 1916 – A local company have undertaken a scheme of converting the old Wheatsheaf Brickworks into a silica brickworks, which promises to develop into an important local industry. A good number of workmen are already employed; the raw material

being obtained from the Bwlchgwyn Stone Quarries.

That last report suggests that the works had been dormant for some time before 1916. The company was formed by seven local men and there are suggestions that the works' renaissance had been requested by the then wartime Ministry of Munitions in order that it could be developed into a silica brick factory to supply the steel industry for the war effort. A Gwersyllt Silica Co letter of March 1917 to Colville Steelworks in Motherwell expressed their desire to supply bricks "at least equal if not superior to our competitors". Gwersyllt sent some bricks to Motherwell for analysis and the steel works replied "with reference to our test of your bricks we beg to inform you that the quality is not equal to Yorkshire but appears to be on a par with the general run of South Wales bricks".

The works enjoyed continuous production for many years, barring a five-month closure during 1926 when the serious coal strike deprived it of fuel. On 17th November, 1950 the employees received notice that the works was to close because of lack of orders; stockpiles of over half a million unsold bricks having accumulated. But the works was reprieved at the last minute:

Wrexham Leader 5th January, 1951 – Gwersyllt Silica Works are to stay open. A month ago a statement was issued to the effect that the works would close and notices were given to the 26 men employed. These notices have now been withdrawn as a direct result of new orders which have been received. A works official has stated that more orders have been received since the decision to close the works was made in November, but the position is still not secure and is to be reviewed in a few weeks.

The firm continued in production until further problems forced them to register a new company on 1st January, 1958 under the same name. I noticed that the main directors were also leading lights within the Bwlchgwyn Silica Co; the same quarry which had been supplying the brickworks with its minerals, so it's not unreasonable to assume that the Gwersyllt Silica Co may have actually been run by them ever since its establishment in 1916. However, the bad financial climate finally overcame all their efforts to keep the works open. By late 1958 the MP for Wrexham was delivering a speech on the district's dire industrial climate and mentioned that the works had been one of the most recent local closures.

The site remained derelict until the Metal Box Company bought it in October 1968 and built a large factory on the clayhole land, followed in later years by a warehouse on the old brickworks site. You can notice today how the factory sits below the level of the road; the grassy rises on its southern and western perimeters being the original banks of the clayhole.

The area was home to an earlier and much smaller site nearby – the 1840 tithe map shows that Evan Jones held Brick Kiln Field just south-east of site 77 at OS 3222 5290, which was eventually obliterated by the construction of the railway.

Gresford Area

SITE 78: WILDERNESS BRICKWORKS

Wrexham Advertiser 16th June 1883 – " We understand that land has been taken in the neighbourhood of the Wilderness Mill for the erection of a new brick, tile and terracotta works on a large scale. The works are to be commenced forthwith".

That land was leased immediately alongside the Chester to Wrexham railway near to the present Gresford Industrial Estate. The original lease of 24th June, 1885 was granted to Mr Edward Stanley Clark of the Llay Hall Works, but he soon took on three partners from Liverpool – Russell and James Rea and Charles William Massey – the lease being transferred to the new company of Messrs Clarke & Rea in October 1885. On 31st July, 1888 the company was floated and registered as Clarke & Rea Ltd. The works' 26 acres had an estimated half a million cubic yards of clay in the land to the north of the factory, containing a clay of a particularly high grade and producing a class of pinky red and buff goods which could rival the products of the Ruabon works. During its 30 or so years of peak quality production the works had an impressive output, but the limitations which would be found within its clayhole would eventually cause its demise.

Wrexham Advertiser 20th December, 1890 – On Tuesday morning at a quarter to six, a steam boiler exploded at the Wilderness terracotta works, fortunately without injury to any of the workpeople. The boilers being covered in with bricks, some were thrown onto the buildings and the GWR. The night shift had just left off work, hence the fortunate immunity from injury. A large number of men are temporarily thrown out of employment. The firm have however sundry alterations and additions to the works in hand, so many have been taken on for labour and it is anticipated full work will be resumed after Christmas.

Wrexham Advertiser 1st October, 1898 – Monday was quite a gala day, for Mr E Stuart Clark, the eldest son of Mr Edward Stanley Clark, attaining his 21st birthday. The whole of the employees at the colliery and brickworks at Llay Hall and terracotta works at the Wilderness had been invited to a fete on Gwersyllt Park, and soon after noon some 700 workmen, their wives and children were gathering preparatory to forming into procession. Headed by the combined bands of Oak Alyn and Rhosrobin Institute, a move was made for Oak Alyn, Mr Clark's residence, and as far as numbers would permit, the visitors were accommodated on the spacious lawn and adjacent banks. Mr S J Young, colliery manager, made a congratulatory address on the auspicious occasion. An adjournment was then made to the park where two huge marquees had been erected. In one, the men were regaled with Melton pork pies large enough to satisfy the appetite of a giant, washed down with copious draughts of nut brown. In the other tent the gentler sex and children found an appetising tea presided over by Mrs Clark and family. A programme of sports had been arranged – the three legged race was very amusing. Roars of fun were caused by the sack race. "Find your own boots" race – people were simply convulsed with this, the incidents being very funny. A tug of war between the surface and underground men of the colliery was the finale of the sports. Mr Fiddler, surface manager, made the presentation to Mr Stuart Clark before the company dispersed. The gifts from the Wilderness consisting of a Morocco leather case containing solid silver cigarette case and matchbox. By the time dusk was approaching, the band playing God Save the Queen as a fitting finale to the day's enjoyment. It is estimated that considerably over two thousand persons were present, and yet there was not the slightest sign of disorder.

That level of generosity shown towards the workmen and their families was not hard to find amongst the brick and coal masters of the Victorian age. Many of them, like Mr Clark, were committed Christians and they were not remiss in showing kindness to their less wealthier brethren; it being said of Mr Clark that "he was ever ready to alleviate distress. His public charities were numerous and his private benefactions untold".

By the turn of the century Mr E Stanley Clark had died, the firm's connection with Massey had also terminated, and in 1903 the partnership with the Rea family had also come to an end. Mr E Stuart Clark purchased the sole rights to the company at an official company auction on 21st November that year. The Wilderness Works, named after the adjacent woodlands and mill, had by this time 8 round kilns for burning red goods and 7 square kilns for blue goods.

During the 1912 coal miners' strike, and in consequence of the poverty resulting from it, Mr Clark allowed scavengers onto his brickworks land. "Quite a large number of pickers have unearthed a rich harvest of coal from a spoil tip at the Wilderness Brickyard" commented the local press.

Not everybody, however, was welcomed onto the property:

Wrexham Advertiser 10th May, 1913 – Five boys were charged by Thomas Price, watchman at the Wilderness Brickworks, with having stolen 39 lbs of nails worth about two shillings. Complainant said he was in company with police constable Owen watching near the clayhole at the works in consequence of much damage which had been done on Sundays. He saw the boys come down the claybank and going into a shed, they took away a bag of nails. Youths were in the habit of going into the claypit. They also let wagons run down the incline and they were smashed at the bottom. There were some wagons in the water which could not be removed. Mr Challenor on behalf of Mr Clark said there was no desire to press the case – it was no use keeping a watchman because the lads stoned him when he interfered. The Chairman said "Then there is a case of terrorism there". Each of the defendants were fined ten shillings.

The northern reaches of Wrexham town were quite a distance from the works in 1913, and in truth the Wilderness was well named – it being fairly isolated in those days. This made it a haven for tramps and "playful" youngsters, and we can get a shrewd idea of just how many trespassers visited the site when we learn that by August 1914 the works was being quoted as losing a massive 5 – 6 tons of coal per week to pilfering.

Despite its early successes the final years proved to be financially disastrous, and the reasons for its closure by 1924 are perfectly outlined in the following report made by Mr E Lloyd Jones, the mineral agent to the landlord Sir Watkin Wynne, in the same year:

"The lease has three years to run, but Mr Stuart Clark has given a years' notice. This brickworks never paid its way and the Clark family who stuck to it and carried it on for years lost a considerable amount of money in it. The prime reasons for the failure of the works were the great thickness of the fey, or over – burden, and the recurring layers of grey rocky marl in the beds of red marl, making it costly to manipulate and difficult to turn to size, shape and colour. The war practically brought these works to a stop in 1915, and soon after they were taken over by the Government for the storage of dangerous explosives. This was one of the last stores held by the Government and was only handed back to the lessees about two years ago. The works are not likely to be used again as a brickworks and the supply of profitable clay has been exhausted. Brickworks shed and chimney – there is a large quantity of good timber and bricks in these".

In June 1924 the council were considering whether the old factory might be adopted as a store yard for road materials and the claypit used as a refuse tip. By July 1926 the factory was being dismantled, and the timber and bricks, as Mr Jones suggested, was sold off. Exactly a year later Mr Clark sold the works to his Llay Hall Company for a paltry £1,000.

The factory stood at OS 3344 5339 and has been completely eradicated by later excavations and land reclamation.

SITE 79: GEORGE DUNFORD – GRESFORD BRICKWORKS

The first recorded brickfield in Gresford was shown on the 1843 tithe map at OS 3540 5425, just to the west of Carthagena Farm. It was probably defunct at that date, as the land was put down to arable usage, and it certainly didn't appear on any subsequent mappings.

The first evidence for our site 78 appeared in the Advertiser of May 1861:

"To be let. A brickyard situate about one half mile from the Plough, Gresford. Every requisite for carrying on the business ready on the premises".

Site 78 is indeed half a mile from the Plough, and the same ad reappeared in March 1862. George Dunford was by far the longest established brickmaker in Gresford, and my belief that he worked from here is based only on the correlation of two facts, namely that he was recorded as being an established Gresford brickmaker throughout the 1870s and 80s, and that the OS map of 1871 showed our site 78 as the only brickfield in the area at that time. The brickfield is still there at OS 3562 5410; or at least the remnants of it; the banks of a large and obviously well worked clayhole excavation being clearly discernible. The clayhole is just off Vicarage Lane and opposite Gatehouse Farm, or Haddocks Farm as it was in Victorian days. The farming family who live there says that the farm was reputed to have once had a brickworks in the yard, which received its clay supply from the clayhole opposite as well as from small pits at the back of the property, and there are indeed some ruins in the yard which look like they may once have had some industrial usage.

The census records tell us that George Dunford was originally from Somerset and was brickmaking in Gresford certainly from 1871 – 81. He also lived in Vicarage Lane with his local born wife Emma, conveniently close to the brickyard, and we have advertisements from the Wrexham Advertiser of 18th November, 1876 and 26th June, 1880, which show that "George Dunford's Gresford Brickworks" manufactured common as well as pressed bricks.

We don't know when operations ceased here, but they certainly had done by the turn of the century.

Coedpoeth Area

SITE 80: VRON COLLIERY & BRICKWORKS

There were three principal brickmaking sites in the Coedpoeth district; the town itself having quite an old and established industrial history. The name Coedpoeth itself refers to an area of densely covered woodland, and throughout the 18th century most of the trees were felled and converted into charcoal to be used in the iron and lead smelting works at Bersham and Minera. In fact, the more ancient name for the district used to be Burntwood – a literal description of the activities which went on there.

The site of Vron Colliery sits atop one of the hills to the north of the village of Coedpoeth, and the colliery historian George Lerry records that it was sunk circa 1806 by a local man. At some point circa 1850 it became the property of Mortimer Maurice and the Scotsman William Low, who did much to open out the works in subsequent years. Evidence that the company made bricks is contained in records of royalty payments from 1860 – 62, wherefrom we learn that they sold many thousands to land sale customers (off site sales).

It was in 1873 that the Vron Colliery took the step of concentrating its brick production at a new factory to the west of the colliery, and the diary of Joseph Hall, one of the colliery's engineers, gives an insight into the proceedings. Note that mention is made of Chadwick, an iron foundry company in Wrexham, and of Johnson's, the Chester engineering firm; both companies now long consigned to the annals of history. The machinery for the new works was purchased from Pattinson's Brickworks, a small works just down the hill from the Vron.

18th March, 1873 – Journey to Pattinson's Brickworks to take dimensions of Engine and Clay Grinding Machine to be fixed at Vron Colliery.

1st April – Jas. Hale commenced taking engines to pieces at Pattinson's Brickworks.

30th April – Journey to Wrexham. Patterns for brass glands for Brick Engine. Chadwick.

19th May – Journey to Wrexham. Two brass stops for Brick Machinery from Chadwick.

29th May – Journey to Johnson's, Chester. Winding barrel make complete with brake and lever and clutch box and lever for Machinery at Brickworks.

9th June – Trial of Claymill to grind mortar.

16th June – Commence grinding clay to make bricks in the new Brickworks. Water Co's water laid on.

12th July – Journey to Chester taking clutchbox to be altered. It belongs to winding barrel of Claymill.

21st July – Journey to Chester to fetch clutchbox for Brickworks from Johnson Co.

21st August – Journey to Wrexham. Patten of firebars for Brickmaker's sheds.

By January 1874 the new works was in production and the Vron Colliery Company Ltd were advertising "bricks of first quality. 3s. 4d. per hundred".

In March 1882 Messrs Maurice & Low were in liquidation, and two years later Mr W F Butler was heading a new company to acquire the concern. From this time onwards it appears that the running of the brickworks was managed as a totally separate concern from the colliery, as the accident register of 1901 lists the Vron Brick Co as a separate firm from the Vron Colliery Co. Mr Butler still had managing control over the brick company, but he was not an experienced brickmaker himself, so in 1889 he invited Charles Mason, previously the manager of Garth Brickworks at Trevor, to take on the running of the brickworks, and for the next two years Mason became its unofficial manager. In early 1891 Butler suggested that the works might be enlarged, and a new partner, Mr Thomas Alexander, was recruited to provide the capital needed to fund the extensions, although Alexander had virtually nothing to do with the practical side of the business. Mason was then officially appointed the works managing director, but Mr Butler simply wouldn't allow him free rein to do his job efficiently. Mason had been successfully working one side of the clay bed, but Butler insisted that he should get his clay from the opposite side, despite Mason's warnings that the clay in that sector was contaminated by lime. Unfortunately Butler had to have his way, and 300,000 bricks were subsequently made and thrown away as unusable. More bad moves were forced upon Mason, until in December 1894 he was given notice to quit. Butler said that the works was to close, but later appointed a new manager in Mason's stead. Mr Butler must have been an incredibly stupid man – not only had he compromised the works' efficiency, but he had consequently broken the terms of Mason's contract of employment and the case was taken to court. The evidence in Mason's favour was overwhelming and he won the case for compensation to the tune of £50 plus his court costs.

By 1903 the Vron Colliery also controlled the Talwrn Colliery, a smaller works lower down the hill at OS 2875 5152. By the end of that year there was serious concern as to whether the coal seams were becoming exhausted, and together with the company having had their operations hindered by incursions of water, this led to the closure of the two collieries and the unemployment of 500 workers.

A fresh input of capital was required to overcome these difficulties and it arrived in early 1904 when the Broughton & Plas Power Co bought the properties, including the brickworks. "They will at once proceed to open the Vron Colliery" reported the Chronicle in July. There seems to be a little confusion as to whether the colliery actually reopened or not, or whether it might have been the Talwrn site which was worked, but there is no doubt that operations at the Vron itself were resumed by March 1907. As to the brickworks, the evidence is strongly in favour of it having continued its operations throughout the periods of difficulty which the colliery had been experiencing.

By December 1905 the brickworks was advertising for tenders to drive a metal lined drift mine into their property – 200 yards long, 6ft. high, 7ft. wide and dipping at a gradient of 1 in 3. There is a record of a collier having claimed injury compensation from the Vron Brick Co in 1908, and it's fair to assume that the Brick Company might well have been operating some sort of mine at this period, although exactly where is not recorded.

The Broughton & Plas Power Co retained ownership of the brickworks until its demise, although by 1911 the brickworks was operating under the style of the Vron Brick & Coal Co; a name which either suggests that the works was mining its own coal supply, or that it had once again been linked with the main colliery. The 1899 25 inch OS map shows the brickworks with an engine house, grinding mill, five kilns and four chimney stacks, but no pits of any description, although the factory was linked to the adjacent colliery by a number of rail lines.

On 16th December, 1911 the plant and machinery of the Vron Brick & Coal Co was to be sold under a distress for rent. The company must have been in a dire situation – everything from the winding engines to the office furniture and even the lamps were up for auction. Interest in the sale was not forthcoming, so the County Court ordered it to be rescheduled for 9th January, 1912, and I think we may assume that this heralded the end of brickmaking at the Vron. During the Great War the brickworks was requisitioned by the Ministry as a factory for the production of slag phosphate as agricultural fertiliser, and I could find no further evidence for its continuance after that time.

The brickworks was centred at OS 2904 5220 and is now nothing but green fields. As to the colliery, the Broughton & Plas Power Co gave the men notice to quit in December 1930, and the last Vron coals were brought up in January 1931, leaving the site to be used as a pumping station for the Plas Power Colliery's extended workings. The site was however temporarily worked as an opencast mine during the Second World War from the end of 1943 to mid-1946.

SITE 81: PATTINSON'S COEDPOETH BRICKWORKS

Our first evidence for this small works is an advertisement from September 1866, the wording of which is suggestive of the works either having been recently established or perhaps taken over by new proprietors:

"Coedpoeth Brick & Tile Works. Proprietors G C & W Pattinson. Parties building can now be

supplied with common and pressed bricks, flooring tiles and paving bricks. Any size or pattern to order. Also draining pipes for agricultural use".

The two brothers George Clark and William Pattinson had some time previously been the proprietors of the Pentre Saeson Colliery & Brickworks; a concern which they apparently left in April 1864. George Clark Pattinson was living in Coedpoeth and seemed to be the one who actively ran the brickworks.

For some reason, it was put up for auction on the 8th March, 1869, and later for sale by private treaty; the reason for the sale not being explained, but the Pattinson brothers retained ownership of it thereafter. The sale advertisement perfectly delineates the layout of a small but well appointed country brickyard of that period:

"3 brick kilns to burn 30, 20 and 10,000 bricks respectively. Brick making shed flued throughout 30 yards by 10 yards. Cast iron clay mill with pan and rollers 9ft. diameter worked by a 10 h.p. horizontal steam engine. Draining pipe machine with table and full set of dies. Patent brick press and a number of brickmaking tables, moulds, barrows and planks together with every other requisite for carrying on an extensive trade. The beds of clay are of the thickness from 6 – 10 yards. The area of the brickworks is 8922 square yards and the area of the brickworks and land is 11,253 square yards".

By September 1877 it seems that the Pattinson brothers were having their doubts about the future viability of the works. It looks like William had arrived to view the operations at Coedpoeth, and the meeting of the two brothers spurred the works foreman to write a warning note to the landlord's agent Mr Walter Eddy. It read:

"Mr Pattinson has been over inspecting the brickworks and is going to write to you tonight on the subject. I greatly fear it will not meet their expectations by what I could hear between his brother and him, but they did not explain it to me. Only ask if there was any good marl clay".

What happened to the works is not recorded, but it had disappeared by the beginning of the Great War. It stood at OS 2863 5137, and is now replaced by housing.

SITE 82: COEDPOETH BRICKYARD

Wrexham Advertiser: Lot 1. All that land containing 4783 square yards now used as a brick and tile work, together with the kiln, ovens, sheds, carpenter's shop, offices and other buildings thereon, situate in Coedpoeth, adjoining and having a frontage to the turnpike road leading from Wrexham to Ruthin of 81 yards, and late in the holding of Mr Thomas Williams, mine proprietor. There is excellent firebrick clay in this land and every convenience for the manufacture thereof, and being in the midst of a large and thriving population a good market could be obtained.

That sale was originally scheduled for 14th August, 1865, but didn't go ahead. Lot 2 in the sale catalogue was the premises of the Royal Oak "situate adjoining lot 1", and here is where we come across a problem with the positioning of the brickyard. The frontage of all the buildings adjoining the public house measures 63 yards, but together with the total width of the Royal Oak the length comes to virtually exactly 81 yards. Could the text of the sale advertisement have been misworded?

If lots 1 and 2 were together supposed to have been 81 yards, that would therefore place the works as having been where the Cross Foxes public house and adjoining buildings now stand, centred at OS 2835 5115. Other descriptions from a later sale of the same site in 1867 corroborate these assumptions.

The sites were eventually split up and sold as six separate parcels on 25th March, 1867, together with the bricks of the kilns, drying sheds and chimney stacks, which were sold off as building materials. Whether the brickworks ended its productive life in 1865 or 1867 is not recorded, as neither is the year of its establishment, although the tithe map of the early 1840s shows no brickworks here.

In trying to imagine a brickworks at this spot, in

what is now a town centre, it is worth remembering one simple fact. In the 1860s the village of Coedpoeth would have been in its infancy. In fact, a place called Adwy 'rclawdd, which is just down the hill, was once the more important of the two villages. As an elderly local remembered in 1896: "Adwy'r clawdd was a village when Coedpoeth was little more than a mountain road".

Site 78

Site 78

Site 81

Site 88

Wrexham Area

SITE 83: STANSTY BRICKYARD

The Stansty – Rhosrobin district of northern Wrexham was home to a nice cross section of Victorian industry on the small scale: collieries, brickyards and the Stansty Ironworks, which was built alongside a brickyard which had been in operation for many years previously. The 1843 tithe shows this yard as Brick Kiln Field – a working "brick bank" in the holding of William Edwards. By 1859 the little works was being operated by David Hughes, and the 1861 census shows us that Gwersyllt born David lived and worked there with his sons Thomas, 24, and John, 15. Also working here at the "Rhosrobin Brickyard" (as the census described it) were labourers Charles Laurence and his brickmaking family. A hand written account of David's brickmaking at the "Rhostansty Brickyard" (another name variation) shows us how modest his operations were: in 1862 he produced 30,000 bricks, in 1863 29,000 and in 1864 25,000. It seems evident that his business was gradually falling off; a fact which led to the appearance of the following:

Wrexham Advertiser 18th June, 1864 – To be sold by auction on 5th July. All that field or parcel of land containing 6a. 1r. 10p. part of which is now used as a Brick Work, and the other part in cultivation situate at Rhos Stansty, now in the holding of Mr David Hughes, brickmaker. The whole of the property is adjacent to the new colliery and forge at Stansty. It would be a good investment for a small capitalist.

I can only imagine that the brickyard might have been later reworked by the new forge company, as the census of 1871 lists David Hughes as living at Stansty Forge as a brickmaker. Whether the brickyard stayed open or not is debatable. The 1881 census lists no brickyard here at all, and no brickmakers living at the Stansty Forge Cottages. This of course does not prove that the yard was totally abandoned – it may have been worked when the occasion arose that bricks were needed, but it was certainly in production at the end of the 19th century, as the Wrexham Advertiser of 28th August, 1897 records that "a man named Edward Davies was brought into the Infirmary with a broken leg received at the brickworks near Stansty Old Forge".

If the brickworks indeed became the property of the Iron Co we should take a little look at the latter's history:

Wrexham Advertiser 21st January, 1865 – On Wednesday last the opening of Stansty Iron Works which are situated close to the old brickworks adjoining the hamlet of Rhosrobin. These works consist of a mill and forge.

The forge was owned by Thomas Watkins and his partner Mr Jones under the style of the Stansty Iron Co, producing chiefly small iron castings and wire rods. By July 1866 however, the company had come to grief with debts of over £10,000; the failure being attributed to "heavy expenses, badness of trade and smallness of capital". James Sparrow of the Ffrwd Iron Works was appointed the trade assignee and it was his duty to oversee the winding-up of the company which culminated in its auction sale on 6th and 7th February, 1867, and in the sale inventory there was mention of a "fire clay house". This may even have been part of the old brickworks site .

The ironworks fell into the hands of Mr Samuel Forrest, who ran it until another bankruptcy in 1876, at which point its contents were again sold off on 20th October, part of the stock being "firebricks and clay". By October the following year the works was still unoccupied and being offered for let. It seems to have been resurrected and was still operational until certainly early 1889, but I could find no authoritative verification of its fate after that time.

The brickyard stood at OS 3264 5244, now a patch of waste ground at the back of the Rhosddu Industrial Estate, with the ironworks having been alongside it to the north.

Another Brick Kiln Field stood not far away at roughly OS 3270 5275 – shown on the 1843 tithe map as an old pasture field, and it was probably an earlier brickmaking site of even greater antiquity.

SITE 84: GEORGE MERCER'S COLLIERY BRICKYARD

What must have been a tiny and short lived works is shown on the 1861 Whitchurch, Wrexham, Mold & Connah's Quay Rly proposal map. Set amongst the farmland of the Mercer family a small "Colliery and Marl Pit" owned by Edward Jones and run by himself and George Mercer stood alongside a "Brick Kiln, Shed and Yard" in the holding of Mercer at OS 3288 5207. None of these workings appear on the 1871 OS, as they were eradicated by the construction of the Wrexham to Chester railway.

SITE 85: WREXHAM COLLIERY

I should mention the nearby Wrexham Colliery, which stood at OS 3286 5224 and part of whose buildings still remain in the present occupation of a pallet supply company. There is no firm evidence that a commercial brickworks ever existed here, but during the works' establishment the small colliery with a "clay works" was shown on a map of the Ruabon Coalfield for 1865. It is very likely that this works was set up to make the bricks needed for the initial building project, and in July 1860 Wrexham Colliery were advertising the sale of nearly 200,000 bricks – probably the remainder of a batch of bricks they had made and not used.

Chester Chronicle 15th October, 1870 – The Wrexham Colliery Co after labouring for about five years in sinking their pits in which they have had to overcome immense difficulties, reached a valuable seam of Main Coal this week. A large number of labourer's cottages will quickly be erected to accommodate the many hundreds of men who will soon be employed.

A company property and assets list for 1872 does list a brick plant on site, but from the time the company renamed itself the Wrexham & Acton Colliery Co circa 1873 no further mention of such was made, and no brick plant appears on the OS maps. The colliery was also known as Rhossdu Colliery, and was closed in 1924.

SITE 86: THOMAS MERCER'S BRICKYARD

"We find at the present day in very small yards in remote places bricks still being made differing only in detail from the methods of the Egyptian period".

Those words quoted by a Victorian brickmaker might well apply to the methods practised here as in many other small country yards, for this whole district was in the 1860s a very quiet, rural location accessed only by narrow lanes, and it was here that Thomas Mercer held a small brickworks close to the tiny colliery run by his son George at site 84. A railway proposal map of 1862 shows Thomas's "Brickworks and Claypits" situated on land owned by Edward Jones at OS 3285 5196. As Thomas Mercer was the farmer of the surrounding lands we can assume this yard to have been an agricultural brickyard. The site is today occupied by housing.

SITE 87: RHOSDDU BRICKWORKS

This site was run by the George Mercer of site 84, listed in the 1861 census as a 31 year old Master Brickmaker. His younger brother William was a journeyman brickmaker, and together they lived at their father's farm. After George had his dealings with the colliery and brickworks at site 84 he set up Rhosddu Brickworks half a mile to the S. E. His advertisement dated 28th May, 1868 reads: "Bricks, bricks, bricks. George Mercer of Stansty begs to inform builders and others that he has commenced to manufacture press and all kinds of bricks for sale in a new yard near the Walnut Tree Tavern, Rhosddu".

The works is shown on the OS map of 1872, by which time it may have been defunct or temporarily closed:

Wrexham Advertiser 9th September, 1871 – To be sold by auction upon the Premises at Rhosddu Brickworks on 13th September, about 2 acres of capital growing swedes and turnips, half an acre of potatoes, a kiln of about 28,000 unburnt bricks, large drying shed, cast iron pump, iron brick press, tables, brick moulds, planks, barrows, picks, spades and other tools. Capital cart, saddle, office desk and sundries, the property of Mr George Mercer under a distress for rent.

The works stood at OS 3344 5149, which is now occupied by garden allotments.

SITE 88: E M JONES RUABON ROAD BRICKWORKS

This site was next to the turnpike gate into Wrexham from the Ruabon Road and existed at a time when the area was little more than open countryside south of the gate, and for many years it was Wrexham town's principal brickworks. The foremost occupant of this brickworks was Edward Meredith Jones, who took the site on lease from the landowning Meredith family of Pentrebychan Hall, whose royalty accounts show that Jones began his first production run in March 1863. However, I believe that E M Jones had a predecessor on the site, and the evidence for such an assumption is contained in the rates books for the Wrexham district, which show that in 1859 an Edward Williams held a brickworks on 1a. 2r. 16p. of land owned by Mr Meredith of Pentrebychan. We also know from surviving documents that Mr Meredith gave a lease of land for a brickyard to the said Edward Williams from 10th May 1855 at a yearly rent of £5 with the stipulation that he make no fewer than 300,000 bricks per year, and this yard is described in the document as being "near to the turnpike gate at Wrexham"; the gate being at OS 3298 4962 adjacent to our site 88.

From 1863 (the year in which E M Jones began brickmaking here) the list of entries in the rates books show the same brickworks had passed from Edward Williams' possession to that of E M Jones.

By September 1863 the Advertiser ran the following ad: "Draining Pipes at E M Jones Timber Yard, Wrexham". Edward Meredith Jones was born in the town on 5th May 1825, and circa 1850 he took over the timber, slate and lime merchants at 12 Charles Street, which had been established since circa 1762, and with the acquisition of his new brickworks he could now supply bricks and terracotta goods from the same outlet. The practical running of the brickworks was in time entrusted to Daniel Collins, a Dudley man who had come to Wrexham around 1868 and continued managing the works until January 1879 when, aged only 38, he fell from a horse drawn vehicle and met his untimely death.

By 1882 the clay land leased to the works was becoming exhausted and Jones approached Pentrebychan Estate for a new lease on adjoining lands. The land agent visited the works and met Jones and his foreman Mr Joseph Collins, and in a letter to his master Col. Meredith he reported on the obvious embarrassment which Mr Jones felt about his works: "Mr Jones and his foreman were with us when we made our inspection and expressed a hope that no objection would be raised on account of the smoke from the kilns and chimney stack or the general unsightliness of the works". The foreman Joseph Collins, later to become the new manager, was not, as we might expect, Daniel Collins' son, as Daniel had been unmarried in the census of 1871, but it does seem likely that he may have been the Joseph Collins who would later take on the Marchwiel Brickyard. Jones was keen to win approval for his request for expansion and followed up with a letter of his own, saying "Of course this will not make any difference in the situation of any buildings. They will remain where they are and the clay will be drawn to the mill by the donkey tramway as at present. I am trying to supply the Lager Beer building, but if I get the contract I shall be in a fix if the clay is stopped". The new take of land was subsequently granted and royalty on the bricks was reduced from 2s. 6d. to 2s. per thousand on account of the poorer quality of the new clay land. It has to be said that what documentation still survives does suggest that most of the clay available to the works seemed to have been of a particularly poor quality, and what bricks I have found made by this works certainly bears this out.

This works was a typical middle-sized brickworks of the period; as witnessed by the number of people working there:

Wrexham Advertiser 24th January, 1885 – The annual supper of the employees at Mr E M Jones' brickyard was held on Saturday evening at the Oak Tree Tavern. The chair was taken by Mr J Collins, the manager. About thirty persons sat down to an excellent spread, greatly enjoyed by all present.

Being on the outskirts of the town, the brickworks had always proved popular with tramps; the manager Mr Collins having said that people were constantly in the habit of sleeping in the yard – a fact which is also borne out by the numerous reports of trespass and damage reported in the local press over the lifetime of the works.

By late 1884 the clay land was yielding supplies whose quality proved to be disappointingly irregular and Mr Jones' solicitor wrote to the landlords, saying "It is evidently necessary that some further extension must be granted unless the brickyard is to be permanently closed within a short period". We must assume that the land applied for further to the south was granted, as the works continued for a good few years after. Despite the poor quality of the clay this modest works maintained a reasonable output, and by 1887 the total for that year's make of bricks had reached 1,222,530. By February 1894 the land agent had brokered a deal to allow Jones to sub-let any of his take which was not being used commercially, and this arrangement probably served as some form of compensation for the clayland being so weak. To this end Jones let portions of his land for agricultural usage and on 12th October, 1895 the following advertisement appeared in the press: "Stack of last year's hay, about 14 tons for sale in Brickyard field, Ruabon Road, Wrexham. Apply Parry, Golden Lion, Llangollen". This arrangement allowed Jones to recoup some of the rent money paid on land which would otherwise have lain fallow and unproductive.

E M Jones finally relinquished the site in 1895 and concentrated on his timber business until his retirement in May 1904. He died from pneumonia on 9th November, 1910. The brickworks lease officially changed hands from 29th September, 1895 and the works became the property of Whitehouse & Co, who ran it under that style until July 1903, when they formed Wrexham Brick & Tile Co in order to bring the works under the same company control as their other brick factory at Kings Mills, which had also previously been established by E M Jones. In July 1905 the Ruabon Road Brickworks was put on the market; the Chronicle stating that it would be sold to an immediate purchaser for just £600 – a clear indication that it was proving a financial liability. It is at this time at the end of its life that we get a description of its physical appearance. The works consisted of *"one large engine, one Lancashire boiler 22 ft long, wire cut brick machine, pipe machine, winding gear, horizontal pug, wagons, rails, blacksmiths shop, stores, office, stabling for 3 horses, foreman's cottage with land and gardens, 4 large arched kilns, 3 large drying sheds and one very large chimney stack. The works stand on 15 acres".*

The factory site has been replaced by housing at OS 3293 4949, whilst the southerly clay land is a large reclaimed field. During the 1890s Wrexham Town Council began filling the disused parts of the clayhole with ashes whilst the works was still functional.

SITE 88 A: EDWARD BRAMLEY'S RUABON ROAD BRICKWORKS

The location for this works is not fully known. A respected local historian active in the 1960s and 70s believed Edward Bramley's works to have been the predecessor to Mr E M Jones at site 88, and this may in a sense have been true. It looks likely that Bramley's operations were themselves preceded by those of a Michael Gummow. In February 1852 Gummow leased land "now used as a brickyard " at Felin Puleston from Henry Meredith. The agreement also stipulated that he should allow a hut and stock of tiles on the brickyard to remain until their owner Mr John Busy could have them removed, so we may assume that Mr Busy was the original occupier of Gummow's take. Gummow himself was a builder, obviously looking to make his own bricks, and was also a well known surveyor and property speculator in the town, eventually rising to become Wrexham's Borough Surveyor.

Our next evidence is contained in the rates lists. Michael Gummow is shown to have had a brickyard of 1a. 2r. 16p. area in the year 1859; this entry later being replaced by the following: 1863 – Edward

Bramley, 1864 – Ann Bramley, 1868 – Caroline Bramley, 1869/70 – Bramley & Jones, and no listings thereafter.

The tantalising problem is this: Why does Bramley's works and E M Jones' works have precisely the same area designated to them? It also seems tempting to believe that the 1869 partnership might have been with E M Jones. Perhaps the two men originally worked the same site independently, using separate kilns, but warranting separate rates listings because they were two autonomous companies.

Wrexham Advertiser – Magistrates Court, 7th March, 1864 – John Jones, William Butler and Ann Butler were in custody having been apprehended by Insp. Lamb and charged with sleeping on a brick kiln on the Ruabon Road. Charles Bramley gave evidence as to the amount of damage done and the prisoners were discharged with a caution.

Another glaring problem faces us. The trade directories from 1868 – 89 advertised Edward Bramley as a brickmaker at Ruabon Road, yet none of the correspondence between E M Jones' brickworks and the Pentrebychan Estate gives any mention of Mr Bramley whatsoever.

As to the question where Edward Bramley actually did have his brickworks, it seems to be just one great mystery.

SITE 89: WILLIAM ROWE'S BRICKYARD

This site is not shown on the tithe map of the early 1840s but is mentioned in a document of 3rd March 1846 wherein Wiliam Roberts, a Wrexham brickmaker, leased from Henry Meredith

"all that piece of clay land now in the occupation of Mr William Rowe in the township of Wrexham Abbot. The said William Rowe to have liberty to use the clay in the said clay field for the purpose of making bricks and draining tiles, to erect kilns and drying sheds thereon and to use so much sand as shall be sufficient for making bricks and tiles".

Wiliam Rowe was to make no less than 50,000 bricks and the same number of tiles each year and I can only imagine that he would have been making them for the new leaseholder Mr Roberts. As to its position, it most probably was the same "Brickyard and Office" shown on the later W. M. & C. Q. Rly map of 1862 in the occupation of John Rowe at OS 3218 4959. We can also refer to a tantalising piece of evidence from the Advertiser of 20th April, 1867, wherein a Samuel Edwards mentions getting bricks from Rowe's Yard which was a mile away from Rhostyllen, a distance which more or less tallies with the OS reference. The site however is not shown on the large scale OS map of 1874.

SITE 90: JOHN ROBERTS BRICKFIELD

This minute works was shown on the tithe map at OS 3240 4956 as a "Brickfield" in the occupation of John Roberts, and had disappeared before or during the construction of the line of the Ruabon to Wrexham railway in 1860.

SITE 91: WREXHAM BRICK & TILE CO

On the south eastern periphery of Wrexham were the two largest of the town's brickworks, situated on either side of the road near Kings Mills, and of all the Wrexham area brickworks these two had the fortune of being situated on a bed of superior marl clay which was an extension of the Ruabon marl beds to the south.

Site 91 was the earlier of the two works and was established by Mr E M Jones, who already had the Ruabon Road Works at site 88. During his ownership it bore the name Kings Mills Brickworks.

Wrexham Advertiser 16th September, 1893 – The Kings Mills Brickworks belong to Mr E M Jones who established them about seven years ago. All machinery here are driven by steam power. The tramway from the clay pits is worked with an endless chain, conveying the clay to the platform to pass through the process. There are two sheds capable of receiving 25,000 bricks, and three kilns, two circular and one rectangular, and will together burn 70,000 bricks.

In actual fact, the company's letterheads and advertisements both place the year of its establishment as 1884. In September 1895 Jones gave up his brickmaking and sold the Kings Mills works to Messrs Phillips & Whitehouse; a sale which was no doubt easily accomplished with the imminent opening of the adjacent Wrexham & Ellesmere Railway being only two months away, affording the opportunity to vastly increase the works' output. The new proprietors eventually renamed their acquisition the Wrexham Brick & Tile Co.

Wrexham Advertiser 10th June 1899 – Tom Birke, aged 22, has been admitted to the Wrexham Infirmary suffering from severe burns which he received whilst working at the Wrexham Brick and Tile works at Kings Mills. He was seized with a fainting fit when close to the kiln, and while in this condition he was very badly scorched, the face, left arm and left portion of the body being the more severely affected. In several places the skin was completely burnt off. On Monday night he was in a state of collapse, but on Thursday he had considerably improved.

In mid-1903 the company was floated in order to raise the capital needed to improve the plant, and at a committee meeting on 23rd October the chairman Mr W B Phillips happily reported that the latest reconstructions at the works had effected a 50 per cent increase on the previous year's productivity. These successes however, were not to last. In November 1907 the company was in serious debt and their main supplier of fuel, Wynnstay Collieries, petitioned for the brickworks' winding up. It was at this time that the works could have disappeared forever but for the intervention of the judge at the bankruptcy hearing, who argued that if the company were wound up their landlords might seize all their assets, leaving everybody out of pocket. By September 1909 the works had been successfully sold to a new syndicate of owners headed by Mr T B Taylor of Wrexham and production began anew, and in December 1909 the Wrexham Brick & Tile Co Ltd became somewhat of a ground breaker when a large advertisement with accompanying illustration of the factory appeared in the Wrexham press – the first such newspaper ad to be produced on such a scale by any of the North Wales brickworks.

In November 1925 the owners' partnership came to an end, and with its dissolution the works was put on the market, but the highest bid of £5,750 fell far short of the value of the factory; the plant and machinery alone having been worth £15,000. Mr Taylor retained ownership of the site until his death in 1930, at which point his executors sold it at auction on 12th June to W & G. R. Oates, the proprietors of the Standard Works at Buckley. The Oates family kept the works until March 1949 when it was closed with the loss of 36 jobs, but not for long. On the opposite side of the road the Abenbury Brickworks had already become the property of Thomas Marshall & Co, and it was they who resurrected the Kings Mills Works shortly after its closure, and from this point onwards the history of the site can be followed in the next chapter.

E M Jones' Kings Mills Works stood at OS 3486 4930 with a clayhole to the east, but a new tunnel kiln plant was later added by Thomas Marshalls at OS 3505 4928.

SITE 92: ABENBURY BRICKWORKS

The close neighbour of site 91, and its later sister works, was the Abenbury Brickworks, which was established as a direct consequence of the construction of the Wrexham and Ellesmere Railway. Because of Victorian society's obsession with railways we find we have a rather unique cataloguing of the brickworks' early growth.

The ceremonial cutting of the first sod of ground for the new line took place on the 11th June, 1892, but the serious work had to wait until the harvests were gathered: "We understand that it is the intention to start the work as soon as the crops are off the ground". The civil engineering company contracted to build the railway was Davies Brothers, run by Llewelyn and Howel Davies, who had inherited the firm which their father had founded in 1835, and they established their main works yard for the railway project on the spot where the new brickworks would later come to be.

Wrexham Advertiser 30th July, 1892 – The work of constructing the new railway is progressing. In the field across the King's Mills turnpike road, works of rather great importance are being made, as here the contractors have erected brick machinery which will convert the marl they are digging out of the viaduct cutting into bricks which they propose using.

The month after that report had appeared the Railway Co actually published a list of the Davies Brothers employees who were labouring on the project, and we find their brickmakers amongst them:

450 navvies – 50 masons – 25 labourers – 20 carpenters – 12 blacksmiths – 20 crane and loco drivers – 35 horses and drivers – 8 watchmen – 3 timekeepers – 20 fencers – 30 brickmakers and quarrymen.

26th November, 1892 – In the field which the contractors have bought there is to be a brick and terracotta works which will be capable of turning out 100,000 bricks per week.

By January 1893 the brickworks was up and running, and the same month also saw the works' first fatality when Isaac Jones, a clay getter, was crushed by a fall of clay from the quarry face. By 1895 the construction of the railway was completed, and on 2nd November the grand official opening was celebrated. The following report is an amalgam of an article which appeared on that same date and an earlier article from 16th September, 1893:

"The land which has been developed by this enterprising firm was purchased in September 1892 and works known as the Abenbury Brickworks or Red Marl Industry were erected for the manufacture of the red and blue bricks required for the stations and some of the bridges on the line. We had the pleasure through the courtesy of Mr Ames, manager, of inspecting the premises and seeing the new and substantial machinery in motion. The driving power of all machinery is given by a double cylinder horizontal engine, all fixed on a concrete base 10 ft-high. The machinery consists of what is usually known as the mixing machine, and also an endless rope – haulage tramway. By this tram the clay and sand for mixing are conveyed from the clay pit to the mill. The sheds which are substantially built cover an area of 8500 square foot, and at the western ends of the sheds are the kilns, 6 in number. These kilns are known as the Improved Newcastle kilns with arrangements for carrying hot air from one to the other, and each kiln takes about four days to burn. The goods manufactured are pressed and wire cut facing bricks, blue bricks, copings, chequered tiles, ridge tiles and finials, floor tiles, wall copings, chimney pots and vases. Now as to the clay. This is equal in quality to the best beds of the Ruabon red and blue marl, and although the depth is not yet proved the face of the clay at present being worked is 40 ft. thick. The marl has proved on analysis to be equal to any in North Wales, and the quantity sufficient for many generations yet to come. A quarry is on the south side of the line known as the Abenbury Quarry, a remarkably fine bed of Lower Permian Sandstone".

The nearby railway viaduct over the River Clywedog is built from this sandstone. The railway to Ellesmere finally closed in September 1962, although a supply line from Wrexham to the brickworks was left intact.

The early years of the 20th century saw a craze for walking races, with many of the local firms having organised their own events:

Wrexham Advertiser 11th July, 1903 – A keenly contested walking match took place on Saturday between the employees of Messrs Davies Brothers. The route chosen was a circular one starting from Abenbury through Wrexham to Holt, then on through Rossett, a distance of about 17 miles. There were about 24 starters and 21 finished the distance. The ages ranged from 18 to 53 and six prizes were offered. The walk was done in excellent time, the average rate being five-and-a-half mph.

In March 1909 notice of the bankruptcy of Davies Brothers was published. Despite the company having made great achievements in the field of civil engineering, including a contract worth £110,000 for the construction of sections of the Vyrnwy Reservoir, the Wrexham and Ellesmere Railway contract had lost them £14,000. As the brothers said: "The cause of our stopping was the heavy loss incurred in carrying out the railway, which depleted our trading capital, followed by the slump in the building trade which caused a falling off at our quarry and brickworks". With £13,000 still outstanding on the brickworks mortgage the company's trustees attempted to sell off the works, but bids fell pathetically short of its worth. The remaining stocks and loose machinery were disposed of at auction and the works closed down, eventually falling into the hands of the mortgagee Lloyds Bank. For three years the works lay idle, suffering badly at the hands of vandals, to the great annoyance of the Bank.

By early September 1912 a syndicate of businessmen had purchased the works and set about its revival, and its subsequent history becomes somewhat vague. We do know that the works was requisitioned as a dynamite stores during the Great War, and that by 1921 its owners were the Oughtbridge Silica Co of Sheffield, who held it until it was again used as an army stores during the Second War. Once the government had relinquished its control of the site it was bought by the Thomas Marshall Co circa February 1947, and the works were converted to the production of refractory blocks for the steel industry. Marshalls supplied the works with fireclay from their Ffrith mine at site 71. Two years later Marshalls also acquired the adjacent Kings Mills Brickworks and for the next twenty years these two works enjoyed lavish financial investment, which included an impressive tunnel kiln plant erected at the Kings Mills site in 1964. The same year also saw Marshalls sell part of the Wrexham works to Moler Products of Colchester, who took over part of the production line. Finally in 1970 the 13 oil and coal fired kilns were converted to natural gas.

During the heydays of the late 1950s the company had seen exports going to 27 countries around the globe, but by April 1971 the declining state of the steel industry was beginning to have its effect throughout the refractory brick trade. "Our main customers are the steel companies in Britain and North America and the level of orders has declined considerably over the past few months" explained Marshalls. 120 of their 140 workforce were reduced to a four-day week and by September 1975 70 men had been made redundant. By October 1980 the Marshalls division had only six men left working at the plant, and although Moler Products were managing a little better, production at both sites finally ceased in 1981.

Davies Bros original Abenbury factory stood at OS 3498 4911 with a clayhole to the east, and by the end of its life the works had expanded in size to an even greater degree than its sister plant at Kings Mills. After closure the two sites were quickly demolished and lay waste until late 2001, when the building of new housing estates eradicated all traces of what had been Wrexham's two largest and most prestigious brickworks.

SITE 93: CLAYS BRICKYARD

In the countryside N.W. of Wrexham Industrial Estate there once stood Clays Brickyard, shown on the 1842 tithe map on the roadside at OS 3713 5137 in the holding of Robert Holmes. Surrounding it was "Further Brickyard Field" to the west and "Claypit Field" to the east. On the opposite side of the lane to the south was "Brick Kiln Field", an area shown on the later 1871 OS as being clayhole excavations.

On 1st November 1851 a large sale of goods took place at Clays, indicative of an isolated country brickyard perhaps finding difficulty surviving: 27,000 firebricks, draining tiles, large quantity of unburnt bricks, a cart and a variety of household furniture being amongst the lots.

The next proprietor of Clays was Mr Parry, and we learn a little of his small scale operations from the Advertiser of 21st June 1856, wherein it is clear that he was following the traditional country practice of using clamp kilns:

"We then looked at the other, the top of this kiln to the depth of four feet was much shattered by the weather".

Mr Parry's customer asked the foreman Mr Millington what he did with the damaged bricks, to which he replied that they sold them cheaply as filling for foundations. The customer insisted that he should have the best bricks *"in the kiln next the road"*.

By 1871 the census listed Thomas Price the brickmoulder living at the brickyard, but after this date we know nothing. I did manage to speak to the last farmer to work this site as arable field, and he told me of how he had had to be careful not to plough too deeply in this area, as the shears would hit the buried rubble of the brickyard floor beneath. All the site to the north of the road has now been landscaped and forms part of the golf club land.

SITE 94: MARCHWIEL BRICKYARD

This small country brickyard was owned by the Evans farming family. The yard appears on the 1871 OS map and the trade directory of 1874 shows the family as the brickmakers at the site, whilst the 1881 census lists 81 year old Meredith Evans of Old Hall, Marchwiel as a farmer and brick manufacturer. Before the Evans family moved into Old Hall, John Birch, the son of the owner of site 95 was resident there in 1871.

In August 1893 Meredith Evans let the brickyard to the father and son team of Joseph and Daniel Collins. I believe that Joseph Collins had earlier been the manager of E M Jones' brickworks at site 88, and he might have named his son Daniel after his former boss (also named Daniel Collins) who had died in tragic circumstances.

E M Jones finally relinquished site 88 in 1895 and perhaps Joseph had got wind of his intentions to do so at some point previously, so perhaps that's why he struck out on his own at Marchwiel in 1893.

As Collins was taking over the Marchwiel site, Meredith Evans instructed his solicitors that "With regard to the brickyard, Messrs Collins was to have the two ovens and sheds with the other plant for £130. We have not made any bricks for the last 2 – 3 years and the sheds were in a somewhat dilapidated state, and they intended taking them down and make new ones. Their size will be 45ft. by 15ft.". Messrs Collins did indeed pay that sum for the plant and machinery and were subsequently charged a reduced rent of £2 for their first year's occupancy; the rent to increase to £50 thereafter, whether the yard proved profitable or not.

Wrexham Advertiser 21st October, 1893 – Joseph Collins, brickmaker Marchwiel, was fined two shillings for allowing a cart belonging to him to be used without having his name upon it. The defendant said the cart had just been rebuilt and the names had been left off by mistake.

In the days before vehicle registration it was required of tradesmen that their vehicles should be signwritten .

It seems that the Collins occupancy might not have lasted very long. On 9th July 1894 there was an auction sale at the brickyard to raise money "under a distress for rent". All the stock on site was included, as well as the two presumably new corrugated sheds together with 16 wheelbarrows, shovels, picks and moulds etc. To compound matters even further, Messrs Collins were fined in court seven days later for employing a boy without the necessary Certificate of Fitness, and for not fencing moving machinery. If they managed to continue after these troubles it could not have been for long, and the Evans family again took control of the site.

Wrexham Advertiser 12th August, 1905 – The old brickworks in the direction of Gibraltar which have been lying idle for some years are about to be reopened, and there is every prospect of employment for a large number of men. It is said that there is a very extensive bed of clay which can be easily worked. In the meantime preparations for the reopening are being rapidly pushed forward.

That new brickworks itself closed with its sell – off on 2nd April, 1909, due to Joseph Evans (Meredith's son) "giving up brickmaking", and the sale included everything down to the one-and-a-half barrels of brick lubricating oil – the largest items being the galvanised drying shed and the 14,000 capacity kiln. The site stood at OS 3599 4750.

SITE 95: RICHARD BIRCH'S BRICKYARD

On the detailed 1861 map for the proposed railway running south from Wrexham to Park Eyton the line passed a small, probably agricultural brickyard owned and occupied by Richard Birch. The census for the same year shows Richard to have been a 55 year old farmer living nearby at Old Hall, so he may well have employed a brickmaker at the yard, if indeed it was at all functional at the time. Kiln Farm at OS 3375 4655 lies very close to the brickyard, and the tithe map of the early 1840s shows Richard to have owned this also. The farm is quite ancient and was used as a malt kiln in Victorian days. The present farmer on the site told me that he had cleared out an old clayhole many years ago which was large enough to have been a brickyard clayhole, and this pit is now a flooded pond south of the farm. There are many small clayholes in this district, including some fair sized holes nearby at OS 3395 4640 which are used as fishing ponds. The brickyard was probably only used as and when required.

SITE 96: MORETON BRICKYARD

The first evidence for this small country brickyard appears on the 1840 tithe map which shows "Brick Kiln Field" and "Further Brick Kiln Field" centred at OS 3225 4550. The "whole of the stock, plant and machinery" at this yard went at auction on 24th August, 1856, but we don't know if it disappeared at this date or was continued by new owners, but by the time the 1871 OS was surveyed it had completely disappeared.

SITE 97: OLD HALL BRICKYARD

The brickyards of the Wrexham area clearly delineate one of the principal differences between Denbighshire and Flintshire, in that the area of the Maelor district were once covered by clay pits and small country brickyards. The extensive lowland fields of this district are rich in alluvial clay deposits immediately below the topsoil, which were easily accessible to the country brickmakers of old, and this accounts for the proliferation of these many yards south of Wrexham; a feature the like of which was never as prolific in the rural areas of the much hillier Flintshire.

This site was shown on the 1879 map as a small shed, kiln and claypit at OS 3392 4300, but all traces of it were eradicated by the turn of the century. There is, according to another historian, the possibility that it was the brickyard serving the Bryn y Pys Estate.

SITE 98: WYNNSTAY ESTATE BRICKYARD

Of all the brickyards servicing the needs of the local landed estates the Wynnstay brickyard was the largest – not surprising when we consider that the nearby Wynnstay Hall was the seat of Denbighshire's most prestigious and wealthy landowner, the Baronet, Sir Watkin Williams Wynne.

The earliest brickmaker whom we know to have been incumbent here was Joseph Steen, and from his royalty accounts in 1855 we learn that he was making the usual run of products for such a works – bricks, floor tiles, various sizes of land drainage pipes and stable floor bricks. His tenancy at the yard seems to have terminated towards the end of that year, as the royalty report specifically mentioned him as being "the late brickmaker", and his appearance in court in January 1856 may well provide the reason as to why his employment was ended. Steen got his coals for the brickyard from Plaskynaston Colliery, and despite having needed only three cart loads to keep him supplied for a certain period, he had taken over twenty; selling off the remainder throughout the neighbourhood. As the coals were charged to the Wynnstay estate, this constituted nothing short of attempted fraud!

The next documented brickmaker who comes to our attention was John Edwards, who was active certainly at the end of the 19th century, and the following text is a reminiscence from one of his youngest employees:

Wrexham Leader 5th June, 1970 – A feature of this brickworks was that it was entirely run by three men and a boy. In 1912 I was that boy, and the men were two brothers John and Edwin Edwards and Mark Williams. Bricks, tiles and drainage pipes were produced here to provide the requirements of the Wynnstay and other estates. John Edwards was in charge, Edwin was the engineer, Mark was the clayhole man and I was in the feeding room. We worked from six in the morning until 5:30pm five days a week. On Saturday we finished at 1 o'clock. Our programme never varied. On Monday and Tuesday we made floor tiles, bricks and pipes. On Wednesday we emptied one of the two kilns. On Thursday we filled it up again; this generally lasted the week out. The other kiln would be cooling off to enable us to start all over again on Monday morning. When the 1914 war broke out production ceased and the men were employed on other work on the estate.

The brickyard's accounts for the year 1909 show an interesting insight into the finances and productivity of a country brickyard, as the following report from the Estate's agent shows:

Paid Edwards..£196
Coal...£267
Repairs to machinery. £23
Feying and taking up fence
(extending clayhole) £20

"The actual cost here given means the cost at the brickyard, so that in the case of pipes sent to other estates, there should be added three shillings per thousand for haulage. The expenditure on coal seems excessive. Edwards lays the blame for this on the boiler. If provision were made for replacing machinery, the cost of brickmaking would be increased about 10 per cent. In the year under consideration there were used on the estate about 130,000 bricks and 160,000 pipes, 7000 floor tiles and some odds and ends, and there were sold 8000 bricks and 100,000 pipes – total purchase money £229".

From those figures we can see that the £229 earned from off-estate sales would not itself have covered the running costs of the yard, and if it were not for all the goods made and used by the Estate itself the works would surely have proved unviable. The only reason why this yard outlived most other country yards was by reason of the demands which the Wynnstay Estate placed upon it.

John Edwards died in August 1932 aged 72 and following the ancient tradition granted to all estate employees Sir Watkin supplied his coffin made from oak felled on the estate.

When exactly the works closed is not recorded. The article from 1970 says that it shut circa 1914, but I have come across newspaper reports which mention the Edwards family "of Wynnstay Brickyard" in 1925 and 1931, although they may only have been living there in the brickyard cottage. A report from 1937 refers to the brickyard as being abandoned, so we know that it was still in situ at that date, and it is entirely possible that it could well have been unoccupied for the previous 23 years.

The works was composed of a small factory with two kilns at OS 3195 4315 and a clayhole to the south east. Wynnstay Estate's timber yard now occupies the site; all traces of the brickyard having disappeared.

SITE 99: BERSHAM COLLIERY

The general historical opinion is that Bersham Colliery was sunk by Messrs Barnes of Liverpool in 1867, but things perhaps started a little earlier than that, as the Wrexham Advertiser lists the auction sale of the Bersham Colliery under a distress for rent on 5th February, 1867, although there is no proof that this was the same site. If it was, I should imagine this to have been the time when Messrs Barnes purchased it. It would then have been only a small affair and amongst the sale assets listed in 1867 were the paraphernalia of early small-scale brickmaking – brick moulds, tables and benches. James Barnes officially formed the Bersham Colliery Co Ltd at its first meeting on 21st October 1868, and the company's balance sheets show that expenditure on making bricks was a regular occurrence. On 19th August, 1872 he reported to his shareholders on the discovery of a seam of fireclay, from which bricks had been made to assess its quality. Before then they must have been using the more basic clays nearer the surface. The site expanded quickly during this period and by early September 1873 a proper brickworks was in course of erection alongside the pit buildings to make use of their new fireclay, and in August 1874 Mr Barnes reported that:

"A mill for grinding the clay, together with kilns and shed has been erected which converts the clay got in sinking into bricks at a moderate cost – as yet all made have been used for the pit and buildings. In a short time I expect to have some for sale".

Within two years of that report the company had found that the profit from their off-site brick sales had succeeded in paying for all the previous expenses incurred in brick production, so the venture had proved a sound commercial move.

Despite a serious fire in March 1897 which destroyed much of the surface works and shut down production in the larger of the two pits, the company managed to resurrect itself without any serious damage to its working capital, and the coal they were raising turned out to be of a particularly high quality – an important commercial factor in those fiercely competitive days of transatlantic steamship crossings. "The fastest passage made to New York has been made by your coal" reported a triumphant Mr Barnes to his shareholders.

In 1899, after running for a train, Mr Barnes suffered a seizure and died suddenly, to be replaced at the head of the company by his nephew Fred Barnes. In July 1911 the colliery was purchased by the Broughton & Plas Power Coal Co, one of the most powerful conglomerates in the district. Whether brickmaking had ceased by this time is unsure, but a detailed description of the works layout, published in the Wrexham Leader of 29th April, 1932, mentioned no brickworks on the site at all.

Bersham's closure on 18th December, 1986 brought deep pit coal production in Denbighshire to its final halt. The original colliery and brickworks stood at OS 3149 4830 and the site is now a modern industrial estate. During the 20th century the colliery had developed a much larger complex just to the south of the original site, and the main winding house and wheel of this later development has been preserved as a memorial to the past – at least for the time being.

Rhos Area

SITES 100, 101, 102: LLWYNEINION BRICKWORKS

My investigations of the three brickworks spaced within close proximity to each other proved somewhat problematic at first, especially as they seemed to be connected with five separate firms, but with some careful examination of all the available evidence I believe I have succeeded in cataloguing as true a picture of their chronological history as can be achieved from our standpoint in time. Firstly, there were two principal industries at Llwyneinion ; the clay works having proved the more durable; the earlier being iron and coal. The iron ore for the Bersham Iron Works came from here in the 1720s and iron production at the Llwyneinion blast furnaces lasted seemingly until the 1860s. At the sale of the land freehold of the Llwyneinion Iron Works Estate in August 1840 the prospectus quoted that "the Iron Works have for several years been celebrated for their excellent quality of the iron there manufactured. A seam of Firebrick Clay 6 ft thick extends under nearly the whole of the property". The company made use of this clay and turned out bricks at a royalty of one shilling per thousand on bricks sold off site, so we can see that even at this early date this general site may very well have functioned as a commercial brickworks, if only on the small scale. That particular company's lease had been taken out in December 1837, but it is believed that brickmaking had been going on even earlier under the ironmaster Thomas Jones. But strangely enough the 1845 tithe map shows no brickworks in this vicinity whatsoever, so we must deduce that it had been conducted in those days by using clamp kilns and not permanently sited kilns, and that the clay had been most likely brought up from the iron and coal workings.

SITE 100: LLWYNEINION OLD BRICKWORKS

The least significant of Llwyneinion's purpose built brickworks is shown on the 1872 OS map at ref 2869 4743, by which time it was designated as an "Old Brickworks", and probably the subject of the following report:

> Chester Chronicle 1851 – The Llwyneinion Firebrick Works near Wrexham. Notice is hereby given that the partnership formerly subsisting between Mr William Charles Hussey Jones and James Searle was dissolved as from 26th May 1851. The business will for the future be carried on by James Searle under the same title. Firebricks of first quality, ornamental and other building bricks. Firebacks, flooring tiles always on sale.

There was a brickworks at site 101 which was primarily a pipe works, so I believe that the above mentioned factory was the one at site 100. The Mr Jones who left went on to establish works at the Leeswood Green Colliery.

By February 1861 the landlords of the Rhos Hall Estate, on which all these works stood, were interested in selling off the property, and the newspaper gives account of the state of the industry upon it at the time. It was reported that a "previous company" had been erecting partially completed blast furnaces, shafts and pumps, as well as having "a large fire and red brick works all complete and ready for work". This could very well have been site 100, as the only other works present at this time was the pipe works of Messrs Hayes & Atkins which had been continuously manufacturing for some time. This would therefore mean that the brickworks' owners had probably been an iron company.

On 21st September, 1869 the site of the Rhos Hall Iron Co, including a brickworks, was auctioned due to its liquidation. I honestly can't confirm that this concern related to our site 100, but it may be the case.

It looks like the brickworks must have lain idle for many years thereafter, and all traces of it had disappeared by 1899. The works is now an overgrown mound and the only visible evidence remaining is the deep clayhole abutting on its southern side.

SITE 101: MESSRS HAYES & ATKINS

This works appears on the 1872 OS at ref 2878 4778 and was designated as a "Tile and Pipe Works" whose style was reported in articles of 1854 and 1856 to have been Messrs Hayes, Brough & Co. of Liverpool. Mr Brough was the partner in charge at the works, whilst Mr William Woolhouse Hayes ran the company's registered office in Liverpool, but by 1860 the proposal map of the North Wales Mineral Rly verified the ownership of the site as having become Messrs Hayes & Atkins. The principal output from these works is also recorded as being glazed sanitary pipes.

Wrexham Advertiser 7th January 1865 – It is gratifying to find at this festive season that those who invest their capital in important enterprises are not unmindfull of the well-being of those in their employ and share with them their creature comforts. On Monday 26th Messrs Hayes, Atkins & Co gave a substantial repast to upwards of 70 guests comprising the workmen, their wives and sweethearts. The dinner took place in a shed tastefully decorated with evergreens and flowers together with a number of mottos such as "Union is Strength", "Success to Messrs Hayes & Atkins", " Llaw wrth llaw, a chalon wrth galon" (hand by hand and heart with heart) etc. The usual loyal and patriotic toasts were given in excellent style, interspersed with some capital songs. Mr Smyth proposed thanks for the good things provided, which called forth the most lusty cheering. The men were regaled with bread and cheese and cwrw da (best ale), while the women were bountifully supplied with tea. The shades of evening having closed, Mr Smyth exhibited a magnificent magic lantern, the views of which ranged from the powerful implements of warfare, galvanic batteries etc, to the comic characters of Punch and Judy. Some brisk cannonading took place throughout the whole of the day, which was kept up on the following day.

The trade directory verifies John Smyth as being the manager of the Llwyneinion Pipe & Fireclay Works.

In November 1866, according to the Wrexham Advertiser, "the inhabitants of Rhos were startled by the appearance of a first class carriage on the new line of railway". This new railway now connected the local industries to the main G.W.R. at Trevor and helped benefit the pipe works' productivity. From 1869, and perhaps shortly before, the works was styled simply as George Atkins & Co.

It's uncertain as to when it finally closed, but the trade directory for 1879 still lists its presence in the market place. A newspaper article from 1889 mentions that G Atkins & Co had ceased trading by that time, and Mr Atkins himself responded from Liverpool in a letter of 5th November that year to explain why the works had closed. He said:

"Your issue of 26 October attributes our giving up the works to being heavily handicapped by having to cart all our manufactures to Wrexham, whereas we had railway communication into our yard for many years before we ceased manufacturing, and only local and land sales were carted. The reason we ceased was that all coal and clay were practically worked out, and as we were on the outcrop of the lowest coal measure there is little probability of anything worth working being found below Llwyneinion. We should as soon expect gold as coal or fireclay. Every practical man in the district will say the same".

Absolutely nothing of the site remains today and its frontage onto the road has been replaced by housing.

SITE 102: POWELL BROTHERS

Wrexham Advertiser 27th June, 1891 – A firm from Buckley has opened new fireclay works at Llwyneinion.
Wrexham Advertiser 21st November, 1891 – Messrs Powell Bros. have erected two large sheds and a kiln at Llwyneinion. Brickmaking was commenced there this week.

The Powell Company had originally been established as a Buckley pottery firm in 1853, although they never seriously got into brickmaking in Flintshire. They sited their Llwyneinion Brickworks on the spot at OS 2885 4751 where some small kilns (probably brick kilns) had been shown on the 1872 OS map, and in time the venture became the largest of the three works by far. In August 1908 Powell Co came close to purchasing the freehold of their site following the death of the landowner Mr George Rooper, a London solicitor. Complications prevented the sale going through, but to the company's advantage, as they finally acquired it in October 1912 for the knock-down price of £1,000.

In 1924 the company's principal owner Mr Isaac Powell died, and ownership eventually transferred to the Llwyneinion Shale Brick Co, formed in February 1926 by a Birkenhead consortium. As its name suggested, the firm was by then making bricks from clay admixed with crushed shale in the form of Engineering, Common and Rustic bricks. The new company lasted for just over three years, as a letter from them explained on 27th September, 1929 that the brickworks was being put up for sale due to the proprietor's ill-health and subsequent retirement. The new owners were the Hartley family, who held the Ruby Works at Rhydymwyn, as well as the Hoole Bank Brickworks near Chester at OS 4336 6933.

Wrexham Advertiser 26th November 1957 – Government cuts in the housing grants and diminished trade have hit brickworks in the Wrexham area. One of the most seriously affected is the Llwyn Einion Works which will be closing down shortly. Already half the staff have become redundant. A spokesman for the works hoped the closure would only be a temporary measure, but in the meantime the works would have to close down completely. This is the third time the factory has closed since it first opened more than 50 years ago, and recently new equipment has been installed at great expense.

I have it on good authority that the works never reopened.

In the proceeding years the large southerly clayhole became flooded and was targeted as the illegal dumping ground for oil waste brought from Ellesmere Port in road tankers from 1961 onwards.

As time rolled by concern developed that this ever-increasing slick could present a serious problem. As the caretaker of the site said: "I saw herons dive into the lake – they never came out again. My daughter's cat fell in once and when it managed to get to the bank, it died". On 5th August, 1980 the inevitable occurred when the slick caught fire and burned for 18 hours, resulting in the mass evacuation of local residents. Clwyd County Council, who had bought the site only three weeks previously, were left with the expense of clearing the site and they took the opportunity to demolish the abandoned works. Today the pool is all that remains – now completely surrounded by strong fencing.

SITE 103: COPPY BRICKWORKS

A little way south of Llwyneinion lies the heartland of Denbighshire's brick industry; the centre of which was Ruabon village, but which together with the surrounding districts of Rhos and Cefn created a hard red brick and terracotta known generically as Ruabon Brick – also commonly referred to in the building trade as Ruabon Red.

Coppy Brickworks became most noted for its glazed bricks whilst under the proprietorship of J C Edwards Ltd, but its genesis began as the Rhos Brick Works Co, which had been formed by a consortium of Yorkshire entrepreneurs, at the head of which was the Leeds brickmaker John Gilbert Robinson. The works was under construction by mid-1872; Mr Crofton the manager hosting a celebration dinner for the works' employees on 10th July at the nearby Sun Inn. By 1877 the site had three small kilns which were supplied with clay and coal from two pit shafts; a separate shaft having been sunk to raise coal for off – sales to the public – a nice way of bringing in some extra revenue. Despite this, the works had been established at a cost of over £10,000 and extra capital was needed to keep the venture afloat, and the "Rhos Brickworks and Colliery" was put on the market on 20th January, 1878. The Yorkshire firm managed to raise the capital needed to retain ownership by forming in October a new company under the style of the "Albert Brick & Coal Co "; Mr Robinson's principal partners by then being Huddersfield businessmen. By 1880 the venture had become a limited company, and in truth the fortunes of their enterprise seemed to have proved somewhat sporadic – from a court case held in March of that year we find their lawyer saying that they "were not Welshmen, but some canny Yorkshiremen who had opened the works in the last few months and were subject to a great deal of trespass". Whatever their difficulties may have been their company could not stay afloat and it eventually took the financial might of Ruabon district's premier firm of J C Edwards Ltd to resuscitate the ailing works and steer it into a new field of endeavour:

Wrexham Advertiser 28th October 1882 – Albert Brickworks. After being at a standstill for a considerable time these valuable works have again recommenced operations. The new company are determined to develop the property vigorously and have every confidence. The fireclay on the land is found to be of the very first quality and a trial kiln of enamelled bricks have given great satisfaction. A large number of boys and several adults have been taken on, and this in the face of depressed state of trade here is a substantial benefit, and a new trade, that of enamelled brickmaking etc will be established in our midst.

That "depressed state of trade" had its inevitable effect, with the Albert Brickworks not fully coming on line until May 1884; the J C E company's letterheads of that year not even bothering to include the Rhos Works as one of its holdings. It soon progressed at a rapid rate however; many new kilns being built shortly thereafter, leading the Advertiser of 26th July, 1884 to predict that "the works will have an extensive and imposing appearance".

Wrexham Advertiser 25th April, 4th July, 1885 – The Albert Brickworks continues to grow in importance. Considerable additions have been made since our last report and the manufacture of building and enamelled brick is now on a very large scale. The present energetic management seem determined to make this concern second to none in the country, for we learn that several

thousand pounds are to be spent forthwith in further additions to the plant. The demand for the splendid enamelled bricks continues to exceed the supply. The amount of traffic afforded by these works is no small boon to the Shropshire Union Railway.

By 1886 J C Edwards had formed the "Rhos Glazed and Enamelled Brick Co" to promote its new range of goods coming out of the works, and in April 1904 new machinery was installed at the Coppy Works, as it was by then called, followed by more extensions to the buildings.

By the beginning of the Great War new trends in architecture had put an end to profitable glazed and enamelled brick manufacture, so the Coppy moved over to producing a more general run of products.

Wrexham Leader 30th March 1951 – Few people would have realised that the grey-haired man who slid down muddy banks and over piles of clay as he showed me round the works was 80 years of age. He was Mr Robert Parry, the present manager who has been associated with the firm for nearly fifty years. Today the grey clay of the mine is manufactured into yellow facing brick and tiles. We walked over to a derelict mining shaft; closed 20 years ago when the works were affected by flooding. Today the clay is wound up from a drift some 500 yards away. An average of 20 men mine the clay from a seam 50 yards beneath the surface. A small winding – house backs onto the shaft and in the distance one sees the small tubs emerge from the ground. The clay arrives at a point where it is dumped for weathering. Mechanisation may have speeded up the industry, but the manufacture of bricks is still a slow process, for nature plays a big part in the operation. Dwarfed by the huge chimney stands a broken wooden structure. This was a Whinsey winding machine; the first type of winding machine invented. A bar attached to a revolving drum was operated by a horse. As the drum revolved the rope was hauled in and the cage came up. That however was many years ago. Today there was no horse. Only a rotting structure remained. Back in the small office, the walls of which are covered by

Workers at the Copi Glazed Brickworks circa 1930. Photo: Tudor Jones.

tiles and bricks of all shapes, colours and sizes, Mr Parry told me how his products have been sent to all parts of the world. One of his proudest boasts is that his company provided the tiling for the bathing pool on board the Queen Mary.

It's interesting to see from that last report how the primitive pit gear had still managed to survive from the Victorian days – perhaps even from the works' earliest beginnings, and the drift mine could well have been the same as was opened in July 1929, of which the Rhos Herald had reported "It is said that the new method of raising clay will not be so costly as the old pit".

In July 1956 the works was acquired by R H Gibbs & Son of Hereford, by which time only quarry flooring tiles were being produced, but as even this product finally became unfashionable it inevitably spelt the death knell for the factory.

Wrexham Leader 26th March, 1963 – Another Wrexham area brickworks is to close. The Copi Works (the Welsh spelling) once world famous for glazed bricks, is to close down gradually over the next few months costing forty men their jobs. The closure now leaves only one brickworks in Rhos – the Pant Works – which are only ticking over. Like most brickworks in the area, Copi had gone over to tile making in recent years, but new rubber and vinyl flooring materials cut heavily into its business. It is understood that remaining orders will be switched to the Worcestershire works of Mr K H R Gibbs. Some employees have already left. If most find other work before August the works will probably close before then.

Coppy did indeed close in 1963. Army Engineers dynamited the 150 ft high chimney stack on 22nd November the following year – nearly blacking out the Rhos when it fell the wrong way, narrowly missing the town's electricity sub-station.

The factory was centred at OS 2876 4674, which is today the site of the Coppy Industrial

Estate.

SITE 104: RHOS BRICKWORKS – KAYE HIRST LTD

Shown marked as "Rhos Brickworks" on the first edition OS map, this works was at that time slightly larger than its nearby neighbour the Albert Works, but it never achieved anything like the Albert's eventual success.

We first find mention of it on a railway map of 1860, at which time it was owned by the Rhos builder John Pritchard and run by the partnership of Rhos men Jacob Davies and Thomas Savage. On 12th June 1861 the partnership of Davies & Savage, "carrying on business of brick, tile and pot manufacturers" was officially dissolved; Davies taking over the concern himself, and we see him in the census for that year listed as a "brick manufacturer employing six men and two boys". A succeeding railway map of 1864 shows that the "Bricksheds, clay pit engine, kilns and ponds" were still owned and occupied by Prichard and Davies, but on 26th August, 1867 the works' boiler, steam engine and clay mill were sold at auction. This could have meant one of two things – either the plant had been replaced by larger machinery or more likely that Davies was having a cash flow problem.

Between March 1872 and August 1875 the Advertiser ran several invitations to purchase a small brickworks at Rhos, and although the works was not specifically named, it seems most likely from its descriptions that the ads referred to this site. During this period all other Rhos works were developing along specifically well-documented paths, so I can only assume that it was this small site 104 which was for sale, especially as only a paltry £800 was being asked for it.

I also believe this site to have been the later home of the Kaye – Hirst Co. They are mentioned in the trade directory of 1883 as being manufacturers at Rhos – a fact borne out by the stampings on their bricks. One of the sale ads for the unnamed Rhos Brickworks did mention that "the clay produces the most superior white facing bricks", and indeed, what few examples I have found of the company's bricks have all been a creamy white in colour. The

Kaye – Hirst Co must surely have operated from this site, as it was the only one in the entire district to have left no documented evidence of its ownership or its history during this specific period.

The factory stood at OS 2891 4652 and was replaced by terraced housing at the end of the 19th century – the name of Kaye – Hirst having also significantly disappeared well before that date.

SITE 105: PONKEY BRICKWORKS, RHOS

Wrexham Advertiser 18th September, 1869 – The new shop at the corner of Henblas St. and Queen St. in Wrexham, erected on the site of a tumble down old building that had been a great eye -sore, is now completed and occupied. It is a great improvement to this conspicuous corner and we hope ere long to see some hovels a few yards further up Queen St. disappear, and something comely rise up in their place. The bricks of the new building, which have been much admired for their colour and smooth surface, are from the Ponkey brick and tile works.

In the days when that report was written the Ponkey Brickworks was working the best of its available claybed, but as we shall see later its reputation was to be much sullied as the quality of its clay deteriorated. The history of the Ponkey district on the eastern side of the Rhos goes back into antiquity; coal mining having been recorded here in the very late 17th century. In 1825 working class "explorers" arrived here from Corwen and Trawsfynydd and found the remains of the earlier coal pits, and they arranged with the local landowners to rework the pits for a wage of ten pence per day. These early 19th century miners lived in makeshift hovels which they erected around their shafts. A map of Rhos drawn in 1861 shows the area was then dotted with these small shafts between the roads and houses – the Rhos itself having been built up around these obstacles with no attempt having been made to fill them in. Indeed, when Ponkey Brickworks was established the old pits came in useful. As the British Architect in 1878 put it:

"At Ponkey hard red bricks are made from the clays in the refuse heaps of old coal pits".

The brickworks was reputed to have been established circa 1866 by Charles Albert Sharp of Leicestershire and a lease dated 1866 exists in the National Library of Wales which grants "the clayland" to Ponkey Brick & Tile Co. The landlord was Mr R H Price of Bersham Hall; the main proprietors being Mr T H Sharp, Henry Dennis and Mr Glennie; Mr Dennis seemingly having been the principal manager, and documents from July 1869 still exist ordering drainage pipes from Messrs Dennis & Glennie's Ponkey Brick & Tile Works.

By 1873 the works, also commonly referred to as Aberderfyn Brickworks, was in the hands of the liquidator and the whole of the stock was sold at auction on 2nd September. The works must have been struggling, as the proprietors were also summoned in December for non-payment of rates. On 1st September 1873 the partnership took out a new lease on the site, which was eventually followed up in April 1877 by the sale of the works; the same partnership again managing to retain its hold. Exactly why this sale was held is not clear – perhaps the works was again in liquidation, but at least the sale prospectus gives us a good description of the extent of the site at that time. The works itself stood on two and a half acres of land with a further 50 acres of mineral land, together with the usual array of buildings, a small water reservoir and a tramway bridge which conveyed the clay from the quarry to the upper storey of the Milling Shed, plus round and square kilns.

I earlier mentioned how the quality of the clay had deteriorated as the bed was worked through, and the following commentary from the Wrexham Advertiser of 1879 bears this out:

"Mr Lynam, surveyor, stated the property was depreciated in rating value owing to the material at Aberderfyn being bad, but he had often seen works where the material was equally as bad. The works were fairly good and some of the buildings of modern type. The works were well laid out with no difficulty in getting materials in. Mr Sharp, manager and part proprietor, then stated that since he had been in possession he had made about 100,000 bricks a month and had to pay a premium to Mr Price the previous occupier. Sharp said the average make of bricks a year would be 960,000, but owing to the bad state of the clay, the extra cost of bricks was 2s. 6d. per thousand. Mr Ford, nationally renowned surveyor and valuer, said he had been over Aberderfyn and never saw clay so inferior in quality and there was no comparison to be made between the clay here and other works in the area. Mr Joseph Higginbottom, who had been engaged in brickmaking himself, thought the marketable value of the Aberderfyn clay to be a temporary one. The clay was perfect rubbish and in the course of his experience he did not think anyone could be found to work such, except in Wales (laughter from onlookers).

On 10th November 1887 the works was sold in consequence of the expiry of the lease, and the site was eventually acquired by Walter Pen Dennis, the son of Henry Dennis, who took the decision to cease brickmaking in favour of pottery manufacture.

In September 1889 the Advertiser was reporting that the Ponkey Potteries were by then in the course of construction, with new sheds, offices, outbuildings and kilns being erected. Had the older works been left to rack and ruin? It might even be conceivable that it had not been functioning since its 1887 sale. By 1891 the following account appeared:

"The works were originally a brick manufactory and were rebuilt in 1889 by Mr W P Dennis. Dennis has fitted up the place with the latest improvements in machinery, engine power etc, and he is already extending the works to meet increased trade. About 100 employees are occupied here. Another shed is in the course of erection and will be built in three stories, each floor being 200 ft by 25 ft. The four departments into which the operations are divided include the manufacture of 1) Garden pots, saucers, seedpans – 2) pan mugs, milk coolers etc – 3) lead pots, dishes, crucibles – 4) fancy goods.

By 1900 however, the OS map showed the works

Ponkey pottery circa 1895. Women workers were not uncommon in the potteries of the district.
Photo: Dennis Gilpin / Nene.

as being disused and it remained so until its acquisition in late 1904 by the Wrexham furniture makers Aston & Son, who set to work converting the factory into their new Aberderfyn Cabinet Works, which was officially opened in July 1905.

The original brickworks factory was sited at OS 2985 4652 with its clayhole to the south. A large brick factory shed still exists on the site, and it is believed that this was one of the buildings erected by the Ponkey Potteries.

SITE 106: PANT BRICKWORKS, RHOS

Of all the brickworks in the Rhos the Pant was the largest; even more so than the Coppy. Situated on the western side of Rhos, the Pant – a Welsh word referring to a dip or hollow in the landscape – was the site of iron and coal workings of which there are recorded leases dating back to 1820. Thomas Jones of Gardden Hall held the ironworks here until his bankruptcy in 1829, after which it was acquired

by Thomas and Richard Greenhow of Wrexham, and the Chester Chronicle of 1840 mentions the main works at Pant as consisting of "blast furnaces, engines, timber yard, pit heads, coke ovens and a mill for grinding fireclay, brick kiln, brick shed with cast iron floor". This floor was heated by steam fed into the space beneath it which heated the brickshed and assisted the drying process. In November 1840 the by then bankrupt Richard Greenhow was selling his interest in the "Pant & Rhos Colliery & Iron Works" (which was also listed in the trade directory for 1835) so it must have been this company which had begun serious brickmaking at the Pant. On 15th October, 1844 the Chronicle listed the sale of the entire Pant Iron Works – a "powerful clay mill" having been up for auction from the same works in the previous December, and by the time the tithe map was published in 1846 there was only the Pant Coal Works listed as left working at this site.

Brickmaking on this site was resurrected with

Employees in the Pant stockyards, 1902. Photo: DRO.

the establishment of the North Wales Coal & Fireclay Co circa 1860, the holdings of which was at some point before 1874 transferred to the Pant Coal, Brick & Fireclay Co, which itself was re registered under the same name on 27th June 1874, and again a year later. We know from the testimony of the Company Secretary Mr Daniel Owen, a farmer by profession, that the works got both its clay and coal from pit shafts. At some point after 1879 the works was transferred to the ownership of Edward Taylor Fitch and William Taylor under the new style of the Pant Brick & Sanitary Pipe Works, the name suggestive that the colliery side of the business had been wound up as a commercial concern.

The most notable period in this works' history began on 2nd January 1886 when the Messrs Fitch & Taylor made contract to hand over the works to Henry Dennis, who was looking to cash in on the latest fashion for glazed brickwork. He reinvigorated the site by establishing the new firm of the Ruabon Glazed Brick & Fireclay Co, which was officially incorporated on 2nd March 1866 to "work the said Brickworks and Mines with the utmost vigilance and attention to the Interest, Profit and Benefit of the Lessor according to the best and most improved mode of carrying on Works of a similar description" – the lessor being their landlord Sir Watkin Williams Wynne. Mr Dennis soon set about enlarging the factory with the intention of converting it to glazed and enamelled brick production – at almost the same time J C Edwards was doing likewise at the Coppy Works. There still remains the letter from the landlord's agent Mr Walter Eddy, who informed Sir Watkin on 5th March, 1887 that "I am going to meet Mr Dennis on Monday at the Rhos about the land for the Enamelled Brickworks".

By 1891 the works had become one of the most prestigious in the entire Ruabon district, as witnessed by this contemporary report:

"The works located at Pant cover about twelve acres. They are widely and justly celebrated and the increasing demand for the tiles, glazed bricks etc of rare make and colour is good proof of the excellent quality of the goods. There are 35 kilns of all kinds and varieties. The number of employees is 380. There are ten engines here and the clay is raised from the company's own

Pant Brickworks in 1906. Photo: DRO.

pits, burning a rich buff colour. The manufactures are white and coloured glazed and enamelled bricks, buff facing bricks and terracotta, encaustic, tesselated and other fancy tiles for pavements and wall linings, sanitary pipes, traps etc".

Reproduced in this book is an example of the Victorian and early Edwardian custom of presenting an "illuminated address" to a person deemed worthy of the honour. These colourful examples of the calligrapher's art were usually drawn on fine vellum and presented as a gift on the occasion of a marriage, anniversary or retirement etc. This example was made in September 1902 and was awarded by the Pant workmen to their manager Mr Till, who was leaving them to take up another appointment at a Leeds factory, and the style of language and sentiment which it conveyed is typical of all such examples of these once extremely popular items. It reads:

"Presented by the employees of the Pant Works, Ruabon to Mr George Till on his resignation as manager of the works. Respected Sir – having heard with the greatest regret that you have resigned the position of manager which you have held for the past six years in these works, we feel it our bounden duty before you leave us to convey to you our grateful appreciation of the kind and gentlemanly treatment we have invariably received at your hands and our deep sense of the loss we shall sustain. We are aware of the difficulties of your position and rarely can a manager secure the goodwill of all those with whom he may be brought into contact, yet notwithstanding this, you will leave us fully assured of having gained the respect and esteem of the whole of the workpeople and employees upon the manufactory. At the close of a connection so honourable to yourself and so full of pleasant and grateful recollections for us, we desire to present you with some lasting token of affectionate regard. We therefore beg your acceptance of this address, and we ensure you our earnest wish and prayer is that the blessing of Almighty God may rest upon yourself and family in the sphere of labour you are about to enter".

Following its closure after the Great War the Pant's connections with the Dennis family and their parent company of Ruabon Coal & Coke came to an end with its purchase in October 1921 by the Gwersyllt Silica Brick Co of site 79.

Rhos Herald 20th September, 1930 – There was a time once when the Pant Brickworks was a hive of industry employing 300 workmen. In the days when Mr Till was manager, followed by Mr Maxwell, the works turned out bricks and pipes to all quarters of the globe. Those were the golden days of local industry. Things today are slightly different at the Pant. After lying idle for some considerable time the works were taken over by Gwersyllt Silica Brick Co. Some 40 men are employed here and they no longer manufacture building bricks or sanitary pipes. The output is confined to what is known locally as a firebrick or silicon brick. The company have earned a reputation in the industry for supplying a first class article.

On 20th August, 1971 Pant Works ceased their remaining silica brick production for the last time and stayed open only long enough to supervise the disposal of what stocks were left on site. Where once 380 souls had worked, only 25 now witnessed its demise. After demolition, what ruins remained lay as a makeshift playground for local children until the Council completely re landscaped the site in the late 1990s; obliterating all physical evidence of this once giant works centred at OS 2864 4588.

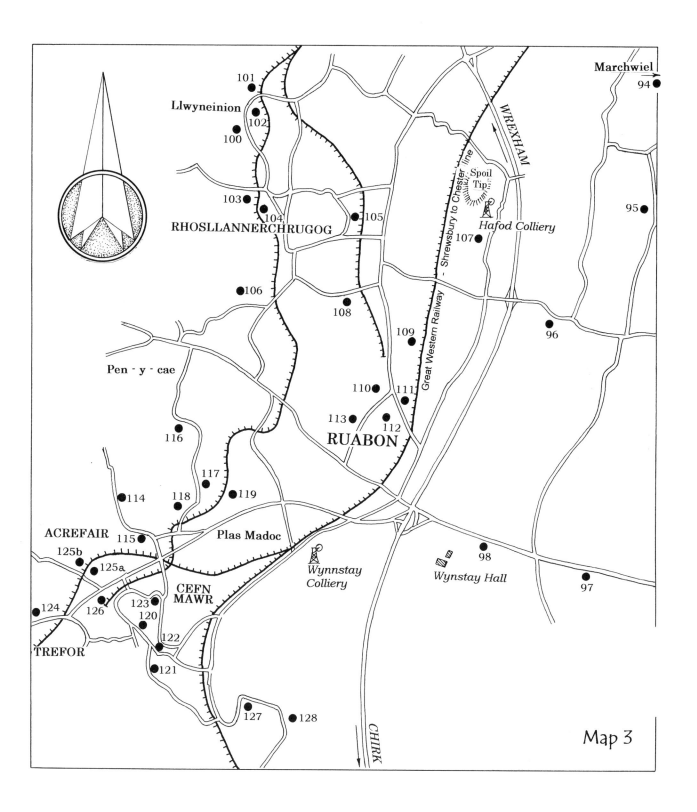

Map 3

Ruabon Area

SITE 107 HAFOD COLLIERY & BRICKWORKS – DENNIS RUABON

The great tile works of Dennis Ruabon at Hafod, east of the Rhos, still exists in production today – the only clay works to have survived in Denbighshire. What is not commonly known however is that brickmaking at this site preceded the construction of this present factory by many years, and began here with the establishment of the Ruabon Coal Co's pit by Mr R C Webster. His new colliery at Hafod y bwch (the older and more complete name for this district) began with the cutting of the first sod of ground on 10th March 1863; the pit being named Ruabon New Colliery, as a Ruabon Colliery was already in existence in the district. Brickmaking was begun almost from the start of the project and we have evidence from January 1866 of the brickmaker Jacob Davies working on the site, although these early makings would have been reserved exclusively for the company's usage and not for land sale (off site sales).

Wrexham Advertiser July 1866 – Extensive rumours had been spread about that there was no coal in Hafod y Bwch ground, but Mr R C Webster's knowledge of geology has proved contrary to the opinions of the whole country. The general saying was that it was useless to commence sinking, as nothing would be proved, but they commenced in spite of all their forebodings, but as soon as they were a few yards down they met with a very sandy ground full of water which stood in defiance to the skill of the best men. The pits were at a standstill when Mr R Harrison came there from Durham to be a master sinker, and after examining the ground, he commenced with energy, placing his men in the right way, conquering all difficulties and soon became masterly by getting the two pits on solid ground, and he has been very successful since the commencement, and now the pits are nearly 400 yards deep. And I am happy to inform the public that the sinkers on Monday last came on a seam of coal of excellent quality which proved to be 8 ft. in thickness. A message was sent to Mr Webster who in a very short time came to see it, and was so much pleased and overjoyed as to make the handsome treat of five shillings to be shared in equal shares between upward of 50 workmen. So three times three to Mr Webster for his treat.

Five shillings must have gone a long way in 1866! In 1867 the company installed a massive steam engine – "the most powerful winding engine in England" as the Advertiser reported, and by August the Ruabon Coal Co was raising its first coal. The colliery was sited at OS 3125 4659 and the 1871 map shows it with an adjoining brickshed and three round kilns slightly to the north east at OS 3129 4662 connected by a short tramway to a clay pit.

Wrexham Advertiser 8th July, 1871 – An inquest was held at the Blue Bell Inn, Rhos on the body of a young man named Edwin Wright who was killed on Wednesday evening at the Hafodybwch brickworks by being either knocked or pulled to the cog wheels by one of the clay wagons. It was only on Wednesday morning that the deceased had commenced working at the Hafod brickworks.

By 18th June 1879 the "Hafodybwch Colliery & Brickworks" was in liquidation with debts of £11,000. Despite being in full production its profitability had been seriously compromised by a trade recession which had continued for many months, and despite the site being valued at £50,000, at the London auction sale on 26th June even half that amount could not be realised – London being the home of the company's most senior shareholders. Into the fray now stepped Henry Dennis, the most famous of all the district's industrial figures and an entrepreneurial genius of unparalleled repute, whose companies and majority holdings included, amongst others, the Pant Brickworks, Wrexham Colliery, the Glyn Valley Tramway, Minera Lead Mines, major local gas, water and sewage companies, Cefn Stone Quarries and industrial concerns in his native Cornwall.

Born in Bodmin, Cornwall in 1825 he left school to study civil engineering at the Borough Surveyor's Office. He later learnt the business of railway engineering as an employee of the Cornwall Railway and in the early 1850s studied the principles of mining. It was at this time that he first visited this district when he was charged with supervising the construction of a tramway to connect Llangollen slate quarry to the canal. After a stint at a lead mine in Spain he returned to Wales and landed the managership of Bryn yr Owen Colliery at OS 2980 4730, during which time he set up in partnership in 1857 with his brother in-law Mr Glennie as mining surveyors and engineers.

By the time the Hafod Colliery was in liquidation Mr Dennis had amassed a considerable personal fortune, and he wasted no time in purchasing the concern and incorporating it as part of his new Ruabon Coal & Coke Company. Brick production at the colliery had by this time certainly been a commercial concern in its own right for many years past, and in response to the growing demand for quality brick and terracotta Mr Dennis took the bold step of building a massive new brickworks south of the colliery at OS 3115 4625 – the site of the present day factory. The machinery at the new "Red Works" was finally set in motion in July 1890 and the following account from 1891 testifies to the factory's speedy success:

"The excellent products of the Hafod Works led us to anticipate at a glance a well laid-out establishment, but we were agreeably and greatly surprised to find it far in advance of anything of the kind we had ever met with in the Kingdom. Entering a large stock yard through which runs a railway siding we could not resist an absolute sense of admiration as we noticed the rich colour and various shapes of the many articles. The works occupy 10 or 11 acres of ground and the clay holes over several acres will shortly be extended to many more. The building bays are 27 in number, while 18 more are in course of construction. Each bay has an upper floor thereby doubling the drying space, the temperature of which is regulated by steam. The upper floors are used for artistic terracotta work,

plaster models and articles requiring special care in making. There are 34 kilns of various description and several others are now being built. Spring barrows run upon iron moulders carrying the bricks from one part of the works to the other. The number of men employed here is about 360, there are also 10 engines, and machines of all the best and latest construction turning out daily 60,000 articles or more. 100 wagons attached to an endless chain 1000 yards long deliver the clay with clockwork regularity at the rate of 7 1/2 hundredweight per minute. Within 8 or 10 ft. of the surface a careful observer can mark the various shades of colour in the marl, the series of clay continuing for 60 yards in depth. Extensive collieries, the largest in North Wales, employing about 1000 hands are also in the possession of this renowned and enterprising firm and are situated near the Hafod Brickworks".

At a gathering on 30th May, 1892 to celebrate the forthcoming wedding of Henry Dyke Dennis, the heir to the empire, it was announced to much applause that "although when the works were started it was said they were much too large, they had found them too small for the orders they had in hand" – a fitting tribute to Henry Dennis' astute commercial foresight.

In 1904 both the Red Works and Hafod Colliery were fitted up with an electric lighting plant supplied by a Leeds contractor.

Henry's flagship works had to keep up with the best of the competition, and it's surprising that he let other companies take the lead in this field. The Ffrwd Colliery had been lit by electricity as early as 1887, Llay Hall in 1889 and Ruabon Brick & Terracotta in 1895.

Towards the end of his life Henry Dennis became interested in motor cars and purchased a six cylinder Napier. On 15th June 1906 he drove it down to Bodmin but was taken ill shortly after arriving and died two days later, and according to reports of the time it was practically his first and last proper ride in it.

Wrexham Advertiser 30th June, 1906 – Mr Dennis lived a strenuous life and was always full

Henry Dennis. Photo: Wrexham Museum.

of hope and confidence. Everything he touched seemed to prosper; he never shirked a difficulty and never feared to undertake apparently impossible tasks. He surmounted all obstacles; he went about any undertaking with the utmost confidence and he reaped his reward. Many summers will come and go ere the influence he exerted in North Wales will cease to be remembered. Much that he was able to get through of late years was due to his wonderful vitality – the passage of time appeared in no way to sap his energy or to impair his vigour of mind. Quite recently the writer inquired of him "To what do you mainly attribute your long life and wonderful energy Mr Dennis?" "Well", came the reply, "I have always been an early riser, take plenty of exercise and invariably get up from the table when I could eat more".

In late 1933 the colliery was purchased by the Llay Main Colliery Co, and from 1934 the brickworks went its own way under the new style of Dennis Ruabon Ltd.

Following the Second War, during which time the brickworks had been requisitioned as a storage depot, there began a programme of expansions and improvements. In expectation of a post war demand for bricks 20,000 tons of surface soil was removed from the clay land to facilitate speedier clay removal when required, and a new mechanical shovel and flood pumps were brought into the clayhole. In 1946 steam power was made redundant by the installation of a sub station to connect the works to the mains electricity; quickly followed by the purchase of new electrical machinery for the factory. The ancient method of hand – barrowing bricks around the yard was also curtailed and a fleet of small petrol driven trucks and trailers employed in their stead.

By 1954 the clayhole had extended to over 25 acres in size; a double track endless tramway connecting it to the factory by running through a specially built tunnel below the Bangor to Johnstown road. Except for the tunnel itself, all traces of this have today disappeared and road trucks now haul the clay. In 1954 however, despite all the improvements, one thing hadn't changed:

"A familiar sound in the pit is the clang of ship's bell, used for signalling the conveyor operator when to stop and start. The bell has been in use since the firm started".

In January 1963 the company's capital was increased by a further £100,000 in order to finance yet further improvements. By 1965 a new 280 ft long gas fired tunnel kiln had been completed – the largest kiln in North Wales – and the smaller kilns began a conversion to oil firing, but in 1970 all the kilns were converted to running off cheaper North Sea gas.

In 1978 the kilns began to receive their fuel from a most novel source. On 29th November the valves were opened to receive methane gas from the underground workings of Bersham Colliery. Bersham had always been plagued by gas; Mr Hall, the Inspector of Mines saying in 1884 that "he had always to complain whenever he visited this colliery and described the pit as one of the most dangerous

The giant Hafod Red Brick Works in 1906. Photo: DRO.

he had been down". The manager Mr Pattinson "said he was never a day in the mine without seeing gas". This new scheme was the ideal way to benefit both companies – the gas being drawn out of the colliery via a two mile long pipeline to Hafod, and this arrangement continued until Bersham's closure at the end of 1986.

By the end of the 1970s the making of bricks had come to an end and the company concentrated its efforts into quarry tile production. The old beehive and rectangular brick kilns were eventually discarded as unsuitable and 1979 saw the construction of six new tile kilns – the beehives being demolished in the 1980s. In March 1997 a management buyout finally severed the last connections with the Dennis family's involvement, and the company, still retaining the surname of its founder, thrives today despite the threat from foreign competition.

As for Hafod Colliery, the National Coal Board closed it in March 1968.

For those readers local to this district one of the most impressive pieces of the Red Works' art can be seen in the facade of Chester Library, originally made for the Westminster Motor Car and Carriage Works of J A Lawton & Co, which opened in March 1902. The site had previously been a smaller carriage works owned by William Hewitt, but this larger factory was much more prestigious and featured 16 double forge hearths on the ground floor. At first glance the exterior architecture might be mistaken for stone, but is in fact a pinky buff terracotta designed and made at the Hafod Red Works.

SITE 108: BRANDIE PITS, RUABON

This brickmaking site was a very small affair connected with the Brandie Pits Colliery – in its day a very famous works; the Colliery Guardian calling it in 1858 "the great Brandy Colliery", and naturally using the more English spelling for their predominantly English readership. Its name actually gives rise to some fascinating theories as to its derivation. The Chronicle in 1856 says that "nearly adjoining the turnpike road the colliery works of the Great Western Railway Co, called the Brandy Colliery are situate", and the works also gets a mention back in 1844. In the days of the stagecoach, this point on the Ruabon road was a staging post and advertisements for coaching firms in 1830 mention the Nettle Post Coach and the Paul Pry Post Coach running daily along this route. Here the horses would have been changed and fed, and fodder – houses would have been a necessity for storing the horse feed. The Welsh for fodder is Ebran and fodder – house therefore becomes Ebrandy. I have read that there was a building in this area called the Ebrandy, which was connected to the local coal pits. The main Brandie Pits were about ten in number, plus some smaller ones, and most of them would have used pit ponies; all of them needing plenty of food on hand. It seems therefore that this district has a strong name connection with the usage of horses.

A railway map of 1863 shows that the main Brandie Works was then owned by the Ruabon Coal Co, the same concern who began sinking the Hafod Colliery that same year, although no brick kilns were specifically mentioned in the very detailed book of reference accompanying the map. Brickmaking by the clamp method would most certainly have occurred here, which might very well have not been mentioned, as clamps were not permanent structures.

By 1873 however, the 25 inch OS map shows Brandie Pits with two brick kilns on the colliery site – the works also having a separate coke oven plant, also shown on the 1863 map. When the Ruabon Coal Co folded around 1880 Henry Dennis' Ruabon Coal & Coke Co purchased the coke works, but I have no definite reference for his also having acquired the colliery. This may well at some point have become the property of Gomer Roberts, who is listed in the directories of 1880 and 1883 as being proprietor of Brandie Works Ruabon. He became bankrupt in that latter year with debts of over £10,000; his assets estimated to realise only £538, whilst the Advertiser of 23rd June noted that "the amount available for unsecured creditors is subject to the possibility of realising the machinery at the brickworks".

By May the following year the paper noted that "the old Brandy Works which have been for a considerable time lying idle will shortly be the scene of a new industry – the manufacture of velvet. A large factory is to be built for the purpose".

Everything connected with the Brandie Works has completely disappeared. The brick kilns were fairly central within the colliery site and, as far as I can judge, were situated at OS 2974 4568 – now an area of scrubland.

SITE 109: VAUXHALL COLLIERY, RUABON

There is precious little to say about the brickmaking at Vauxhall Colliery other than that the trade directories of 1874 – 76 listed the colliery as being brick manufacturers. The historian Lerry says that the first pit was sunk in 1857 and named Kenyon Colliery in honour of the landlord Lord Kenyon of Gredington. The later firm of the Vauxhall Coal Co Ltd was registered on 15th June 1871 for the purpose of working the former Kenyon Colliery of Messrs George Forrester & Co, which had previously been placed at auction in October 1869 by order of their mortgagees.

The Rhos Herald reported that the site finally ceased production on 12th May 1928 after a very uncertain period during which the miners had been placed on day-to-day contracts, and by June 1930 the company itself went into liquidation following the realisation that it could never reopen the works.

In its day Vauxhall had been one of Ruabon's major industries employing 600 men and boys. In 1967 the site was redeveloped as the Vauxhall Industrial Estate and one of the colliery's original buildings still stands at OS 3050 4534. On the eastern side of the adjacent railway line is a massive area of spoil tips which were once connected to the pits by an aerial tramway – the size of this tip being an indication of the site's one-time prosperity.

SITE 110: GARDDEN LODGE COLLIERY – RUABON BRICK & TERRACOTTA CO

This is the story of two brickmaking firms on the same site, the earliest of which was a small colliery:

Chester Chronicle 1859 – Gardden Lodge Colliery Co. They have now a branch line from the works to the G.W.R.. Main Coal. Quaker Coal. Ruabon Yard Coal. This celebrated coal is used by Her Majesty at Windsor Castle and is acknowledged to be the best quality raised in North Wales.

We can trace Gardden Lodge Colliery certainly back to 1851. The works, along with the tenancy of Gardden Lodge Farm, was acquired in early 1875 by the newly formed Gardden Lodge Coal, Coke & Firebrick Co – a firm set up by Lancastrian merchants and cotton dealers. By September the following year the company was in liquidation and was put up for auction, although not by reason of its weakness in the market place – the works was in full production. The sale was put back to January 1877, at which point the company managed to retain the works under the same name, and although it was only a relatively small works its success was assured for the next few years. One thing about this colliery however was never in doubt. Being situated on the great Ruabon marl bed the works were consistently recorded as raising large quantities of fireclay, which in April 1877 caused a fatal accident to the collier Moses Williams, who was working a seam of coal when it gave way under the weight of the clay seam above it and crushed him to death.

Wrexham Advertiser 16th April, 1881 – The Gardden Lodge Coal Co Ltd of Ruabon have about 30,000 tons of first class well seasoned clay in stock, which is daily increasing, and are prepared to make arrangements for the disposal of the clay or with persons willing to establish a firebrick works.

Note how the reference to brickmaking had by then been dropped from their company name. That advertisement reappeared in May 1883 and suggests that the company might have been interested in expanding their operations to include a proper brickworks. In fact, it might be effectively argued that they had ceased commercial brickmaking by this time, as why else should they have been selling off such a large stock of clay. But by July that year the company was again in liquidation and the entire site was dismantled in February 1884 at an auction sale whose numerous lots required two days for its disposal.

The site seemingly remained unoccupied until the freehold was purchased by the Ruabon Brick & Terracotta Co, whose intention was to develop the site into a large brickworks; its principal director being J. W. Haigh, a native of Todmorden in Lancashire, who had collieries at Burnley and Dudley. The new company was officially registered on 5th December, 1887 and from this point onwards we shall be referring to it by its then

abbreviation of "The Ruabon Co".

It wasn't long before the company began a series of wrangles with the G. W. R. who had sidings laid into the new factory from their Bryn yr Owen branch. These squabbles blew up between 1889 and 1897 and revolved around the issues of land rights, mineral excavation, subsidence, compensation etc, and resulted in the sidings being closed between November 1892 and July 1893, during which time the Ruabon Co were urgently forced to find alternative means of moving their goods out of their factory. "Wanted immediately. 50 or 60 horses and carts for carrying bricks from their works to Ruabon Station" ran the advertisement placed in the Chronicle of 31st December.

The British Clayworker tells us that one of the main promoters of the Ruabon Co was Henry Jenks; a man whose vitality as managing director did as much to ensure the growth of the company as the excellent quality of the clay itself. The works soon became colloquially known as Jenks Works, but it seems that his fame may have also extended into infamy. Henry had apparently in the early 1890s been tried in the Manchester Courts on a charge of "behaving in an immoral way" towards a woman he had met on a train, and the following account strongly suggests that his apparently amorous nature had produced an illegitimate child much closer to home – his home actually being the house called Gardden Lodge:

Wrexham Advertiser – Ruabon Petty Sessions 11th November, 1892 – Thomas Dickin, farmer, was brought up charged with malicious libel against Henry Jenks, managing director of Ruabon Brick & Terracotta Co, who had married a sister of the defendant and had had difficulties with him. On the morning of 25th October a postcard was in the company letter bag addressed to "Henry Jenks, Company Floater". On the other side was "I saw one of your thieves today, Felon. This is to inform you that your bastard is removed from Mrs Walsh', Selattyn, to near Pentrecoed where no doubt you will be able to see him. Have you floated that company yet?" The day when the postcard appeared to have been posted, the defendant accosted him while he was driving from his house to Ruabon station. He called out "Pull up you b... scamp. I will break your b... neck for you ". Jenks drove onto the station where the defendant came up and used such abusive language that he was ordered off the station by the station master.

Jenks Works became one of the very first to make use of electricity by installing lighting plant throughout the entire factory in 1895; much earlier than most other companies, and in the same year, as Henry explained himself:

"At a short distance from the chief works, others have been erected for the manufacture of ordinary bricks from the surface clay, and in another part of the estate some 240 houses are being erected by this company for the convenience of their workmen. These the men may if they choose purchase by a series of instalments absolutely less than the rent charged in the neighbourhood for interior accommodation".

On 25th July, 1900 the Ruabon Co petitioned to wind up the firm with debts of £45,773; the new company of Ruabon Brick & Terracotta Co Ltd being formed in March 1901 to raise the capital needed to continue the business. The principal directors J W Haigh and Mr J Collinge, another Lancashire colliery owner, had been for some time supporting the ailing works with vast sums from their personal funds, and had lost the lot in the winding up. Perhaps this stress had taken its toll on Mr Haigh's health, as shortly after the company's reformation he had gone on holiday to Harrogate to recover from a severe cold, but died there on 9th July, 1901.

At precisely the same time the new limited company was formed a seam of coal was found on their estate, and the company took on "about 12 practical miners" to work it. We know from a court case that Wynnstay Collieries had previously been supplying the Ruabon Co's needs, and it seems odd that the brickworks had not taken more advantages of the site's previous incarnation as a colliery. We can see how the old pit shafts had been totally neglected from this next story:

Wrexham Advertiser 23rd December, 1905 – An extraordinary and to some extent appalling phenomenon caused serious damage at the works of the Ruabon B & TC Co. The works are close by two disused pit shafts. One of these, 900 ft deep, is on the premises but fenced off by a brick wall 12 ft-high. This enclosure is bounded by the engine house, the drying room and a large brick kiln. On Wednesday morning a strange roaring sound was heard within the pit shaft, and a hole having been made in the wall for the purpose of finding out the cause, the enclosure was seen to have become a great whirlpool of water which had welled up from the pit with irresistible force, and as it gradually sank down again, had formed into a vortex. The foundations of the pit – covering were rapidly undermined. Gaps in the earth began to appear as the rock and soil was sucked downwards by the torrent; the abyss crept gradually outward as the whirlpool swept bricks and other obstructions into its maw, until at length the whole pit – covering fell in with a roar like thunder, followed the instant after by the collapse of the chimney stack 30 ft high, which toppled into the torrent with a mighty splash.

For most of the First War the works had been closed and used as an explosives store, but reopened again in mid-1919 under the new managership of Mr W A Gray, who had for the previous 27 years been a senior figure at J C Edwards Ltd. From the evidence of David Williams, once an office boy at the works, it appears that the Ruabon Co were also ahead of the competition in introducing one of the latest fashions into the local brick industry. He wrote "It was soon after the end of the war that the new manager brought into production something new in the area, namely the rustic faced brick, and that was specified for building the War Memorial Hospital.

Wrexham Leader 11th June 1937 – The Ruabon Brick and Terracotta Co employs about 200 men throughout the year and it is now under the management of Mr F Packard. There are 34 kilns on the works, one of which is the largest of its kind in the country. The goods manufactured

Ruabon Brick & Terracotta Works in its final years. Note the pipes feeding the kiln fireholes, which have been converted to oil firing. Photo: Gwilym Griffiths.

at Ruabon are high-class brick facings in red, brown and buff. All classes of red, brown and blue engineering bricks, flooring quarries, sills, ridge tiles, chimney pots, finials, pier-caps, fireplaces, flue liners, firebricks, sand faced and multi-coloured bricks. The latest brick introduction is the "Sand – rust" brick, which embodies the texture of the Old English hand made brick and has in its range many beautiful colour shades.

It was also at this time that the total electrification of the factory machinery at Gardden Works, as it was by then known, was completed.

Reuben Haigh, the son of J W Haigh, continuing in his father's role as the company's chairman, was by this time regarded as one of the great men of the district. He gave much of his time to farming his Gardden Estate lands and was in the 1930s the Hon Director of the Shire Horse Society and President of the Royal Welsh Agricultural Society. During my investigations I met an elderly gentleman who knew Reuben and said he was the nicest man it was possible to meet, and that he was also well renowned throughout the district for keeping his farm in the very best order. He also told me that Reuben had a private brickyard close by the Gardden Works where he made bricks for local use, as well as to keep his hand in at the craft – as more of a hobby than a serious business.

Gardden Works had become one of the largest, productive, profitable and prestigious of our district's brickworks, but as the practices within the building industry changed it finally found itself going the same way as its contemporaries. Reuben Haigh died in March 1951, aged 72 – the last of the original line linking the company with its illustrious past. By 1958 the factory could justify making only floor tiles, and in June 1959 a slump in tile orders forced the works onto a four-day week. In February 1960 Dennis Ruabon Ltd took over ownership of the works and managed to offset closure until the running of two such huge factories became financially unrealistic, and in May 1975 Dennis Ltd announced Gardden's closure.

The factory stood at OS 3005 4486 and received clay from underground pit workings as well as two opencast clayholes, one of which was sited north east of Gardden Works "between Afongoch stream and the path to Vauxhall Colliery", as the lease described it. From this clayhole the clay was transported to Gardden Works via an underground tunnel beneath the main road. The factory site today is occupied by Gardden Industrial Estate.

SITE 111: MONK & NEWELL BRICKWORKS, RUABON

Ruabon village itself was once famous for the three giant brickworks which stood almost alongside each other; Gardden Works being the largest. Tatham Works at site 112 was the earlier of the three, and Monk & Newell was the next to be established.

Wrexham Advertiser 7th July 1883 – "Those of our readers who pass through Ruabon on the G W R have no doubt noticed the extensive and picturesque block of buildings in course of erection and now rapidly approaching completion on the north west side of Ruabon station. These handsome buildings are the property of Messrs Monk, Newell and Bryon. The first two gentlemen are eminent contractors of Liverpool. Mr Bryon was until recently the manager of the Penybont Works and he is moreover the inventor or originator of red terracotta in Ruabon. On visiting the Ruabon works we were surprised to find that although the first brick was only laid on 1st March, the buildings are so far advanced as to admit of manufactures being commenced on Monday next. The elevation fronting the railway is comprised of ten high pitched gables; eight forming the drying rooms, 26 ft span; the machinery room 40 ft and the engine room 18 ft span. The brick making machinery as may be expected is of the most modern type and being manufactured by Mr W Hughes, Plaskynaston. It is proposed to build 40 kilns, 14 of which are already erected. The chimney stack which was finished on Saturday is without doubt the largest and finest in the district being 18 ft square at its base and 174 ft from the bottom of its bed of concrete which is 6 ft thick. Each brick and terracotta drying room is fitted up with 800 shelves each 13 ft long and heated with continuous underfloor steam piping. The roofing and tile drying room is one of the largest we have ever seen in any clay works, being 250 ft by 70 ft and capable of turning out nearly one million bricks and tiles per month. The clay at the point where it will be first obtained is of a distance of 200 yards from the machinery house and will be carried in small railway wagons and worked by an endless chain. Brickworks as a rule are a nuisance by reason of smoke, but here large flues are so constructed round the works as to carry all smoke away into the main stack. We were shown the modelling shop, the firm having permanently engaged the services of an eminent skilled artist in Mr H M Whyte of London. A large railway cutting is through the centre of the works for loading and getting in coal whilst there is also a second railway to connect the works with the neighbouring Vauxhall Colliery, converting what was at the beginning of the year an area of grass grown fields into a scene of bustling industry".

It wasn't long before Mr Bryon's exact position within the company came into question; Monk and Newell refuting that he ever really had a legal stake in the venture, and in mid-1885 he was paid £200 to quit the firm. His only remaining legacy in the recorded history of the company is the preceding article and the company's listing in an 1883 trade directory as being Messrs Monk, Newell, Bryon Co. Mr Bryon had previously been J C Edwards' chief modeller, and his work was exhibited at the Wynnstay Floral Fete and Industrial Exhibition of August 1872, of which the Advertiser said "The models in clay are somewhat inferior with the exception of that exhibited by Mr E Bryon, Trefynant modeller to Mr J C Edwards; a design for a fountain, the figure being a merman, and the manner in which the shape and position of the figure were brought out, showed an acquaintance with anatomy which Mr Bryon is so skilled. We understand that Mr Bryon had prepared several other articles for exhibition, but owing to the carelessness of the man in charge, they were completely spoiled in the kiln".

Wrexham Advertiser 1st October, 1887 – On Saturday the workmen belonging to Messrs Monk and Newell combined in a trip to Manchester. The special train left Ruabon at 6am and arrived in Manchester soon after nine, which gave the excursionists ample time to pay a visit to the exhibition as well as Bellevue. The firm, in addition to allowing the works to stand for a day, gave a handsome donation towards defraying expenses. A very pleasing incident marked the day's proceedings, it being the presentation to Mr Gibson the station master of a silver mounted pen holder and pencil case combined, by the workmen, for the interest he had taken in the trip and the men.

The firm continued their regular contributions to the workmen's summer trips for some years. On their 1903 day trip to Blackpool the company "very generously gave £10 towards their employees trip, and the gift, which is an annual one, was highly appreciated by the workmen". It's also worth noting how much respect was shown towards the local station master; a social phenomenon which has long been lost and forgotten by we present day folk. It should be understood that the establishment of the railways had benefited the ordinary working man by opening up the country to a degree never before imagined or realised, and in those more respectful and authoritarian days of Victoria's reign the station master was as highly regarded in society as the local mayor or police sergeant; a situation which continued to exist in the more rural communities until the strident improvements in road transportation during the 1940s. By 1895 Mr Gibson had been succeeded at Ruabon station by Mr Fussell, at which time he was similarly honoured by the Monk & Newell workmen with the gift of another silver pencil case.

Wrexham Advertiser 5th October, 1889 – This usually quiet village was painfully aroused on Monday by a shocking fatal accident which happened to a man named John R Jones, employed as a loader of bricks into railway trucks. Occasionally it happens that the packing or strapping of the goods in the truck cannot be completed before the wagon leaves the yard by the afternoon train. On such occasion the packers follow the truck onto the GWR siding where the work is completed. On Monday this practice was carried out by Jones and others who had commenced their task about 4:30pm, all three men being fully under the impression that the shunting was over. The deceased, who was standing on the inside and close to the edge of the truck, did not notice any movement of the wagon he was in until a sudden jerk caused him to lose his balance. Two of his fellow workmen saw him fall and made haste to see if he was hurt, when to their horror they found the unfortunate man's body lying across the rail, one loaded and four empty wagons having passed over him.

That accident happened when the trucks were taken from Monk & Newell to Gardden Lodge Junction to be weighed. The loading and shunting of brickyard trucks had by this date become an intensely busy activity and the increase in brick traffic on the railways from both this and Gardden Works had become so great that "a considerable amount of shunting work is done during the night", and large lamps had to be fitted at both Ruabon goods yard and Gardden Lodge Junction to make this work easier.

Wrexham Advertiser 3rd February, 1900 – A successful competitive meeting took place in the Welsh Baptist chapel on Wednesday evening when Mr Richard Price presided over a crowded congregation. Considerable interest was centred in the Male Voice Choir's competition. The choirs from the brickworks of Messrs H Dennis, Monk & Newell and H R Bowers competed. The three choirs gave a capital rendition of "Horaeth" and the adjudicator awarded the prize to Messrs Monk & Newell's choir.

On 30th June 1899 the new lease on "the clay and brickworks at Pentreclawdd" (Monk & Newell) was granted to John Newell; Thomas Monk having died ten years previously on 5th November 1889 at his home, Woodchurch Farm, Birkenhead. From 1917 the works were occupied by the Ministry of Munitions, but upon their relinquishing the site in

early 1919 it was put up for auction in May that year, but without any serious interest being shown. In September however it was bought by a Liverpool syndicate headed by Thomas Dugdale Stubbs, who was also managing director of Caernarfon Brickworks. He paid £10,100 for the lease on the Ruabon works, and circa March 1920 he sold it to his own company The North Wales Brick & Tile Co, who began manufacturing the bricks at the old Monk & Newell factory under the trade name of Rubric, at which point the old name of Monk & Newell technically ceased to exist. By this time the works had its original 14 round kilns plus 5 square brick kilns and 2 square tile kilns; the 40 kilns originally envisaged never having materialised.

As we have seen with many other of our brickworks the inter-war years proved to be a precarious time for the industry and by November 1924 a petition had been presented by one of the company's creditors to wind it up. To protect the works from any future creditor's claims, Stubbs eventually transferred the company's lease back into his own name in June 1927.

Wrexham Advertiser 28th July, 1928 – On Wednesday evening a sad fatality occurred in a disused clay pit belonging to the Monk & Newell brickworks. Two brothers went to the pit which is full of water for a bathe, accompanied by a companion. Walter Davies, aged 16, must have got into difficulties and though the companion made gallant attempts to aid, he eventually sank. The police were quickly on the scene and attempts were made to recover the body by diving. When these proved futile grappling irons were used. A little before midnight the scene at the pool was eerie in the extreme. The gentle rays of a young moon stroked the ripples of water, in the depth of which a promising life had met its end. The precincts of the tragedy were thronged with anxious people. Passing motorists frequently stopped to offer their kindly aid. The search was resumed early on Thursday morning and a large crowd had assembled. The body was discovered in about 5 ft of water at the side of an old truck. At the inquest: Coroner – Are there any precautions posted up around there? Companion – No sir.

Site 91

Site 92

Site 102

Site 104

Site 105

Site 107

Site 110

Site 114

The clayhole was quite a size and perhaps most of it had indeed been left unworked since before the war. The coroner summed up by expressing his concern that people still had to use clay pits to bathe themselves. "In a district of 20,000 people there was not one public bath house", he said. Bathrooms simply didn't exist in the working men's houses of those days.

In July 1929 Stubbs' severe financial difficulties saw him being examined for bankruptcy with debts of £13,702, and the Wrexham Leader reported that "early in its career the company (North Wales Brick & Tile) became short of funds and was subsequently carried on by overdrafts. All his resources had gone in the effort to keep the brickworks going". His potential assets stood at £22,527 – dependent on his being able to realise the sale of the Ruabon brickworks, and it is from this time, July 1929, that we find our last evidence of the brickworks being in production from a letter issued by the company. Part of it reads "I do not think it would be possible to sell all the blue bricks we can make every week. When Monk & Newell had the works we have always been able to deliver large orders for blue goods. Red bricks are more profitable. It is not advisable to turn over the plant to making just one or two items".

We don't know who wrote that letter, but it could have been Mr C Morgan, the manager who had been retained in the 1919 transfer of ownership, at which time he had been with Monk & Newell for 36 years. By now the landlord Sir Philip Simon Yorke of Erddig Hall thought it wise to step in and try to save the ailing works, so in September 1929 he published an advertisement offering it for sale, followed up in November by his attempt to get a grant under the Trade Facilities Act to reopen the by then closed factory, but no interest was shown by local government. During these troubled times Sir Philip had been wrangling with Stubbs over certain validities of the leasehold in consequence of Stubbs' bankruptcy, and Sir Philip was much relieved when Stubbs finally decided to give up his claims. A solicitor's letter dated 7th October, 1930 reads "I am glad to hear that Capt. Stubbs has left the works since it would have been inconvenient to have had to eject him". By this time the fate of the works had been well and truly sealed and it never reopened.

The abandoned factory seems to have still been there in 1939 at OS 3040 4463, but was later replaced by housing. The flooded clayhole was let to a local angling club and still exists today.

SITE 112: TATHAM BRICKWORKS, RUABON

The earliest of the three large Ruabon brickworks enjoyed its heydays whilst under the proprietorship of Mr H R Bowers, one of the district's pioneers in the field of quality red brick manufacture, and he built the Tatham Works on a site which had already been proved as a brickmaking facility. A railway map for the proposed route of the W,M & CQ Extension in 1862 shows the original brickyard of Messrs Daniel Owens & Co as being little more than a single building with no permanent kilns erected on land owned by Colonel Frederick Richard West. Daniel may well have been the same gentleman who was later to be a director of the

Pant Coal, Brick & Fireclay Co at site 106. An indenture of lease in December 1862 also exists in which the trustees of Colonel West granted the brickearth and clay at Tatham to Daniel Owen, John Davies, William Pritchard and the Rhos builder John Pritchard, who was also part owner of the Rhos brickworks at site 104.

The lease on this minor brickworks was transferred to Mr H R Bowers from 1st January, 1868 at a dead rent of £25 per annum with a royalty of 1s. 6p. per thousand bricks and one penny for each chimney pot, and Bowers built his new factory on exactly the same spot as was shown on the railway map for Daniel Owen's works.

Wrexham Advertiser 19th June, 1869 – On Monday afternoon an accident occurred at the Tatham brickworks near Afongoch, which proved fatal. A young man named Edward Daniels, about 19 years of age, was helping to erect a large chimney, when by some mishap he fell from the top and was killed almost instantaneously.

Unfortunately, I have not been able to uncover a single piece of documentation to enable us to follow how the works developed during the next twenty or so years, save for one solitary mention in a rates assessment case in February 1880, when the surveyor Mr Marshall stated that he had visited the works and "considered them in a very bad state indeed". It does seem that Mr Bowers had lavished more attention on his other works at Penbedw, and in truth we simply don't know exactly how productive the Tatham site had proved. Bowers died in 1902, but some say that he sold the works to the Ruabon Brick & Terracotta Co in 1888, although I have not been able to corroborate that evidence. It is odd that a railway proposal map of 1895 lists the occupier of the works as being H R Bowers, and a newspaper report from July 1897 also mentions "Mr H R Bowers' Tatham and Penbedw works", so I personally doubt that the Bowers company relinquished Tatham until after his death.

The factory had a tramway connection to a clayhole south of the works, which then ran south east to loading stages on the GWR, but on the evening of Wednesday 23rd March 1898 a new main line siding was officially opened into the works itself, allowing for 20 wagons to be loaded simultaneously, this being a great advantage over the "toy railway", as the Advertiser called the old tramway.

Again, we know nothing about the history of the works in the early 20th century until February 1927, at which point we have some correspondence from the Ruabon Co to the Wynnstay Estate Office. We must assume that Wynnstay had by this time acquired the land – Col. West had apparently died in 1862. The Ruabon Co explained: "Regarding Tatham lease. It is on a part of this land that we wish to install an electric haulage plant for which purpose we are now at work installing an electric supply to these works. The second point we would like altered is the term of years. Could you please make this 60 years instead of 40. We feel sure that you will consider this a reasonable time when you realise what we are doing at Tatham". What the Ruabon Co had been doing was quite adventurous. By 1937 the company's manager Mr Packard had designed and built two remarkable kilns on the Tatham site. One was the largest down – draught round kiln in the country, and the other was the first concrete monolithic kiln yet constructed. This was a kiln cast as a single moulding from reinforced concrete with no brickwork joints to leak any internal gases, thereby ensuring minimal heat losses, resulting in a reduction in both the firing time and fuel expenses.

Wrexham Leader 11th June, 1937 – Both works (Gardden Lodge and Tatham) have now been entirely electrified, obsolete plant has been taken out and all the drives are served with the latest motor and equipment. The whole of the changeover has been designed by Mr W R Ebrey in conjunction with Mr Packard. To those who knew the plants at the Gardden and Tatham works prior to electrification, the entire absence of heavy gear wheels, long shafting and cumbersome units will now seem as though a new era has been set up; comparative silence prevails where formerly the rumble of machinery must have proved destructive to the workers. All the goods produced at the Tatham works are now being dried from the waste heat of the kilns.

Tatham Brickworks with Ruabon Brick & Terracotta above it in the early 1930s. Photo: Dennis Gilpin / Nene.

During the Second War the Tatham Works was requisitioned by the Government as a dispersal warehouse for Bakelite Ltd, who retained the factory until May 1948, but the actual freehold on the land, together with the brickworks lease and Tatham Farm, was sold outright by Wynnstay Estate to Reuben Haigh of the Ruabon Co for £6,250 earlier in November 1945. Once Bakelite had vacated the premises the Ruabon Co had sole usage of the site to do as it pleased. But what exactly they did here and for how long is again unsure. We do know that in March 1961 the 170 ft chimney was demolished to allow the Ruabon Co to have access to the clay seam below, and it is known that the company used Tatham's clayhole to supply their Gardden Works. It seems unlikely that brickmaking had resumed after the war, especially as the Wrexham Leader explained in 1961 that the main works' chimney had been out of use since

before the Second War. The works was sited at OS 3019 4455 and the clayhole is now a tree planted landfill site.

SITE 113: OFFA COTTAGES BRICKFIELD, RUABON

At OS 2980 4443 was a small country brickfield of 1a. 19p. area on the opposite side of the road from Offa Cottage. In October 1881 the brickfield was let by Wynnstay Estate to Robert Pemberton at a rental of £5 per annum. A railway map of 1895 shows Pemberton as still in occupation of this field, but by that date it was not listed as a brickmaking site.

In February 1930 the Estate let a brickfield of 3r. 28p. (much smaller than the above mentioned) to Richard Owen of Offa Cottage, Ruabon. Could this conceivably have been the same site? Had only part of the original field been let? Surely the reference to "a brickfield" was a remnant from an older age, as why would anybody have wanted to bother making bricks on such a small scale in as late as 1930?

Whatever the truth may have been, what is certain is that at some point in the distant past a small working brickfield existed here. The site is still an open field to this day.

Acrefair Area

SITE 114: H R BOWERS PENBEDW BRICKWORKS, ACREFAIR

Henry Richard Bowers was born on 19th June, 1821 and was one of the three brothers who ran Bowers Bros grocery and druggists store at 101 Eastgate Street, Chester, opposite the present Browns department store. Their father had founded the business – "Surpassed by none and Equalled by few" – in 1780, and up until 1843 they also had a second shop in Northgate Street. Such was the repute of the business that in 1869 they were appointed a Royal Warrant, but by this time Henry had left the firm to set up a fireclay works at Penbedw, north of Acrefair – a wild and windswept area located on the slope of a hillside at OS 2746 4364 with the works offices fronting onto the narrow lane which is still today named Bowers Road.

The site had in the 1840s been occupied by the well-known local industrialist Gomer Roberts, who had used it as a waste tip. Gomer was also dumping waste a few hundred yards to the north at OS 2742 4391, which had according to the tithe map itself previously been used as a brickyard, and a small pond, probably the original claypit, now marks the spot.

As to the Penbedw Works, it is the local legend that this was the first works in the Wrexham – Ruabon area to produce fine quality bricks from the famous Ruabon marl, and the evidence seems to bear this out. The first positive reference to Henry's occupation here was the company's first known advertisement in the Chester Chronicle on 25th November, 1854, which read:

"Bowers' Penbedw Fireclay Works. Superior glazed stoneware pipes, firebricks, white facing bricks, made by the most approved machinery".

To be able to manufacture such items, Bowers must have had some decent kilns erected by this time, and we may be able to trace the works back even further. At a rates assessment case in February 1880 "Bowers stated he had originally taken the works at Penbedw 28 years ago", which

would suggest its having begun in 1852, so he most certainly deserves the accolade of being at least one of the better organised of the early Ruabon pioneers.

Wrexham Advertiser 21st March, 1863 – Mr H R Bowers, proprietor of the Penbedw Works, presented his workmen on the 10th with a quantity of beef; the single men with 2lb each and the married men with 4lb each. This is not the first time for Mr Bowers to show his great kindness towards his workmen – on times of general elevation he usually presented them their full time wages. Such good deeds as this ought not to be hidden, as the employers and workmen of this district may have an example worthy of imitation.

His family were ardent Wesleyan Methodists and a sense of Christian duty was strongly to the fore in his character. The aforementioned account of his paying his men their full-time wages may be a reference to the custom of withholding "pence money" as a means of inducing the men to hold to their terms of contract without leaving before completing their time. The following excerpt from the Advertiser of 15th June, 1889 also speaks well of Mr Bowers' reputation:

"Mr Thomas Edwards on behalf of the men said he felt it a great privilege to meet his employer and son that day. They as workmen had benefited much by the kindness of their respected employer. He had allowed them to work full-time during the quiet part of the year when the yard was literally packed with goods, whilst other manufacturers in the district had only allowed the men to work half-time. He also paid their wages weekly, which was a great advantage to them".

Mr Bowers exhibited his company's wares at the Eisteddfod of 1866; the venue for the "host of sturdy Welshmen and fair Welsh women" that year being at Chester. Holding Welsh Eisteddfodau at

English venues was not uncommon in those days. The Gorsedd – the ritualistic centre of the event – was set up on the Roodee racecourse and an exhibition of Welsh industries was held in the spacious Music Hall Theatre; the participants of which included the Flintshire Oil & Cannel Co exhibiting specimens of their paraffins and coke, the Saltney anchorsmiths Wood Bros, Powell's Buckley pottery, Griffiths Bros of Caergwrle, who manufactured spades and shovels, and Mr Bowers' works:

Wrexham Advertiser 8th September, 1866 – The first stall to the right of the entrance contained a complete assortment of fire clay goods from the works of Mr H R Bowers of Penbedw. The excellence of the articles manufactured by Mr Bowers is well-known, and to him belongs the credit of originating the manufacture of a new class of goods in Ruabon, and thereby utilising the excellent beds of clay in connection with the Ruabon Coal Measures.

Mr Bowers received the silver medal for his exhibits. Apart from the car industry, industrial exhibitions today are virtually exclusively restricted to specialist trade conventions, but Victorian society loved to celebrate its industrial diversity at regular exhibitions set up all over the country for the widespread appreciation of the general public.

By 1879 the works had 11 kilns, and for such a prestigious company this seems to have been quite a modest number. Perhaps the company's acquisition of the Tatham site in 1868 is the reason for this, as most of the company's common brick seemed to have originated from there, leaving Penbedw to produce the finer articles.

Wrexham Advertiser 5th June 1879 – On Sunday evening at about half past 5 o'clock a fire was discovered to have broken out in the barn adjoining the Penbedw Brickworks. The discovery was first made by a boy who at once acquainted the foreman Mr Thomas Edwards. Mr Edwards was quickly upon the spot, but only just in time to save a number of valuable horses which were in the stables attached to the barn.

The barn was stored with a large quantity of straw which had taken fire by some means. Mr Edwards found the stable filled with dense smoke and experienced much difficulty in removing the animals, they being extremely restive. The rapidly increasing flames were put out but not before the whole of the straw had been consumed and considerable damage done to the building.

The stables were extremely necessary to Penbedw Works; more so than at most other works by reason of its lack of railway accommodation. The following report of Mr Bowers' Penbedw site in 1880 bears this out and tells us much else besides:

"The whole of the Penbedw clay was got from open cuttings and the best clay was about 12 yards deep. The goods were loaded on a siding at Acrefair and carted there from the works about a third of a mile. There was no railway at Penbedw. With regard to the question of cartage, he had employed three horses and carts to go to the railway station and Bowers put down for such a horse and cart with a man's wages £1-17-6 a week, or a total per annum for the three horses and carts of £292-10-0. In addition to this it cost him about £90 a year for the cartage of slack to the works, which would be obviated if he had the advantage of a railway siding. Seacome's Delph Works paid about two pence per ton to the branch line at Plasmadoc, whilst Bowers paid something like ten pence for cartage. The Penbedw brick output in 1879 was 6448 tons from 11 kilns and the water was supplied from the Cefn Water Works.

The lack of a railway would also have contributed to the restricted output of Penbedw Works – if it hadn't been for the railway siding close by at Acrefair, Penbedw would probably have never achieved the notoriety it did.

For the last few years of his life Henry had become quite invalid and retired to his home in Chester, leaving the works in the hands of his sons Harry and Herbert. Harry came in daily from Chester by train to Wrexham, whilst Herbert lodged locally, returning to Chester with his brother at weekends. Henry died on 20th May, 1902, aged 81, and in October the following year the company took out further mortgages of £10,000, the reason for which is not explained, but the terracotta industry was soon to face bleak times. By 1912 the company was in liquidation and was put up for sale in June as a going concern. With no interest forthcoming it was again offered for sale in November, but this time it was clear that the intention was to dispose of it for its material assets and not for the continuation of brick manufacture.

The main body of the works remained in ruins until the entire hillside was decimated by large scale opencast clay mining by Rhos Fireclays Ltd in the 1970s. All that remains today are a few overgrown patches of rubble adjacent to the roadside.

SITE 115: COWAN'S CAMBRIAN BRICKWORKS, ACREFAIR

Just north of Acrefair stood a small, short lived brickworks on Bowers Road, which you would have passed to reach the much larger Penbedw Works further to the north.

In 1865 the landowner Mr G H Whalley granted the lease on the coal and fireclay to Mr T W Cowan, who established his "Trefynant Colliery & Fireclay Works", advertised throughout 1866 as suppliers of bricks, ridge tiles, chimney tops etc. It wasn't very long however until the whole of the works' plant and stock were offered for sale in November 1866 and again in the following year, including such sundries as the carpenter's benches, smith's tools and anvils. The subsequent history of the works is missing for the next eight years, but it seems that it survived and became known as the Cambrian Fireclay Works. By 1874 the lease had been transferred to Mr John Jackson, a local man, and his partner Mr Hall, and in September of that year Messrs Hall & Jackson managed to secure a total loan of £1,500 on the works, dependent on a more favourable lease being secured from Mr Whalley. It was evident that the works needed further capital to survive, and to this end Mr Jackson, together with a new partnership of Liverpool men, formed the Ruabon

Fireclay & Sanitary Pipe Co on 3rd March, 1875; a venture which never managed to properly get off the ground.

In August 1875 Jackson teamed up with a totally new partnership of Manchester businessmen under the style of the Cambrian Sanitary Pipe & Terracotta Co, but this venture failed to resurrect the ailing company's fortunes and the courts ordered the entire dispersal of the works at auction on 17th December, 1875, put back to 7th February, 1876. The reason for the failure was partly blamed on the new lease promised in 1874 never having materialised, which resulted in the mortgagees of the £1,500 loan having sued for the return of the money. That, plus poor brick sales, sealed the fate of the works.

The factory stood at OS 2767 4328 and is remembered in the name of one of the houses built on the site – Cambrian House.

SITE 116: PLAS ISA COAL, IRON AND BRICK WORKS, ACREFAIR

The road from Acrefair to Penycae is now a quiet backwater set amidst mostly open countryside, and the traveller today would be entirely unaware that it was once the access to some important and diverse industrial undertakings, the northernmost of which was the Plas Isa Works – a minor colliery, blast furnace and brickworks at OS 2805 4442.

"The Plas Isa Coal and Iron Work belonging to Sir Watkin Williams Wynne was in lease up to 1849 to Messrs Roberts Rogers Co who carried on the works for nearly 20 years in which time a large extent of the coal was worked. In July of 1849 they failed and there was a sale by auction of the machinery and other effects".

So reads part of a document discovered amongst the papers of the Wynnstay Estate, which suggests the site was in operation from the late 1820s. The Roberts of the partnership was Gomer Roberts, whom we have come across before, and whose diverse industrial interests during the 1840s-60s covered the Ruabon – Acrefair district like few others did. The 1844 tithe verifies the site as having earlier been *Gomer Roberts & Co's furnace yard*, but which was put down to being a waste tip at the time – perhaps a spoil site for the colliery workings.

The site still had great potential for future undertakings, so to prevent it from being broken up at the 1849 auction Sir Watkin himself purchased most of the machinery, and the site, due to the iron trade being so depressed, was left idle until February 1852.

"At that time Mr Giller who had suffered a loss of about £800 by Messrs Roberts Rogers became the tenant with the promise that after opening and seeing his way, a lease for 14 years would be granted him, upon he paid a yearly dead rent of £135 in consideration for the use of machinery belonging to Sir Watkin".

Samuel Giller's occupancy at the Plas Isa Ironworks is listed in the trade directory of 1856 and a newspaper article in 1855 mentions

"The Plas Isa Works belonging to Messrs Giller & Co, whom it appears raise and sell coal for the British Iron Company".

The British Iron Co was a large iron works in Acrefair itself, to whom many small local collieries were supplying fuel. In 1858 the Advertiser was offering "Good firebricks at 22 shillings per thousand for cash payment at Plas Isa Coal, Coke and Brick Works", and we know that Giller & Co were making bricks from the example illustrated in this book, which bears the stamping G & Co. We also know how much coal was being raised at this time from a royalty account which states that "in 1858 the coal worked for the complete year was 585 1/2 tons", which would mean that the colliery workings were very minor indeed. This is also suggested by the evidence of Mr G H Whalley MP, a local landowner who part owned the site with Sir Watkin. At a railway bill hearing in 1862 he said of the works: "Mr Giller works it, or at any rate he pays me a rent for my tramway. He is making bricks there and I believe gets coal. It is now 12 years since the tramway was made". The lack of any proper railway to the works was probably the cause of its always having remained so small. Mr

Whalley's evidence puts the building of the tramway at circa 1850 – an odd situation as the site would have been idle at this time – and it was connected by the tramway to the main line at Plasmadoc via Plas yn Wern Brickworks.

Plas Isa's brickworks undoubtedly became the principal reason for the site continuing to exist. The 1862 railway hearing stated that the blast furnace and colliery were closed during that year, whilst the mineral agent Mr E Jones stated in 1872 that the furnace had been idle for the previous ten years. As for the brickworks, we definitely know that it was functional from the following inclusions which appeared in the Wrexham Advertiser between 1860-63:

April 1860 – To brickmakers. Wanted. An experienced man competent to take the entire making of bricks on contract.
Apply at Plasisa Brickworks near Ruabon.
May 1860 – Superior strong building bricks at 21 shillings per thousand. Apply to Mr Hanson, Plasisa Brickworks.
December 1861 – Firebricks of the best quality. Nearly indestructible by fire. Plas Isa Brickworks, Ruabon.
February 1863 – Superior draining pipes made of the best fireclay. Red and blue flooring tiles and strong pallett made bricks. Plas Isa Works near Ruabon.

And although the name of Plas Isa is not specifically mentioned, I believe the following advertisements related to the works, especially as the name of Evan Jones is mentioned – probably the mineral agent who was mentioned above:

Wrexham Advertiser July 1863 – To brick burners. Wanted, an experienced steady man who has been accustomed to burn fire clay and common clay. None need apply whose character will not bear the strictest scrutiny. Apply to Mr Evan Jones, Penycae near Ruabon.
Wrexham Advertiser August 1863 – Brickworks to be let. With sheds, kilns, powerful machinery and every convenience for manufacturing fire clay and common clay. As no further outlay will be required the concern is well worth the

attention of any respectable working man possessing some capital. Apply to Mr Evan Jones, Plas Isa, Ruabon.

The works was sold under many lots at an auction on 16th July, 1866, including the 54 ft by 26 ft brickshed, double brick kiln, 2 round kilns and 1 square kiln, together with the old blast furnace engine. By 1872 the site was being referred to as Plas Isa Old Works and the OS map for that period shows little more than spoil heaps, although the works must have been resurrected in some part, as we have evidence from a court hearing in December 1879 which stated that the works had by that time been standing idle for two years.

Any attempts to locate it from studying the old OS maps will prove futile. The only reference to it is the marking "old shaft" on the 1900 edition, but Mr Whalley's estate plans of 1877 clearly show it marked as "Plasisa Blast Furnace".

In 1924 the landowner Sir Watkin contracted Campbell Jones & Edwards Co to remove all the slag waste from the site, and for this reason all that remains to be seen today are rolling fields.

SITE 117: PLAS UCHA BRICKWORKS, ACREFAIR

Coming down the road from Plas Isa we can today see an embankment of trees which was marked on Mr Whalley's estate map as then being a small "Colliery Pit and Claybank" on the east of the road at OS 2825 4420 in the holding of John Jackson, the last occupier of the nearby Cambrian Brickworks.

A little to the south was Plas Ucha Brickworks at OS 2828 4386; another small and short lived works, much like the Cambrian. It has to be said that verifying its historical existence proved difficult at first, and it was even once suggested by an earlier historian that the few Victorian references to it were a misspelt reference to Plas Isa at site 116.

The British Architect 1878 – Up the hill to the north of Garth Trevor and situated about two miles west of the village of Ruabon are the more recently developed works of Messrs Smith & Thomas at Plas Ucha. This firm works the clays associated with the Wall & Bench coal, which here are adapted for use and yield good bricks of a pale yellow colour that are rapidly finding their way into the market.

This area was in the 1860s leased to the New British Iron Co at Acrefair, a sprawling ironworks complex whose holdings included many small colliery pits dotted throughout the northern reaches of Acrefair, from which they mined coal for their works. It was on the site of the future Plas Ucha Brickworks that they worked their No. 18 Delph Pit – a small shaft from which they also extracted fireclay which was then used by the Plas yn Wern Brickworks (site 119).

Before the Plas Ucha Brickworks was built it appears that the No. 18 pit first became known as the Plas Ucha Colliery. On 10th November, 1874 the Wrexham Districts Highways Board granted an application made by Mr Smith of the Plas Ucha Colliery to lay down a tramway from his works northwards to Plas Isa Works. The tramway was subsequently built and is shown on an Indenture map of 1881 running up along the road from Plas Ucha, but it had been removed by the turn of the century and therefore does not feature on either the first or second edition OS maps.

In 1877 the landowner Mr Whalley mortgaged his Acrefair lands to Sir Francis Hicks, John Boustead and Jeremiah Colman, and it is from the plans drawn up for this transaction that we are able to positively locate our brickworks. It is shown as being in the holding of Messrs Thomas & Smith (Mr Smith most likely being the proprietor of the earlier colliery) and the legend for the plan reads:

"Cottage and garden, tramway, pond and pit bank on which Works, Drying Sheds and Kilns are erected, let under lease dated 25th March, 1876. The tramway runs down the road through Sycamore ".

We can therefore take this date as being the time when the colliery probably became a brickworks, and we can also see further mention of the tramway; Sycamore having then been a local district between this brickworks and Plas Isa

Works.

The brickworks was also known by the general name for this area – Delph. An insurance valuation of 1876 mentions that

"The No. 18 Delph Fireclay Works held by Mr Smith and Mr E W Thomas is a small working". That quote also helps to connect the brickworks with the earlier No. 18 coal pit, but we must take one thing into important consideration, in that we should not confuse this works with the larger and much more impressive Delph Works nearby at site 118.

Wrexham Advertiser 25th November, 1876 – On Saturday a man named David Jones who is employed at the Plas Ucha Brickworks was braking a wagon of bricks down the branch leading from the works when he accidentally got under the wheels, and his leg below the knee was literally smashed. He was at once conveyed to the Ruabon Cottage Hospital where amputation was considered necessary.

David Jones unfortunately died from his injuries, leaving a wife and five children. The branch line was a standard gauge siding running into the works from the south, where it connected to the main line at Acrefair.

Messrs Smith & Thomas had only just over three years occupancy at the works. On 29th October 1879 the entire plant of the "Plas Ucha Coal & Brick Works" was auctioned under a distress for rent in various lots: "The whole of the remaining plant of the works comprising a pair of winding engines and the whole of the shedding and brick kilns". It is clear then, that the works had comprised not only the brick plant, but the original colliery as well – hence the existence of the pit winding engines.

The new landowners Jeremiah Colman and John Boustead must have acquired the site, as a later Indenture of 29th September, 1881 records them letting the complete works, illustrated by a detailed plan, to the Oswestry engineer Thomas Mason, who took on

"the premises known as the Delph Works, the carriage of the goods to and from the kilns to

the main GWR by means of the Plas Madoc Branch Rly which is connected with the premises by a siding".

The works never saw the new century. The 1900 OS map showed the main factory in outline only, suggesting it as having been unused, and the six kilns shown on the Indenture plan had been demolished. Where the factory once was now stands a small stone and brick shed, perhaps part of the original works. According to a local man the last usage for this building was as a small chapel school room.

SITE 118: DELPH FIRECLAY WORKS, ACREFAIR

The third brickmaking site on the Delph Road was the most southerly and by far the largest and most successful. Before it's establishment the area was used by the New British Iron Co as a dump for colliery waste, and was connected to their works by one of their many tramways networking this district. According to an article in a trades publication of 1940 the brickworks was founded in 1868 by Thomas Henry Seacome from Wem in Shropshire, who developed it to produce not only bricks but glazed sanitary pipes, the product for which the works became most noted. Almost nothing is recorded concerning the works' development, other than the general opinion that it was regarded as being extremely well laid out. A London surveyor and manufacturer remarked that he had never seen a better designed brickworks in his life, and that if he had constructed his own works to Seacome's design he should have saved £1,000.

Wrexham Advertiser 11th January, 1873 – Mr T H Seacome of the Delph works has this season in continuance of his annual custom of favouring his workmen with Christmas gifts, instituted a novel and noble precedent for the district. In former years the gifts have been in money, but this time he issued an address to his workmen, about 80 in number, in which he wished them a happy Christmas and informed them that he intended to give them each a bank

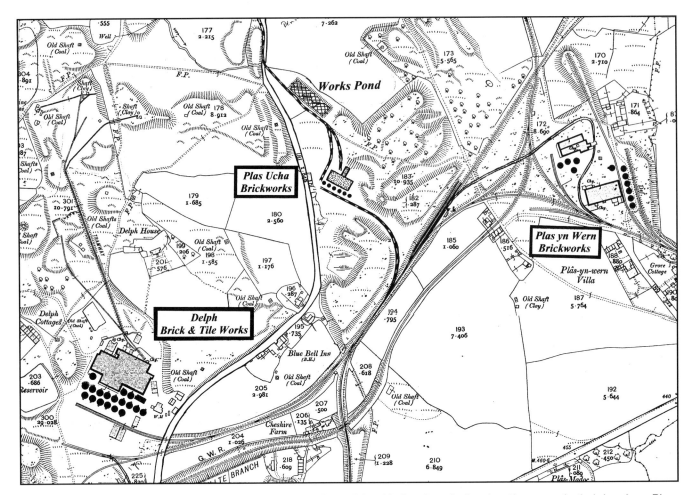

This composite map shows three brickworks sites north of Acrefair, with the sites depicted as they were in their heydays. Plas Ucha Brickworks is shown circa 1882 with its six little kilns serviced by a branch of main line railway, whilst a forked tramway connects it with the main road to run northwards to the coal pits at Plas Issa. The Delph Works is shown as it was in 1912, and Plas yn Wern as it was circa 1900.

book in the Rhosymedre Post Office Savings Bank with a deposit of four shillings for each married man and two shillings for each single man and boy. The address then speaks of the benefit of saving and what may be done when husband and wife agree to carry out principles of frugality and honest independence, and the men and boys are urged to continue adding to their banking account. In order to encourage this, Mr Seacome promises in a few months to add to the savings of those who still continue to have money in the bank. We trust that other employers of labour will follow the example of Mr Seacome. The Savings Bank offers the greatest facilities for the purpose, and by giving the men a start, the masters will, as in the present case, infuse into them a spirit of thrift and carefulness.

Mr Seacome's intention was to persuade his workmen from wasting their money on drink.

The fireclay for the works was raised from underground workings, some of which extended far from the site of the factory itself. They had three pits named No. 1, No. 3 and No. 5. Mr Acton, solicitor to the company, said of the workings that

"the place was not a colliery in the strict sense

of the word, as only about four tons of coal was taken out in a day, but the place came under the Coal Mines Act. Fireclay was what the place was used for chiefly and 40 tons a day was brought out".

And these were not state of-the-art pits. I talked with a local man who remembered in the 1950s being told by one of the old Delph workers that they had to crawl along the narrow tunnels lighting their way with tallow candles. He remembered seeing baskets of burning straw being lowered down the small shafts to burn off the accumulated gases, before the men, no more than two at a time, were lowered down the shafts in crude wooden crate – like cages. Up until the 1970s these ancient pit head gears were still in place over these small shafts.

In 1877 Seacome discovered that his miners had unwittingly tunnelled beyond the boundaries of his "take", and had entered upon the lands leased from Col. Cornwallis West by the adjacent Plas yn Wern Brickworks. The following excerpt is from Mr Seacome's letter to the mineral agent Walter Eddy, who represented Col West:

"My dear Sir, referring to our conversation yesterday, I have to enclose a tracing showing the extent my miners have unfortunately encroached with Mr West's land. Until late last spring Thomas Hughes superintended my miners working. I was impelled to employ Jones the Surveyor of the New British Iron Company to look after my clay pits. Upon his informing me my men had gone beyond my boundary, I at once directed them to cease such working, and to inform me how much clay belonging to Mr West had been taken. Please be so good as not to mention this little affair to anyone unconnected with Mr West, for it is undesirable for Mr Whalley to hear of it, and with kind regards I remain very truly yours, Thomas H Seacome. 11th September, 1877".

The Mr Whalley whom Seacome rather sheepishly didn't want to become privy to the affair was his own landlord G H Whalley, who would not have taken kindly to the fact that his tenant's brickworks was mining clay upon which he could not enjoy charging a royalty.

For some unexplained reason the works was closed and boarded up in the early 1880s, and the invitation to purchase the leasehold interest in the "Delph Brick & Fireclay Works" was published in November 1883 by the executors of the late Henry Harrison. The lease referred to ran from March 1868, and we might surmise that the said Mr Harrison may have become a principal partner or even the owner in that year. Whatever the case, the works was acquired by Henry Wyndham of London, together with its "stabling for six horses, stores, manager's house, 3 offices, carpenters and blacksmith's shops, weighing machine house, 5 drying sheds, 10 kilns and 3 gins for raising clay from the pits".

Industrial Cheshire, published circa 1940 – The record of this firm is one of steady progress during the past 70 years, and at the present time Messrs Wyndham & Phillips are recognised as one of the leading manufacturers in this country of Glazed Vitrified Stoneware. The works were established in 1868 by the late Thomas H Seacome. In the year 1883 the business was bought by the late Henry Wyndham, civil and consulting engineer of London. In 1902 Mr Wyndham took into partnership with himself the late Mr R T Phillips, who had been manager both under Mr Seacome and Mr Wyndham for several years. The title of the firm was then changed to Wyndham & Phillips, and in 1906 the late Mr Phillips took over the entire business when it was made into a private limited company.

That article stated that the company became Messrs Wyndham & Phillips in 1902, but it's interesting to note that a report of the Ruabon Petty Sessions earlier in December 1896 clearly specifies the defendants as having been Messrs Wyndham & Phillips. However, it wasn't uncommon for a principal manager to have been included within the official title of companies during Victorian times, so we may at least assume that Mr Phillips was important enough to have warranted a mention in the company name, even though it may have not been officially called such.

By the late 1930s the company was still enjoying confident sales to countries as diverse as Canada, India, all of the African continent, Egypt, and South and Central America.

In 1943 the Company Secretary Mr James Holt explained a little about the works' practices. He said

"Actually we have two pit shafts here, which are numbered No. 2 and No. 5, but for some time we have used only No. 5. In 1938 the employees numbered 32. Manufacturing coal was raised, but it was not and still is not the primary object of our mining, which is the winning of stoneware clay and fireclay for the manufacture of salt glazed drain pipes, firebricks, buff and white facing bricks, chimney tops etc. The coal is not marketable, but we use it as small fuel or slack to start off kiln fires during the airing process of burning pipes and bricks".

By the start of the 1950s the clay pits had been closed and clay was brought in from Shropshire until the Delph closed on 4th January 1955 with the loss of 40 jobs. It was briefly reopened in December 1956 by G F Sumner & Sons of Wrexham, but had closed again by 1958.

By the early 1960s the giant chemical company Monsanto had taken over the site to burn chemical waste from their Acrefair plant, and the works land was also used as a tip for oil and rubbish. For this reason public pressure forced the District Council to act on the matter and the council wrote to Monsanto, complaining that the site was "resembling a battlefield". From 1964 Hucon Ltd was also operating at the old factory, making pre-cast concrete blocks using the ash and waste from Monsanto's incinerators, but they relocated to Ruthin in 1969 due to the old Delph buildings having become too dilapidated to continue using.

Rhos Fireclays Ltd then applied to develop the site as an opencast mine and were granted council permission for this in 1971. N S M Construction Ltd were contracted to mine the clay for Rhos Fireclays, as well as coal for the National Coal Board, and in 1972 they imported a massive 113 ton mechanical excavator from Germany; the

largest of its kind then employed in Britain, and so big that it had to be transported from Birkenhead Docks in separate sections. The first truck loads of minerals were taken away from the Delph in January 1973, and as the operations delved deeper into the ground they eventually began uncovering the old mining tunnels of the Delph Brickworks, some of which had tools and clay smoking pipes still left abandoned within.

The opencast mining ceased in 1986 and the site today is completely flattened; the old works once having stood at OS 2801 4359.

SITE 119: PLAS YN WERN BRICKWORKS AND ASSOCIATED COMPANIES.

The length of this chapter is indicative of the complexities of its subject matter; this brickworks being inextricably linked to the histories of four other industries: Plasmadoc Colliery, Plas yn Wern Sawmills, the New British Iron Co and Wynnstay Colliery. I contemplated treating each works under a separate heading, but as their inter-relations with each other were so inseparable, to do so would have inevitably caused confusion, so we shall follow their developments alongside each other.

The New British Iron Co was the largest industrial concern in the Ruabon – Acrefair district, whose main works were centred at OS 2820 4310 on the site of the present Air Products factory. Edward Lloyd Rowland of Ruabon held the original Acrefair Ironworks until it was sold in 1825 to the then British Iron Company; the focal point of the works being it's two impressive 43 ft high stone blast furnaces. In 1843 the company registered itself under the revamped style of the New British Iron Co, which went on to produce every description of iron and steel at a site comprising furnaces, kilns, coke ovens, pit shafts, spoil dumps and a maze of railway and tramway lines on land owned by Sir Watkin Williams Wynne.

Just over half a mile north east was the district known as Plas yn Wern; also referred to as Plasmadoc. Here lay the lands of Mr George Hammond Whalley, the MP for Peterborough, whose ancient ancestor Edward Whalley had been a cousin of Oliver Cromwell and whose signature stood next to Cromwell's on the execution warrant of King Charles I. It was here at Plas yn Wern that Gomer Roberts (here he is again) let from Whalley the small Plas Madoc Colliery in the 1840s, at or adjacent to the site of our future brickworks. It was here at "Gomer Roberts Coal Works, Acrefair" that on 26th February 1844 a boiler explosion killed one man, injured 15 more, scalded two boys to death and threw brick rubble for a distance of over half a mile. As a tribute to Gomer I think it's worth mentioning what the Advertiser said of him at the time of his death in June 1884:

"Gomer Roberts, a prominent figure in all important movements connected with Ruabon parish, has just passed away. In everything, taking him for all, it will be difficult to meet with his like again".

Plas Madoc Colliery was advertised for letting in January 1851, described as

"now at work consisting of 200 acres, only a small portion of which has been worked. The firebrick clays are of excellent quality and the estate is surrounded by the extensive works belonging to the British Iron Co";

those works being the small coal pits and waste sites connected to the main complex at Acrefair by their many numerous tramways.

Back at Acrefair (which in those days was referred to as being part of Cefn Mawr) the traveller and author George Barrow visited the district in 1854, and coming across the ironworks during the hours of darkness recorded:

"I should probably have tumbled half a dozen times but for the light of the Cefn furnaces which cast their red glow on my path. Two enormous sheets of flame shot up high into the air from ovens, illuminating two spectral chimneys high as steeples; also smoky buildings and grimy figures moving about. There was a clanging of engines, a noise of shovels, and a falling of coals truly horrible".

Another traveller two years later was also impressed by the "smoky chimneys, huge furnaces and hissing steam engines". For its day the size and nature of this ironworks was, certainly for this district, far in excess of anything else to be seen locally.

Three quarters of a mile east of the Cefn furnaces lay the Wynnstay Colliery, originally sunk as the small Green Pits, supposedly circa 1846. At the National Library of Wales an old letter exists which discusses the Wynnstay Colliery and makes reference to "the terms of the original agreement made in 1856". That agreement was with the New British Iron Co and probably referred to the colliery's contract to supply coals to the ironworks. In August 1858 the Colliery Guardian reported that "The New British Iron Co are sinking a monster coal pit adjoining the railway a quarter of a mile from Ruabon. Adjoining the shaft a very large engine house is being erected". I imagine this must have referred to the Wynnstay Colliery, as the descriptions are accurate enough, in which case the Iron Co must have had much to do with developing the works, although the colliery did not officially become part of the New British Co until the Wynnstay Estate leased it to them in 1865.

By 1856 the then named Plas yn Wern Colliery (Plas Madoc Colliery) had passed into the hands of John Neal Lomax of Chester, who sold at auction on 20th October its "saw mills, steam engine, very excellent clay mill etc". This could have been the year in which the brickworks was properly established, as the trade directories for 1856 onwards list John N Lomax & Co as brickmakers at Plas yn Wern. In 1864 the "Plasmadoc Brickworks "appeared on a railway proposal plan, detailing Mr Lomax as being its occupier. Thanks to the plan we can for the first time locate its precise position, and it stood at OS 2858 4388, in exactly the same spot as the fully established Plas yn Wern Brickworks on the 1871 OS map. It is therefore not unreasonable to assume that Lomax's brickworks grew up around his earlier colliery and saw mills – and we also have another interesting fact to play with. In January 1865 the Advertiser announced that Messrs Bradley, Thomas & Co had just completed furnishing their Steam Saw Mills at Plas yn Wern. Were these built on the site of the earlier colliery sawmills?

I believe so, because thanks to Mr Whalley's map of his Acrefair Estate we can see that a "Saw Mill" is marked at exactly the same spot as the brickworks is on the railway plan – the same shape of buildings with exactly the same arrangement of tramway looping around their eastern frontage. We can therefore make only one assumption – Lomax's Brickworks and Bradley's Sawmills each occupied one of the two buildings shown to have been adjacent to each other on both the Whalley map and the railway plan.

Returning to the activities of the New British Co, the "day book" of the mineral agent Walter Eddy recorded that a new mineral lease of their ironworks site was taken out on 25th March, 1865, and the actual lease for that year still exists, which reads:

"They shall not at any time raise for sale either in the raw or manufactured state, any fireclay except such as they shall require for use at their own works or shall supply to the Plas yn Wern Brickworks – and supply and deliver on their own trucks at the Plas yn Wern brickworks, fireclay, coal and slack for the use of the brickworks".

This verifies that by 1865 the New British Co were co-operating with the Plas yn Wern Brickworks held by Mr Lomax. We can also see how the Ironworks, together with its subsidiary the Wynnstay Colliery, were supplying coal and clay to the brickworks via the tramway previously mentioned, which was leased to Lomax and described in the Indenture as being a *"short branch railway laid down by the New British Iron Co on land belonging to Mr Whalley and let by him to Mr Lomax as part of the Plas yn Wern Brickyard".* A commonly held belief is that the Ironworks Co owned the brickworks, but until the 1880s it seems clear that the two concerns were separately owned. In fact, the ironworks very probably did have their own brickworks on their main Acrefair site – as suggested by the wording "at their own works" in the 1865 lease – and the 1871 OS map clearly shows a separate shed and two marked kilns at OS 2830 43282 north west of the main foundry buildings.

In 1875 Lomax relinquished the brickworks; his last entry in the trade directories having appeared in 1874. The Advertiser of 9th October, 1875 reported the formation of the new "Plas yn Wern Fire Clay Co", which was to take over the operations at the works. The principal shareholders were listed as being the landlord Mr Whalley himself, J C Smith of Southport, C J Tashaw of Manchester and other Manchester businessmen. Mr Whalley gave the running of the works to Messrs J Stevens & McTachan Co, and his estate map of 1877 records that he let the works to them by Indenture of 1st September , 1875. In the following year a report was commissioned for insurance purposes. It reads:

"The Plas yn Wern Brickworks are held by Mr Stevens and others under a certain rent of £1,500 a year, the minerals being supplied them by the N B I C under their covenant. And they further engage to pay £550 for converting the old shale heaps into common bricks and for working other fireclay not included in the lease to the Ironworks. These brickworks have been largely added to and will be equipped with the best machinery, and will with such clay as they have upon the estate carry on a very profitable trade and certainly produce a traffic over the private railway largely in excess of the past tenants. The quality of the brick is first class and the demand both for the home and continental markets is increasing".

This text gives further proof of the brickworks' independently owned status and explains that most of their supplies came to them by means of a contract held with the New British Iron Co.

Wrexham Advertiser 27th May, 1876 – On Saturday morning the smithy at the Plas yn Wern Brickworks was discovered to be on fire. A number of willing hands were soon on the spot, and to prevent the flames extending to other parts of the building, they stripped off the roof. The damage was not considerable.

In 1878 the British Architect verified the ownership of the works by naming them as "the property of Mr

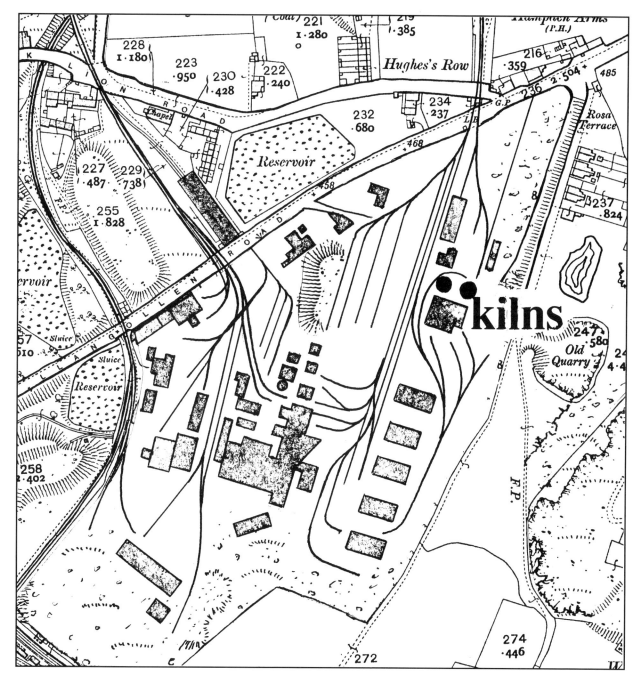

The New British Iron Co in 1879. Evidence strongly suggests that the ironworks may have had its own brickworks, and the kilns shown here may well be the same. The three lines of railway running northwards connect to the extensive mineral workings north of Acrefair.

G H Whalley".

At this point let's make a diversion into an alternative aspect of the New British Co's activities. In the chapter on how workers' pay was structured I discussed the practice of issuing tokens in lieu of money. The New British Co was once at the forefront of this type of practice, and upon their estates being finally sold off when the company closed in 1890, the many sale lots included shops owned by them as well as the Duke of Wellington public house at Cefn – places where their workers could have exchanged their tokens for food and drink. For companies to have also had their own farms to provide these foodstuffs was not uncommon. For instance, the Cefn Coal Co is recorded as having been the leaseholders of Christionydd Farm, and when the New British Co's Wynnstay Colliery treated their workers to a seasonal supper in January 1872 the Advertiser made reference to the company's farm labourers as also having been included in the festivities. Their farms grew the produce to stock the company's "truck shops" in Cefn, and the newspapers used regularly to make reference to prizes awarded for produce grown by them; the following article being typical of many suchlike:

Wrexham Advertiser 25th November 1876 – The six swedes on view at Mr Strachan's shop, High Street, Wrexham grown by Mr Roberts of Berse weigh 75 lbs. Also several swedes grown by Mr E Teneh weighing 13 lbs. each. Mr Strachan also shows nine extra fine swedes grown by the New British Iron Co weighing 13 lbs.

By 1879 the Plas yn Wern Fireclay Co Ltd (still a separate concern from the ironworks) was advertising its white and cream facing bricks, and by this year a new plant had been added to the original works. Evidence given at a rates assessment hearing tells us that the works was in the hands of a contractor – I should imagine that to have referred to Messrs Stevens & McTachan's running of the works for Mr Whalley's company – and the text also mentions that the new works with its five kilns was larger than the original factory which had only one, and which was by that time "not in first-class condition".

Wrexham Advertiser 5th June 1880 – Samuel Evans and David Edwards, colliers of Ponkey, were summoned by the Plas yn Wern Fire Clay Co Ltd for stealing garden tiles. PC David Jones said that he found 13 tiles placed around a little grave in the Groes churchyard, and he found the grave belonged to David Edwards. The defendants said the tiles were found on the road. Edward Green, the foreman of the company, said he had given information about the loss the company was sustaining from thefts of this kind. He balanced up his stock at the end of the month and found a great deficiency. The tiles produced were of a new and registered pattern which was the sole property of the company. They had not sold any tiles of the pattern in question in the neighbourhood. The magistrate said it was a very suspicious case, but there was no evidence to connect the defendants with the thefts.

The mineral agent Walter Eddy visited the site on 15th July, 1881 and toured the works with the manager Mr Bushby. By now the number of operational kilns had doubled to 10, and Mr Bushby made the interesting comment that the works was having to sell their bricks at a very low price in order to ensure enough sales to meet the exorbitant dead rent of £1,500 per annum. He was also upset with the coal supplied them from the New British Co, as the proportions of slack to solid coal was lower than he would have liked; meaning that it was costing them more to burn the bricks with the solid coal.

On 22nd February 1882 Mr G H Whalley, the principal player in the brickworks company, filed for his personal bankruptcy, and although I could find no evidence to support the supposition, I imagine that this must have been the period during which the New British Iron Co acquired ownership of the works. It is very possible that they acquired it during 1881, at which time Mr Whalley would have needed the cash. Whatever the case, the brickworks was certainly in the hands of the Iron Co by May 1887, at which point a continued slump in the iron trade had forced the laying off of a considerable number of the ironworkers. Total closure of the ironworks itself followed in 1888, and it wasn't long before the repercussions were felt within the company's other holdings:

Wrexham Advertiser 1st June 1889 – All the workmen employed at the Green Pits and the Plas yn Wern brickworks have been temporarily thrown out of employment pending the change of ownership of the works. Since the formation of the works (Wynnstay Colliery) 25 years ago, the collieries have been owned and worked by the N B I C but the works have been handed over to a new company.

That new company, Wynnstay Collieries Co Ltd, was registered on 20th June, 1889 to take over the Green Pits and the brickworks at Plas yn Wern. The New British site was disposed of at auction over four days in early October 1890 – the site being acquired by the Chester engineers Messrs Hughes & Lancaster who established a new works in mid-1891; eventually succeeded in 1947 by Messrs Butterly & Derby and later by the present owners Air Products Ltd.

Wrexham Advertiser 20th November 1897 – On Sunday whilst a number of little boys were playing with some trucks in Plas yn Wern siding, by some means the wagons were put in motion and one of the boys named John Roberts had his thigh broken. He was conveyed to the hospital.

I noticed during my researches that trespassing by youngsters was particularly prevalent at this brickworks. As today, the site was located in a quiet rural area, and as we have seen before, works like these could suffer from more of their fair share of trespassing and theft. In September 1906 the Wynnstay Colliery Co stated in court that coal pilfering from the railway trucks in the Plas yn Wern siding was becoming a very serious matter, and the bold offenders even used the brickyard wheelbarrows to cart away their booty.

Wrexham Advertiser 20th December 1913 – William Pennington, 17, Daniel Lloyd, 14, and Samuel Harrison, 15, were charged with having ripped off, with intent to steal, lead fixed to a shed at Plas yn Wern. About 2:30pm Benjamin Jones, a foreman in the employ of the Wynnstay Colliery Co had occasion to go to the brickyards on business. He was accompanied by a fitter Henry Jones. When he entered a shed he heard a noise on the roof. He went upstairs and saw a large hole in the roof and through the aperture saw the defendants. The boys bolted but Harrison was caught. When asked what they were doing on the roof he said that they had been there since 10 o'clock. It was found that about 130 lbs of lead had been ripped off. In giving evidence Mr Jones said that this was not the first time for that sort of thing to happen, but they had not been able to catch the offenders before. Pennington was fined £1 and costs and the other boys 10 shillings and costs each.

The brickworks' parent company at Wynnstay Colliery eventually closed on 13th July, 1927, throwing 1200 men out of work. Wynnstay had not suffered alone, as 368 collieries had recently closed throughout Great Britain following the crippling national coal strike. The primary cause had been the old story of too much over-production by too many companies, leading to the price of coal having plummeted, and although the landlord Sir Watkin had offered to waive the colliery's royalties for the next three years, it was regarded that the financial climate was too precarious to risk taking any more losses. Sir Watkin had already received no royalties for the previous two years, and during the colliery's last few weeks it had been losing over £600 each week.

As went the colliery, so followed the brickworks. Plas yn Wern had always received its best clays and coals from the pits at the New British site and the Wynnstay Colliery, and the fate of Wynnstay inevitably heralded the death of the brickworks.

Wrexham Advertiser 6th July, 1929 – So far as can be ascertained negotiations are still proceeding with reference to the proposed new industry for Cefn. The site for this project is the old Plas yn Wern brickyard, and if the idea materialises, silica bricks will be made at the new works. The buildings on this site were purchased some time ago by Mr W F Humphreys of Acrefair, who contemplated erecting a number of houses in Acrefair with the bricks. The buildings have not been demolished in view of the possibility of a London syndicate deciding to reopen the works.

The reopening never materialised. Today the site is an area of grasslands and trees. At the Wynnstay Colliery site the road from Ruabon to Rhosymedre now cuts right over the old works; two of the colliery buildings still having survived on either side – one being the large stone engine house mentioned in the 1858 report, and the other a ruined brick engine house.

Site 115

Site 117

Site 118

Site 124

Cefn Mawr Area

SITE 120: PLASKYNASTON POTTERIES

This was a small works manufacturing terracotta and earthenware at a site in the Plaskynaston district to the west of the district collectively known as Cefn Mawr. It being a pottery, I would not have included it in this encyclopaedia of brickworks other than for the fact that it became one of the works of the J C Edwards empire. The works is shown on the 1871 OS at ref 2767 4239 and is very probably the earlier site of Messrs Bayley & Bradley's Cefn Potteries listed in the trade directories of 1856-8. The first reference to J C Edwards being here was found in the Wrexham Advertiser of 10th August, 1872, in which the company was named as making items such as flowerpots and seed pans at their Plaskynaston Potteries. The company was also still producing here in 1891, but by 1895 the pottery had ceased to be listed as one of the company's holdings. It may even have been closed in 1892, as the list of collected donations to the Ruabon Accident Hospital from the works of J C Edwards showed a paltry sum of three shillings and three pence in 1891 from the Plaskynaston pottery workers, but nothing the year after. By the time the 1899 OS was published the works was shown as being disused.

Two other works feature in this immediate district, and we should take account of them. Just to the north from site 120 was the original Plas Kynaston Chemical Works – still very small in 1871. It was established at OS 2768 4262 in 1867 by the German chemist Robert Ferdinand Graesser as a plant for extracting oil and wax from the easily available local colliery shale. In 1920 the Monsanto Company bought a half interest in the plant and went on to develop the giant works which eventually swallowed up most of the Plaskynaston district, including the pottery and the Plaskynaston Foundry at OS 2768 4272. This foundry lay to the north of the original chemical works and was famous as being the works of Messrs W H Hughes, the locally renowned manufacturer of brick and tile making machinery. It was this works which made the machinery for the new Monk & Newell brickworks in 1883.

Before we investigate the three other small brickworks located in Plaskynaston district, I can't help but include some fascinating facts concerning the area – all the more interesting for those who know the Cefn of today!

Wrexham Advertiser 1863-70 or 80 years ago the whole place was a common claimed by the freeholder for the use of their stock. Now the Cefn is full of strangers from all parts of the kingdom; crowded with shops, public houses and beerhouses; one selling American bacon at double profits and the other brewing and selling damaged beverages sufficiently strong to kill a bird.

That report typifies how the district had by 1863 started to become a magnet for industry, and workers soon flocked in looking for employment. Indeed, my own great-grandfather came here from Ashton under Lyne to work in the Plaskynaston Colliery. But what would be almost impossible to imagine today is how the town began to develop as a base for the tourist industry in the years between the two world wars:

Wrexham Advertiser 1929 – The Cefn Mawr district seems to be coming into favour as a holiday resort, at least judging by the number of people who spend their holidays in the district. It was only the other week when a writer in a Sunday newspaper wrote "My train stopped at a station called Cefn – the most beautiful spot in Britain". Just a few months ago a first division team was passing through Cefn on their way to Liverpool and when passing over the viaduct, one of the players remarked "I have travelled many miles but have never seen a more beautiful sight".

By summer 1931 "large numbers of visitors" were reported in the district, staying mainly in the small villages of Garth and Trevor just down the road, but I doubt such activity goes on today!

SITE 121: DOLYDD ROAD BRICKWORKS, CEFN

In the British Clayworker of March 1896 "two practical men" were advertising for a brickmaker to undertake the making and burning of bricks at Dolydd Road, Cefn, and by August 1898 the same journal followed up with:

> "Mr Brogden at his Cefn Brickworks has struck the Cribbwr, a 6 ft coal seam of the best quality. The question of developing the works as a colliery has not yet been decided".

At the turn of the Victorian century Dolydd Road was a narrow lane bordered by open fields, but the 1899 OS map shows an industrial excavation with a few sheds at OS 2776 4201 on the opposite side of the lane to what appears to be a large spoil heap. Although not marked as a brickworks, the coincidence of its being there, plus mention of Mr Brogden's brickworks in Cefn at almost the same time cannot be ignored.

SITE 122: JAMES DAVIES BRICKYARD, CEFN

The discovery of the existence of this small brickworks and pottery was made from some obscure documents which I came across mainly by accident. The brickworks comprised a shed and claymill located near the top of Queen Street, Cefn with a six fire -holed brick kiln at OS 2780 4224. The pottery works was on the southern side of the road opposite the brickworks. In the early 1800s it was the property of Robert Jones, who upon his death in 1818 bequeathed both works to his wife Jane. On her death they passed to her son in law James Davies, who sold the pottery to Exuperius Pickering in October 1842, at which time the brickworks had apparently closed down.

The documents I found also included a plan of the site, which showed a small tramway which ran past this site from a quarry in the south to the chemical factory and Plaskynaston Foundry in the north, and an interesting reference to it appeared in 1900, by which time it had become defunct:

> Wrexham Advertiser 1900 – Cefn is a typical Welsh mining village; that is to say it is one conglomeration of houses and one labyrinth of streets and courts. I followed the windings of the main road and heeded not the many narrow, dark and zigzag passages which branched off up the hill on the right and down on the left. The roadway all along was muddy, and attempts had been made here and there to fill the holes with ashes, broken bricks, rubble and macadam. By and by I found myself on a road which led me towards what I imagined to be a chemical works. On each side of the road there was a deep ditch, and I should think this is a most dangerous place in the dark. The roadway was strewn with refuse and there were deep cart ruts, where the water lodged, giving off unpleasant smells. A strong nauseous effluvia pervaded the atmosphere around the factory, and as there were houses close by, apparently the people have to live every day of every week of the year in a foul atmosphere. A stream running through the valley just below the factory was changed into an inky hue. The surface of a pond not far off was stagnant with the foul frothy matter which lodged on its surface. An old tramway road, which runs in front of several rows of houses, was up to the ankles in sludge, and bits of broken drainage pipes were thrown about, so that with great care one might step from one to the other and thus avoid the mire.

SITE 123: BEN HUGHES BRICKWORKS, CEFN

This brickworks was shown on the OS maps of the 1870s as a shed and kiln (not marked as such) and appeared in the Trade Directories of 1874-6 as Piercey Hughes Cefn Brickworks – "manufacturer of every description of fireclay goods, bricks, chimney pots etc". The works was colloquially known as Ben Hughes Brickworks, and although I could find no surviving evidence to corroborate this site as such, its position was verified by the late historian Mr Ivor Edwards, whose grandfather was a personal friend of Ben Hughes. The works was positioned at OS 2785 4273.

SITE 124: ROBERTS & MAGINNIS BRICKWORKS, GARTH

The impressive factory at Garth was developed

from a very insignificant country works, which featured an incident in its early history which reads more like a scene from the Wild West. We know from the railway maps that the site was farmland in 1858, and the first tenant to establish a brickyard here was John Wright:

Wrexham Advertiser 9th August, 1862 – Club law at Garth. Mr Whalley appeared before the bench to complain of one of his tenants being forcibly turned out of a brickyard by John Wright and a number of men that he brought with him. The tenant is Mr Moses Evans of the Australia Arms, who stated to the bench that on 30th July John Wright, Edwin Wright, Charles Wright and two other men came and took forcible possession of a brickyard that he had rented from Mr Whalley for the last four months. Before that time the brickyard was held by John Wright. They put a lock on the gate and stuck up a paper cautioning him against entering. The wife of John Wright had a pistol and said she would shoot anyone who attempted to enter. The bench agreed to grant warrants for their apprehension.

Moses Evans had therefore succeeded John Wright circa April 1862, most likely because Wright could not manage to pay his rents. Incidentally, the works later became known as Australia Brickworks after the adjacent inn at which Moses Evans would have probably been lodging.

Moving on to 1864, the map for the proposed Garth Mineral Rly gives us a more comprehensive picture of the area. The brickyard is shown, still in the occupation of Evans, with its single tiny kiln near the roadside where the offices of the future works were to be, and behind the kiln was a small claybank and brickshed. Due west of the brickyard was a small stone quarry held by Thomas and Jonathan Roberts, whilst behind that to the north west was a small colliery shaft held by Joseph Wright; obviously a relative of the infamous John. In October and November 1866 the "Australia Brickworks, Trevor" was offered for letting by Moses Evans, due to his recent bankruptcy in April with debts of £1,273, and by 1868 the trade directories were showing that the quarry owners J H & T

Roberts had taken on the works. As an interesting footnote, the old Welsh name for this district was Chwrele, which means "quarry", and how that name came to be changed was all down to the men in charge of the Great Western Railway:

Wrexham Advertiser 12th June 1869 – About midway between Ruabon and Llangollen on a branch of the G W R there is a station called Trevor. When the branch was first opened this station was named Chwrele, but as English travellers always despaired of pronouncing the word, the nearest approach to the sound any Saxon was ever known to accomplish being Gorilla, the name was changed to the more melliferous one of Trevor. All this was very considerable of the directors, but being all Englishmen themselves, perhaps we have not much to thank them for.

By 1870 a certain Mr Charles Mason had acquired the works with a working capital of over £2,500 to back him up. He continued the business until having to take out a £2,000 mortgage in 1873; easily enough accomplished as the place was valued at over £7,000, and in 1875-6 he entered into partnership with Mr Anthony Shelmerdine, who contributed a further £1,500 for the privilege.

The British Architect 1878 – At Garth Trevor on the lower edge of the Coal Measures, from the shaly and iron stained clays and sandstone, Mr Charles Mason produces large quantities of good, sound and serviceable cherry red bricks, which are well adapted for all ordinary building purposes. The clay of the "Chwarele coal" occurs abundantly on this property. Its productions are of much the same character as those of the Llwyneinion clay. It has not however as yet been worked to any extent by Mr Mason.

It seems that whichever persons had held these works, things had not fared well for any of them. On 1st October 1880 the "Trevor Fireclay Works & Colliery" held an auction of stock "under distress for rent", which indicates how poorly their trade had proved, and in 1881 Mason decided to retire from the business:

Wrexham Advertiser 17th December, 1881 – A meeting of gentlemen interested in the Garth Brick & Tile Works was held at the Wynnstay Arms, Oswestry last week with a view to forming a limited company for the purpose of carrying on the works.

The outcome of that meeting resulted in Mr Shelmerdine's father in law Mr Neil advancing the company a further £2,000 to assist in developing the works; presumably to increase the works' competitive capability. Shelmerdine also persuaded Mason to accept £1,500 to become a sleeping partner in the company and he also paid off the outstanding mortgage, but in order to achieve this he pledged the credit of the firm to such an extent that the company couldn't balance its books and went bust in March 1882. But due unfortunately to some awkward technicalities, it was Charles Mason who found himself legally responsible for debts of £2,000 on the company's behalf, and the stress on his mind took its toll. Mason became for a long time insane and eventually regained enough of his reason to take on less demanding work as an engine driver (whether on the railways or the operator of a stationary steam engine is not specified). When fully recovered he eventually took up the position as manager of the Vron Works at Coedpoeth in 1889.

The works eventually fell into the hands of Messrs Roberts & Maginnis – when is not clear, but some say they held it by 1885. Perhaps they acquired it after the 1882 bankruptcy. John F Maginnis lived at Derwen Hall, Garth and was the company's financial manager, whilst Roberts was the technical operator.

Wrexham Advertiser 6th November 1909 – A serious accident occurred at the Australia Brickworks on Tuesday afternoon when Oliver Evans, aged 18, had his right hand taken off by the machinery. It appears that Evans was engaged in filling at the pipe mill when he got his arm into the mill. The hand was completely torn off and the arm badly crushed. Dr Macdonald was quickly in attendance and the boy was conveyed by motor car to Ruabon where it was found necessary to amputate the arm above the elbow.

By the outbreak of the First War the new company had abandoned the production of building bricks in favour of the manufacture of silica bricks for the steel industry; Maginnis having practical connections with the Colville Steelworks in Glasgow. The company also began producing gannister, a plastic cement substance used to mould the channels into which molten iron was tapped from steel furnaces. This substance was an amalgam of water, silica, sandstone, broken silica brick fragments and fireclay which the company imported from Shropshire. The silica stone was mined from two sources, one being a mine in the hills which was reached by horse and cart, and in the early 20th century by an aerial ropeway system. The other source was a level mine which ran into the hillside directly at the back of the works and which was worked by donkeys pulling tubs. This led to the brickworks earning the nickname of The Donkey Works, which lasted in local parlance long after the use of donkeys had ceased. From the 1930s onwards the stone was brought in from nearby Minera as well as from other Welsh counties.

By 1922 the company was classifying themselves as the "Welsh Silica Brick & Gannister Works".

I can now clear up a popular misconception, even held by the knowledgeable colliery historian George Lerry. Due to the somewhat misssworded text of certain published documents it has been believed that the works was the property of J C Edwards Ltd during the 1920s and 40s. We can turn to the evidence of Mr William Lacey, one of R & M's directors, who worked at the factory between 1940-74. I was lucky enough to talk to him concerning many aspects of the works' history, and he assured me that the only connection to J C Edwards Ltd was that the Garth Works leased part of their lands from J C E and had no other involvement with them whatsoever.

The 1960s saw some new practices at Garth. The kilns were converted to oil firing and the method of shipping out the products was also changed. At that time there was much industrial unrest within British Railways, and the problems caused to all the local industries became quite serious; to such an extent that the attitude at Garth Brickworks became, in Mr Lacey's own words, "Sod you – keep your bloody railways". The branch line which crossed the Ruabon to Llangollen road into the factory was abandoned and road transportation was used thereafter; to the unexpected benefit of the company, as they not only realised a financial saving but gained greater flexibility over the movement of materials.

The works eventually shut in 1979 – a victim of the recession in the steel industry.

Before we end, I will mention three stories which Mr Lacey told me about the works.

* The old level drift mine, the entrance to which stood at the back of the site, is a complicated maze of tunnels running for miles into the hillside. After it ceased being used some of the more intrepid locals used to sneak in there to work the seams of coal exposed within. During the 1960s one of the men, known to have visited the place regularly, disappeared and was never seen again, and for many years the rumours in the neighbourhood were that he had most probably lost his way within the tunnels and had never found his way out again.

* The works' power plant was a second hand steam engine which the company purchased for £750 in the 1920s. It generated the electricity which powered the crushers and mills as well as supplying waste steam which was used to dry the bricks overnight. In all its working days, apart from stoppages for maintenance, it was never known to give a moment's trouble and never broke down. It continued in use until the 1979 closure and is now displayed at the Blist's Hill Museum at Ironbridge. I myself saw the engine working at Garth in mid-1977.

* The works was supposed to have a ghost. The engineers looking after the night shift operations used to lock themselves in their workshop to feel more secure.

The factory was centred at OS 2651 4254 and is now demolished, although there are some ruins at the back of the site, and the gutted offices still remain on the roadside. In the north west corner of the site is a pool. This is some 70 ft deep and is actually part of the old Garth Quarry, worked by

Messrs Roberts back in the Victorian days.

SITES 125 A,B: EDWARD EVANS BRICKYARD AND EVAN ROBERTS BRICK KILN, TREFYNANT

a) The tithe map of 1840 shows Edward Evans as the occupant of Trefynant Farm, north west of Acrefair, and the trade directory of 1844 lists him as being a brickmaker at Trefynant. We know that he lived at Trefynant House at OS 2708 4287 in December 1830, a property including a

"smithy, stone quarry, mines and a brickyard. The premises are known to contain valuable strata of coal and fireclay, the latter being an entire bed of 12 ft thickness and now in actual work".

Edward was one of the small time farmer – brickmakers, and the 1851 census shows that he had two brickmakers in his employ – 16 year old John Jones and 18 year old Ann Williams, who both actually lived in his household together with his servant.

His clay quarry appears on an 1853 railway map close to Trefynant House at roughly OS 2715 43 05, but it was later obliterated by the construction of the railway. The long deceased local historian Ivor Edwards wrote that Edward was purported to have had a water wheel on the Trefynant Brook to power his clay softening mill.

b) We have another minor site close by at OS 2710 4310, shown on an 1858 railway map as a pasture field with a brick kiln held by Evan Roberts, but a similar map of 1864 shows him working the area as farmland only. Whether this farmer utilised his kiln as a commercial concern, as did his neighbour Edward Evans, we shall never know.

SITE 126: J C EDWARDS TREFYNANT BRICKWORKS

"Less than a quarter of a century ago Mr James Coster Edwards commenced the manufacture of fireclay goods at Trefynant. These consisted of firebricks, chimney tops, glazed sanitary pipes of various kinds and more recently ornamental terracotta designs. The quality of the clay and

the high class work no doubt contributed to a rapid growth in the demand for the produce of these works, and sanitary legislation also further increased the consumption. To meet the requirements of the market, the spirited proprietor added kiln to kiln, shed to shed, machine to machine, until the works became, next to the New British Iron Works, the most prominent object in the landscape and the busiest commercial hive in the valley of the Dee".

That Victorian quotation paid tribute to probably the most remarkable success enjoyed by any brickmaking company in either Flintshire or Denbighshire. The Flintshire works of Catheralls and Hancocks may well have been the much earlier pioneers in the industry, and the Penbedw Works of Mr H R Bowers may well have been accorded the accolade of being the first company in Ruabon to make fine use of the exceptional local marl, but whereas most of the other larger companies might have had only two factories to their name, J C Edwards realised four: the large Coppy Works producing glazed and enamelled bricks and tiles, the Plaskynaston Pottery manufacturing household and garden earthenware, the massive Penybont Terracotta Works making the best red marl architectural brick, and the large Trefynant Works, turning out a whole range of goods, in particular the glazed sanitary pipeware. Within the Victorian brick industry nationwide, the company and the personage of J C Edwards himself was held in the highest regard, and for this reason this and the chapter on Penybont will be somewhat more comprehensive, as befitting this company's overall stature.

James Coster Edwards perhaps owed his fortunes to his father William, who preceded his son as a brickmaker and most probably introduced him to the craft. James was born on 20th November 1828 at, according to the census, Llangollen. At this time his father was a clerk at Pickering's Wharf at Trefynant, shown on the tithe map as having been around OS 2745 4260; now part of the Flexsys Chemical site. Exuperius Pickering was a local industrialist who had lime, coal and slate works as well as canal wharfage at Pontcysyllte

and Trefynant, and it is believed that William took over the Trefynant lime kilns in 1835. William's position in society allowed him to have James, along with his three brothers and three sisters, educated "under the guidance of an old and eccentric Scotsman". That was Alexander Mahaty who had come to the district to work on the construction of the Pontcysyllte aqueduct before settling at Cefn Mawr and establishing a school in the Gorffwysfa Chapel. The famous aqueduct had opened in 1805, and in those pre-railway days the canals were seen as being the marvel of the age; the newspapers predicting that the aqueduct was "destined to carry the riches of the mineral kingdom into the world of industry and thence to every part of the universe".

James' first employment was probably the job he had in a draper's shop in Wrexham, but he later secured a position closer to home as a storeman at the New British Iron Works; his parental home being Trefynant Cottage. The first mention of his father's brickmaking activities appears on a railway map of 1852, in which a "Firebrick & Tile Works" is shown at OS 2699 4301 in occupation of William Edwards and his partner William Williams, and the young James must surely have learnt a thing or two from them.

When exactly James set up on his own is not recorded, but he most definitely had established the Trefynant Brickworks by 1856. We know this from a court case from June that year which related to a transaction that had taken place in Spring 1855, in which both he and his father were involved. Their solicitor made the following statement: "*Mr James Coster Edwards is a brick and tile manufacturer at Trefynant and is also the owner of several canal boats which he uses for his own purposes, and when not so employed he sometimes hires out to parties who may want them. His father is engaged in business on his own account at Trefynant although he had a wharf of his own at Pontcysyllte".*

The 1856 trade directory confirms James to have also been a coal merchant at Trefynant, and it was surely from his wharfage on the canal at Trefynant that he conducted this side of his business.

The first ever illustrated representation of

Trefynant Brickworks appeared on a railway map of 1860, showing a small site on the roadside at OS 2733 4275 with the works office on the opposite side of the road and a stone's throw from the office of his father's limekiln business. As the British Clayworker later said of James' operations:

"His productions at the onset did not necessitate a bigger staff than a man and two boys",

and indeed this fact had even during James' lifetime already become almost a folklore legend amongst the Ruabon clayworkers.

In 1859 James married Elizabeth Edwards of Mold, and by 1861 they were living at Tanyclawdd House at Ruabon with their house servant and the nurse for their one year old son Edward Lloyd.

Wrexham Advertiser 9th December, 1865 – On Tuesday an inquest on the body of Robert Jones, who had been killed at the Trefynant works. The deceased was taking a strap off some portion of the machinery used for grinding clay, and instead of giving notice to the engineman to slacken speed, he tried to do it with the machinery in full motion. He became entangled in the wheels and his head taken half off.

By the year that report was written the works had grown to include six kilns, whilst his father's old brickworks was demolished the year after and "Brickfield Terrace" built in its place; itself only to be demolished two years later.

Wrexham Advertiser 6th January, 1866 – Trefynant Works, owing to the spirited manner in which Mr J C Edwards has developed them, have become a most important feature in the industry. Mr Edwards has been considerably aided by the advantageous position in which they are located. Having a frontage to the Shropshire Union Canal tramway and within a few hundred yards from the canal, a siding was all that was necessary to get into all markets to which the canal has access. The Llangollen Railway opened up a new prospect, and fortunately the Trevor station on that line was located at the nearest point to the works, the road being the only separation between the railway land and that of Mr Edwards. The conveyance of the Canal Company's tramway into a locomotive line took place last summer, resulting in Mr Edwards having parallel lines of railway on each side of his works. In order to utilise these advantages to the utmost he has now completed a new junction from the Shropshire Union Railway to the Llangollen Railway, and in celebration of the opening on Wednesday last he invited his workmen from 80-90 in number to a sumptuous repast in the great hall at his residence, Trevor Hall. Songs in English and Welsh resounded through the hall, and never was a jollier party assembled in the fine old mansion. For the evening, Mr Edwards had provided an excellent entertainment consisting of a concert of vocal and instrumental music, to which he had invited in addition to his staff, all his friends and neighbours and all the tenants on the Trevor Hall Estate. The scene of the entertainment was the new commodious National Schools room in Trevor, which was beautifully decorated with evergreens and flowers; several mottos in English and Welsh tastefully intermingled. The room was crowded – nearly 500 persons being present.

It obviously hadn't taken long for James to have accumulated quite a fortune. Trevor Hall is an imposing mansion house at OS 2563 4230, and the 1871 census shows that he had by then a governess, nurse, cook and housemaid residing with his family, which now included his second son James Coster Jnr, born in 1863.

On 7th August, 1867 a serious fire destroyed one of the "large new sheds" at the works. It had been supposedly started in quite an unusual way –

"the heat from the drying bricks becoming so great that it ignited the wooden planks on which they were laid".

The clay at Trefynant was gotten by both methods – opencast holes and pit mines; the opencast exposing a strata of coal:

Wrexham Advertiser 5th February, 1876 – On Saturday afternoon two boys named Roberts and Williams were picking coal in an opencast where clay is obtained from Mr Edwards' Trefynant works. From what we can learn, they were getting coal from the thin seam which is under the bed of clay, when a quantity of the latter gave way, burying both beneath the debris. Help was fortunately at hand and strenuous efforts made to extrocate the poor fellows. Roberts was taken out quite dead and Williams has received injuries almost beyond all hope of recovery.

The underground pits were quite extensive and the clay lay under a seam of coal called the Half Yard Coal. The clay was mined out leaving the coal to form a roof over the "roads", and these roads along which the miners travelled to the clay faces were recorded as being approx 5 ft high by 5 ft wide. This

Victorian brick press workers at Trefynant. Photo: DRO.

clay burnt to produce wares of a pale buff colour, perfect for the sanitary stoneware pipes which were one of Trefynant's principal productions.

Wrexham Advertiser 2nd October 1886 – The whole of the employees at Trefynant, Penybont, Rhos and Plaskynaston Potteries belonging to Mr J C Edwards were on Saturday the recipients of their master's generosity in the form of a trip to the Liverpool Exhibition. The workmen and boys numbered upwards of 800 and the fare of everyone was paid. As many wives and friends accompanied them, including some members of Mr Edwards' family, the party nearly reached a thousand people.

Wrexham Advertiser 15th October, 1887 – On Saturday evening about 6 o'clock a serious fire broke out at the Trefynant Brick and Tile Works. The fire was discovered in one of the large bricksheds by the watcher, who at once alarmed the neighbourhood by violently ringing the works bell. Several hundred workmen from various parts of the district were speedily on the scene and rendered every possible help in extinguishing the flames. The roof was quickly stripped and floods of water poured in upon the flames. Mr Edwards and his son Mr Lloyd Edwards arrived on the scene and with Mr Jonathan Powell the foreman, personally superintended. The Wynnstay fire engine, accompanied by Sir Watkin Williams Wynn, arrived at 7 o'clock, but fortunately their services were not required. The fire caused great excitement and large crowds of people hastened to the works. As it is, the damage is not serious and is covered by insurance. The origin of the fire is unknown.

The aforementioned foreman Mr Powell had joined the company on 6th February 1860 and had become the works' oldest employee by the time of his death on 22nd March, 1904.

In June 1892 the Edwards family celebrated the marriage of the eldest son Edward Lloyd, and in true Victorian style the works employees were not forgotten:

Wrexham Advertiser 25th June, 1892 – It would be difficult to imagine a more happy relationship between employer and employed than that of which evidence was given at Trevor Hall on Saturday. Mr J C Edwards whose famous clay productions have brought wealth and renown to himself and prosperity to the district has the secret of making himself popular with his men. To those who know Mr Edwards it is not much of a secret either, for kindness and consideration on the part of the master as here, make labour troubles difficult if not impossible. Mr and Mrs Edwards decided to entertain the whole of the workmen and other employees at dinner, and a large tent was erected on a field just below Trevor Hall and preparations were made to satisfy the cravings of the 1000 visitors expected. The time fixed for dinner was 4 o'clock, but some minutes before, the guests arrived, having assembled at the Trefynant works. The band of the Ruabon Company of Volunteers led the way past the hall, at the porch of which Mr and Mrs Edwards and family stood as the long procession marched past, saluting as it went. After dinner sports were held.

The sports events included a tug of war between the men of the Trefynant clay pit and those from the Penybont clayhole; the Trefynant team winning the first prize of £1. John Evans of the Trefynant works won the contest of climbing a rope to reach a leg of mutton; the mutton becoming his trophy. There were races for the lads under 18, and a 50 yard race for the men over 60, the recipient of the first prize of 5 shillings being George Smith of the Encaustic Tile Works. These works were a part of the Trefynant site, being situated to the south west of the main factory, and were not part of the earlier original works. They were built to produce small decorative tiles with patterns of more than one colour of clay.

In the catalogue of 1890 the company invited architects and contractors to visit the company's works to see for themselves the extent of their capabilities. James' astute business sense knew just how to treat a potential customer, and he made sure of promising that a carriage would be waiting at Ruabon station to collect those guests who had made appointment to tour the works. The catalogue also boasted of the Coppy, Trefynant and Penybont Works' combined powers, with nearly 70 machine presses driven by 16 engines of 500 aggregate horse power, 80 kilns consuming 3000 tons of coal per month and gas lighting throughout the factories. Each of the works was interconnected by telephone and a private phone line linked the central office at Trefynant to Ruabon Post Office, ensuring that potential customers might have the most immediate attention. The 1890s were probably the heydays of the company, and the British Clayworker made a particular point of saluting James' achievements by saying:

"In a business which has for its field of labour the entire globe it is superfluous to mention any of the big undertakings in which Mr Edwards has been engaged. In Manchester, Liverpool and Birmingham the Ruabon work is well known. Shipments especially in sanitary ware are constantly made with India, Africa and North and South America, while a new church at Newfoundland is built with the Ruabon productions. Tesselated tiles have found their way as far as a Rajah's palace, while an order for 30 miles of pipes for Brazil is now under way".

One thing always shines forth concerning James, in that in all his dealings both personal and professional he was regarded in the most highest esteem. "Success came to Mr Edwards in an abundant measure, but it failed to do to him what it often does to others" observed the Advertiser. He became a JP and the Deputy Lieutenant for Denbighshire, and was the county's High Sheriff for the term 1892-3. At a presentation ceremony for one of his sons in June 1881 a representative of his workforce proclaimed: "Many of us have grown grey in the service of your respected father whom we hold in dear remembrance, and have always found in him a kind, sincere friend. Our affection for him is not the mere growth of a day, but is the outcome of years, and it is especially gratifying to us at the present time to be able to record these feelings when the relations between employer and

James Coster Edwards

him as "J. C." Mr Edwards had old fashioned ideas and old fashioned methods of executing them. The reasons might be found in the fact that he had too big a heart to discharge men who had grown grey in his service or to introduce forms of machinery that would necessitate the reduction of the number of his workmen. Few men in the trade were better-known or more widely respected and few have built up a business of such enormous proportions in so short a space of time; unrivalled of its kind; one known in every quarter of the globe.

Wrexham Advertiser 4th April, 1896 – The funeral took place on Tuesday in Llantysillio Churchyard and was witnessed by a vast concourse of people, estimated at over two thousand. Special train arrangements were made for those attending, three extra trains being run from Ruabon to Berwyn, which conveyed upwards of a thousand persons, most of whom however alighted at Llangollen. At 1 o'clock the courtege left Trevor Hall, the procession being joined on the way to Llangollen, and in that town by the workmen and the greater part of the public. At Llangollen the procession was four deep and extended with traps and carriages for over a mile and a half and was watched by crowds of people. The courtege reached the churchyard about 3 o'clock. The grave was lined with moss relieved with bunches of primroses and white flowers.

employed in some parts of the country are unhappily not of this friendly character".

In planning for his retirement James had built a house at OS 2501 4183, now the Bryn Howel hotel on the road from Trevor to Llangollen, but he never got to occupy it. In 1896 he went to Guernsey to recuperate from a bout of illness, but his condition deteriorated to the point where he had to undergo an emergency operation, and from that Sunday evening until his death on the morning of Thursday 26 March he never regained consciousness. He died aged 68 at Guernsey's Government House Hotel.

British Clayworker April 1896 – To obtain the fairest estimate of his character is to hear the opinion of the workpeople whose pleasure it was to serve under him, who were just familiar enough and yet respectable enough to speak of

Following James' death, the company continued to flourish under the directorship of his two sons; the heydays of the turn-of-the-century being as active in the field of sports as it was in the craft of brickmaking:

Wrexham Advertiser 11th July 1903 – The walk in connection with the employees of Messrs J C Edwards took place on Saturday and was a great success. Punctually at 3:00pm twenty two competitors started and the excitement began. There were some about 17 years of age, one over 40, some wore strong heavily nailed boots, others had shoes, and one even wore thin cycling slippers for the 15 mile walk. A big crowd of people which had congregated at the head of the steepest hill on the route were put into the greatest excitement when the walkers came into sight. The tremendous number of cyclists and followers became a great nuisance. The crowd on the Crane – the finishing point – was very dense, people even getting on the roofs of buildings to view the final. At a committee meeting on Monday it was decided that there should be a walking match for boys under 17 on Saturday week of about five miles.

The Crane is a junction in the centre of Cefn Mawr. The Trefynant Works also had its own cricket club as well as a football team. Football featured very strongly amongst the local factories throughout the 1920s and 30s; most of the Welsh industries from brickworks, collieries, electricity companies, chemical works to even large shops such as the local Co-op competing in the inter – works competitions. In Victorian days there was even a team calling itself the "Buckley Bricks".

Being such a large factory, Trefynant had its fair share of disasters. Another fire on 22nd May 1904 gutted two blocks of the pipe department, and in November 1927 a weekend of intense gales felled a 60 ft chimney, wrecking the boiler house and adjoining sheds.

In 1934 James Coster Jnr died, eventually followed in March 1956 by the then 96 year old Edward Lloyd. The works had already begun to go the same way as its neighbours, and in July 1956 R H Gibbs & Co acquired the company's holdings, by which time Trefynant was producing only red floor tiles. By January 1958 even the market for that item had collapsed to the extent that a gradual shutdown was initiated, and by September the works had closed. By March 1959 the adjacent Monsanto Chemical Works were negotiating the purchase of the site, which they still own to this day; the old brickworks having been mostly demolished and left to become overgrown by trees and undergrowth. As to the company's main office building situated on the Llangollen road, this was spared demolition and reopened as the Garth & Trevor Community Centre in December 1964, but it has long since disappeared, the only original remnants of the works to survive intact being the two brick piers of

the office gates at OS 2709 4269.

One day, no doubt, all that exists of even them will be a reference in a book.

SITE 127: JOHN THOMAS' BRICKYARD, NEWBRIDGE

The tithe map for 1839 shows a Brickyard and House in the occupation of John Thomas at OS 2878 4171 near Newbridge. The accounts ledger of the Chirk Castle Estate registers that in January 1841 John Thomas of Newbridge was paid for bricks and tiles supplied for the building of Plas Offa farm, and by June 1852 Mr Thomas was advertising in the Chronicle that his "brick and tile works with sheds and pug mill" were to let. The site has long since been redeveloped.

SITE 128: J C EDWARDS PENYBONT BRICKWORKS

Wrexham Advertiser 1881 – Mr Edwards became the proprietor of the Penybont brickworks which had been opened by the late Mr Ward of Black Park, and here he has developed a new industry in red terracotta that would have astounded the former proprietor, had he only lived to see the work of his successor.

It is certainly the accepted opinion that Mr T E Ward established the first very small brickworks at this site. Mr Ward was a successful local industrialist who had a number of concerns throughout the early to mid-19th century, most notably the Black Park Colliery between Chirk and Penybont.

However, during my investigations it began to look extremely likely that the Penybont site's early history was a lot more involved than others have realised. Firstly, the 1839 tithe map shows nothing on this site whatsoever, so if Ward started the works it had to be after that date. Unfortunately, try as I did, I could find no other maps available until the 1871 OS, and to trace the site's history I had to make use of the census records as best I could. The returns for 1861 list 38 year old Wiliam Fieldhouse as a brickmaker employing six men and two boys at "Penybont Brickyard". So where was that? Was it our Penybont Works earlier established by Mr Ward, or could it have been John Thomas' old yard just one third of a mile away at site 127. Its positioning within the census listings suggest Penybont Brickyard as having been surrounded by Ty Maen (to the south), Gelli (to the west) and Newbridge (also to the west), so it strikes me as possible that William Fieldhouse was working site 128 in 1861.

Now let's ask a more puzzling question. The Wrexham Advertiser for 13th March, 1869 ran the following:

"Penybont Brick & Tile Works near Chirk. Having taken from Colonel Myddelton Biddulph the above works, late in the occupation of J Dicken Esq, the public are respectfully informed that a supply of good bricks, crests, tiles and draining pipes are always in hand. The durability and superiority remains unequalled. Benjamin Gething".

It could easily be argued that Penybont is not that far away from Chirk, and there is no other district of the same name which I could find other than our Penybont site. Therefore, can we assume that Mr Fieldhouse had passed it on to Mr Dicken, who then passed it on to Mr Gething in March 1869? It's a tricky question, especially as other historians have placed the year of J C Edwards' acquisition as being anything from 1865-68!

Putting all this aside, let's now regard the testimony of John Cook, who was with J C E when they acquired the site. John recorded its early days, but neglected to mention the year. He said:

"At this time the works were in a very obscure position, being surrounded by fields on every side, and the approach to the works was down a long lane with high hedges on each side so that you had to almost reach the works before you really knew that there was such in existence. But this state of things was destined to be altered. The works at this period was very small and consisted of one small engine, small boiler, rollers, pan, two sheds and some two or three kilns. The best possible use was made of these for some twelve months or so".

J C E replaced the hand presses with machines powered from a new 90 ft long boiler. They then improved the water supply to the works and had a drainage channel dug from the clayhole to prevent its flooding. All the clay at this works was obtained from an open clayhole; no pits being necessary to reach it, as it formed a natural outcrop on this hillside, and I think it's fair to say that the products made from the particularly pure marl at Penybont were regarded amongst the architects and clayworkers of this land as being if not the best, then amongst the best. "Perhaps a better red brick, smoother, more uniform in texture and colour and more impervious to moisture, is not produced than the pressed bricks from the clay of these works" remarked The British Architect journal in 1878. Even at a time when a severe trade depression was gripping the rest of the district's brickworks in that very year, the continued demand for Penybont's products was a testament to their superlative quality:

Wrexham Advertiser 13th July, 1878 – The Penybont brickyard has been greatly enlarged recently, still within the last few months, the men are working night and day and with this cannot execute more than about half the orders they have on hand for pressed bricks and especially roofing tiles. Mr J C Edwards employs a large number of men full-time, a fact much appreciated these bad times.

But if one thing could bring even Penybont to a standstill it was the severity of the winter weather, and at such times when the working man would usually have been laid off from continuing his employment, the exemplary Mr Edwards would try his best to alleviate their hardship:

Wrexham Advertiser 8th February, 1879 – Mr J C Edwards has very kindly distributed large quantities of coal to the widows and poor during the past week. We think that the system adopted by Mr Edwards is a wise one. Instead of doling out a loaf of bread and a little soup, he has generously allowed his men with a number of other workmen who are not able to work at their usual employment through the severe weather, to work a few days per week in improving the estate at Penybont, thus enabling them to maintain their self regard. We are also pleased to hear that Mr Edwards has generously made advances to those of his men who have families, to enable them to meet the necessity of the times.

If any further evidence of the greatness of this man were sought, then we should take the following account into consideration:

Wrexham Advertiser 20th May 1882 – At a meeting of men it was proposed and carried that in consideration of the respect held at all times towards Mr J C Edwards and the many contracts that gentlemen has in hand, that no objection be made to coal being forwarded to his several extensive clayworks.

That decision was taken by the men of Plaskynaston and Black Park collieries, who had been on strike for the previous four weeks. If any body of workers could have been expected to wield the iron hand it would have been the colliers, and for them to pass such an exemption in times of industrial dispute was indicative of more than mere courteousness.

By 1880 the extensions carried out over the previous years had become a point of note; The British Architect in its April edition remarking that "To those who see them for the first time, the Penybont Works are a revelation in size, costliness and efficiency". Such was Mr Edwards' fame throughout the national brickmaking community that he introduced in that year an annual "Edwards Terracotta Competition". This was instigated to promote and encourage the art and use of architectural terracotta design and was backed up by the lure of a then massive prize of £160 for the best entry. No other individual ever showed such a shrewd and forward-thinking attitude in the demonstration of his business sense. J C also took the step in early 1882 of building a block of "model dwellings" near to the entrance of the Penybont Works. These were occupied by his works' managers and were used, if you like, as "living catalogue illustrations" to be examined by contractors, architects and customers who visited his most prestigious works. They are still in existence today.

In 1884 the works laid in gas from the Cefn & Rhosymedre Gas Co; the pipes reaching the works via the road bridge over the Dee. In fact, the local authority originally refused to allow the pipes to cross the bridge, as they regarded consenting to Mr Edwards' request could have provoked possible charges of favouritism from other local companies, but they relented when it was pointed out to them that Mr Edwards employed more people at Penybont than there were living in Chirk! It's possible to judge just how huge Penybont Works was from the relative sizes of the donations collected for the Ruabon Accident Hospital from his separate factories. In 1892 the Rhos glazed brickworks, itself no mean affair, realised a contribution of £1-10-0. The big Trefynant Works collected £3-0-9, but Penybont managed £8-4-5. By 1896 Penybont had 45 kilns in operation and employed more than 500 workers. 300 tons of clay were daily extracted from the clayhole which was from 70-90 ft deep and serviced by a network of tramways on its various levels; the clay trams being winched up by any of the five steam engines around the excavation.

By the turn of the century J C was dead; the company becoming entrusted to his sons. Despite J

C's passing however the prestige of his family's name within the district had not diminished; a fact well illustrated by the reactions of the populace of Cefn and Acrefair to the great turning point of the Boer War:

Wrexham Advertiser 9th June, 1900 – The news of the fall of Pretoria which reached Cefn was received with the greatest enthusiasm. All the hooters were put on and works vied with each other as to which could make the loudest noise. Trefynant Works, which had the gratification of being first in the field, had two whistles and a bell going. At Penybont Works preparations had been going on for several days and immediately the welcome tidings arrived, half eaten dinners were cast aside and a procession was formed in which every man including the manager joined. They were headed by a splendid Union Jack supported by four men. The works' brass band was very much in evidence. Effigies of Kruger were carried on hand barrows – also a Boer on the gallows. They paraded the streets of Newbridge and Rhosymedre and arriving at Cefn a halt was made. Mr Gethin Davies' excellent Drum and Fife Band now joined the procession which had been greatly augmented en route by employees from the other works in the district, women and children. Proceeding through Cefn they were met by a large body of men from Acrefair Engineering Works and by this time the crowd must have numbered

The extensive Penybont Works circa 1930. Photo: Dennis Gilpin / Nene.

between five and six thousand people. Reaching Trefynant Offices they awaited the arrival of Mr E Lloyd Edwards, whom they prevailed upon to make a speech. Mr Emlyn Davis then led the vast throng in the singing of the English and Welsh national anthems and several patriotic songs, after which the return journey was made to Cefn Bank. Here the effigies of Kruger and the Boer were regaled with a large amount of paraffin oil and set fire to amidst loud cheering. Never has there been such wild excitement as on this occasion.

During the First World War it was decided that a suggestion from Chirk Parish Council be adopted whereby a fund be set up to relieve the want of the families of the men who had joined the army. Each of the company's men paid two pence each per week and the boys one penny. Shortly after the onset of the war Mr E Lloyd Edwards addressed his Penybont workers:

Wrexham Advertiser 29th August, 1914 – Mr Edwards, who met with a hearty reception, explained the courses which led to the war and he wished the men to look upon him and Mr Coster Edwards as their fathers in a sense. They wished to do all they could to help the men during the war. They would so far as possible see that the dependants of those who went to the front had a sufficient money to enable them to live comfortably until the return of the breadwinner. They did not think of making profit during the war. He wanted them to understand that as long as they possibly could they would keep the works open.

After the war the Garth and Trevor War Memorial was built on land donated by the company with bricks and terracotta also provided at no cost.

Wrexham Advertiser 10th December, 1927 – On Saturday last the medals awarded by the Institute of Clayworkers for long service were presented to William Jones and Edward Thomas of Penybont Brickworks. Mr Jones has a record of 66 years service and Mr Thomas 54 years. Mr E Lloyd Edwards said he was proud of the fact

that more than 117 men had a record of over thirty years service with the firm. On Saturday the men assembled at the office for the presentation of medals to Joshua Powell whose record is 65 years service, John Jones 58 years and Edwin Davies 53 years. Mr Edwards said it was a very great pleasure to meet that day because they were honouring the men who had served so faithfully. There were 660 hands employed, of whom 160 were boys or girls under 21. Some of them began like boys and finished as men. Mr J C Lloyd Edwards, junior partner, said he hoped all the young men would grow up with him in the same spirit as they had worked with his father. If that would be done it would certainly be a great thing.

Unfortunately the hopes of the young Mr Edwards, grandson of the company's founder, never came to fruition. He died in December 1930 aged only 32 years old.

The years of the Depression finally took its toll on Penybont's productivity, but the company entertained great hopes that its fortunes might be upturned by the possibility of their bricks being used in road building. Back in 1923 Penybont had succeeded in perfecting a new type of hard brick which they had consequently supplied to the county council for their 100 yard trial of brick paving on the main road through Rhosymedre. J C E hoped that Britain might follow the trend common in America, where brick was extensively used as a road surfacing. In 1909 the Indianapolis Speedway motor racing circuit had replaced its two-and-a-half miles of tarmac track with 3 1/2 million bricks, resulting in the track's speed record being broken as soon as it was reopened, but despite the faith the Americans had in brick roads, our local councils were fearful of the higher costs of using bricks. A concerned Mr E Lloyd Edwards wrote to the council on 23rd November, 1931, and his inquiry paints a telling picture of the times:

"Can you tell me whether you are contemplating using any bricks for road making this next year? Our brick making machinery is almost idle owing to bad trade in building and our men are of course either on the dole or working very short

time. This could all be changed if you and your authorities would adopt bricks for a mile or two or three as roads".

The road experiment was however never repeated.

After the Second War there was a welcome boom in the demand for tiles, and by 1948 Penybont had accrued orders for 17 million quarry tiles. But tiles were a commodity soon to hit on hard times. In July 1956 the company was taken over by R H Gibbs & Son, who decided in January 1958 to undertake a refit of the tile making machinery. Unfortunately the new machinery proved problematic with the tiles showing a tendency to crack, and production fell off dramatically as attempts were sought to rectify the problem. By this time in its history less than 100 men were left at this giant and mostly under used factory. In October 1961 the Buckley firm of Castle Firebrick announced their decision to purchase the Penybont Works; Gibbs having decided on closure three months earlier, but it was clear that Castle never intended to work the site as a going concern, and company memorandums from that year outlined the options for the 70 workers left, penning such comments as "prepared to work in Buckley", "will accept demolition work" and "will retire when Penybont closes".

Today, all that remains of the site are the model dwellings and some office buildings, the original brickworks having been centred at OS 2924 4155. The huge northerly clayhole is gradually being filled in with landfill waste.

Decline and Fall

Wrexham Advertiser 18th October, 1902 – The brick and terracotta industry for which Ruabon is noted is at present exceptionally good and at some of the works the employees have to work overtime in order to meet the demand for the material which is being largely used throughout the whole of the United Kingdom and also abroad.

The last two decades of the 19th century together with the very early years of the 20th saw the British brick industry enjoying its halcyon years, having been placed in that position by the impetus given to it by the rapid growth of the water and sewage utilities, plus the improvements which were being made in sweeping away most of the sub-standard housing of the earlier decades. But it wasn't long before those with the benefit of foresight began to suspect that a change might become inevitable. In 1908 the British Clayworker, the published archive of the industry's fortunes, ran an article headed "Is our Industry to be displaced", and the subject of their fears was "concrete". Concrete had been used by the Victorians, but mostly only as an industrial flooring material, and the architecturally ambitious ways in which it had been used by the ancient Romans had been ignored for centuries. Now its possibilities were being rediscovered, and as the 20th century rolled on it was to be seen being used in ever more increasing applications.

Writing in 1936 Lord Strabolgi, predicting what life would be like 20 years later, thought that "bricks will have given way to the beautiful coloured materials of the concrete type". His predictions were certainly going in the right direction, although colour has never properly been taken advantage of by the concrete industry – no matter what decade!

There were many contributory factors which saw the brick industry's decline – over-production, economic hardship, disorganisation, lack of manpower, poor investment and a change to cheaper and more quickly installed building materials, but although most of those causes didn't kick in until the mid-20th century, it's true to say that over-production had already killed off some brickworks even during the Victorian heydays. The "boom and bust" economy has always claimed its victims, and many of the smaller brickworks simply couldn't survive in a marketplace in which demand had begun falling off, leaving too many brickworks trying to compete for what markets remained. This same principle also decimated the smaller end of the colliery industry, and it's worth remembering that the fates of both the brick and coal trades fared along quite similar lines. Consider this observation made in 1882 by the general manager of the Great Western Railway:

> *"The high prices of coal in 1873-4 induced people to put money into collieries and it was obvious that there would not be markets for such large quantities, and the proprietors were competing with each other. The Wrexham coal district was suffering in the same way as others from over-production and this prevented the proprietors from making any profit".*

And when an industry makes no profit, there's only one result… closure. The coal industry had always had somewhat of a disadvantage over that of the brick, in that it took much more effort and financial capital to reach and win the coal seams, whereas most of our district's clay supplies were more easily won from opencast clayholes. By the 1890s the more accessible coal seams had mostly been exploited, and the cost of digging out the deeper seams inevitably proved too restrictive for the smaller companies. This state of affairs caused some consternation throughout the districts where thousands of men were employed in the mines, and especially in Flintshire. Herbert Gladstone MP, speaking at a dinner in 1902, was moved to admit that "coal was being rapidly worked out in the existing mines, and things looked rather formidable". And I suppose it's also fair to say that a similar situation was actually responsible for closing a few of our brickworks. Exhaustion of the more profitable clay seams, and a contractual inability to extend clayholes beyond their leased boundaries did cause some works to cease operations – the Wilderness Works at Gresford and Brookhill Works at Buckley being examples of two such once famous works to meet with this fate.

It was the 1950s which saw those remaining local brickworks besieged by a wave of change which irreparably weakened the industry across the board. By 1954 the trends in building technology were noticeably swinging towards the increased use of concrete, breeze block and clinker block, and the stockyards in the brickworks became chocked with unsold bricks. This trend was a natural result of the demand for cheap post-war housing, which continued for some time, and by March 1957 the stockpiles in the brickyards had reached an all-time record. To make matters worse, local builders were sourcing their brick supplies from cheaper producers.

"The biggest culprits are the private builders, and about 40 per cent of the building in this area is being done by private firms. If private builders had made a point of buying local bricks, brickworks might not have had to close",

complained one of the Ruabon manufacturers, writing anonymously to the Wrexham Leader in 1958. The Welsh building trade was for a time taking advantage of the cheaper bricks made by the Lancashire factories owned by the National Coal Board, which was offloading its surplus brick stocks directly into the Welsh markets, and undercutting the prices of locally made bricks.

In 1958 the Wrexham MP Idwal Jones raised the plight of the local works in the House of Commons, suggesting that the usage of the new breeze blocks was leading to houses being jerry-built, and that a materials standard for housebuilding should be introduced, but the government, keen to encourage a speedy post-war building programme, responded that progress was to be expected, and a decline in the use of more traditional brick would become a consequential inevitability.

At this point we should be asking ourselves why our local works found it well nigh impossible to produce a product at a price to rival that of the English brickyards, and the answer to the question would delineate the principal reasons which more than any other factor became responsible for the death of the brick industry in North East Wales. I believe our problem was twofold – a lack of foresight by the managements, and a serious negligence in investing capital to develop new production techniques. Our local industry failed to understand that modern building practices were beginning to demand bricks which were lighter and which had better insulating properties, but once this became understood, our brickworks were not financially strong enough to develop the technology to produce them. Our brickworks had long existed within the old climate of "splendid isolation", with extremely little interaction between the separate companies. Better co-operation might have allowed for a better understanding of how clay technology could be developed to run more in line with changing national trends. This singular lack of co-operation between the brick companies had in their earlier years been born of a desire to prevent their competitors from stealing any leads on each other, and was a phenomenon noticed back in the Victorian days by the English maker Alfred Crossley, who knew the brickyards of America, where, in complete contrast to practices in Britain, they invited him to inspect their processes with open arms. He wrote:

British Clayworker 1895 – A trait of character perhaps the most apparent in the English clay manufacturer is his conservatism. Americans would probably consider this too mild a term. There is not the same ambition to keep up with the procession that there is in America. Hence it is that there are any number of works going on in the same old way that they were 20 or 30 years ago. English business methods are often cumbersome, so that while a man here is getting through the preliminaries, an American would have done the business. Another thing that is conspicuous here by its absence is a genuine fraternal feeling. In the U.S., if a brickmaker from Chicago happens to be in St Louis and calls on some firm there, he is pretty sure of a kindly reception. "Why, how d 'ye do? Come in. Haven't got much to show you, but come and see what we're doing anyhow". But such is not the case here. One may go to some old brickyard and have the pleasure of looking through the fence but not be allowed to go closer, lest he should appropriate some ideas in the art of brickmaking. English machinery, speaking generally, is behind the times as compared with America. Neither has the brickmaker the variety to choose from.

It's no surprise then, that every new improvement ever developed in Britain immediately had a patent slapped upon it, thereby impeding its free usage and preventing the industry from experimenting with its possibilities. And America was not alone when it came to encouraging the dissemination of knowledge. France had gone as far as creating an Industrial Society, which regularly met to investigate any developments made in the sciences and industry, and awarding prizes for good inventions and improvements, thereby encouraging industrialists to make the effort to improve their manufacturing techniques and bring them to universal attention. As the British Clayworker remarked, "They do things better in France".

As we have seen, Mr Crossley was criticising British brickyard practices back in 1895, and things were no different half a century later. We had to wait until as late as 1952 for Mr Jackson, the National Secretary of the Institute of Clay Technology, to stress that the Welsh companies should be encouraging inter-works visits, to enable the various managers to exchange ideas in manufacturing techniques. The Institute had been originally founded back in 1927 as the National Association of Clayworks Managers, but a local North Wales Branch was not established until July 1950 – a perfect illustration of our district's short-sightedness and sluggishness in recognising the need for change.

As an illustration of just how competitive our local brickworks could be, I can relate a rather amusing anecdote concerning Castle Firebrick Co of the 1960s. It used to be the occasional practice on a quiet Sunday afternoon that representatives of that company might drive up to the Ruby Brickworks at Rhydymwyn in order to ascertain how much stock they had on their yards. If the Ruby's stocks had run down, then it was assumed that they would have been unable to fulfil any bulk orders, and Castle could subsequently have

considered raising the prices on their own bricks to take advantage of this. Conversely, if the Ruby's yards were glutted by bricks, then Castle would have been able to steal the lead by dropping their prices, thereby giving themselves an obvious advantage in the market place.

Our woeful insularity had also resulted in an apathy in the field of technological education. At a speedily convened meeting to discuss education within the industry, held at Wrexham School of Technology in 1951, it was admitted that "there were many diversities of opinion which existed between undertakings in the various clayworking districts". In any other mid-20th century industry it had long been the practice for boys of 13 years of age to train for 2-3 years in industrial apprenticeships, but in North East Wales in particular this was a situation which had never existed for those contemplating any future as brickworkers. On 10th September, 1954, after many years procrastination, another meeting to discuss the situation was held between the trade unions, the local colleges and 21 representatives from various brickworks in Flintshire and Denbighshire. Their agenda was the establishment of a scheme to train boys entering the clay industry in the proper skills of the craft, thereby hopefully creating a new generation of dedicated and educated technicians, instead of the army of disinterested, unskilled labourers who were then populating the brickyards. In the aftermath of the Second World War many of the skilled men had not returned to their old jobs, and those filling their positions were hardly qualified in the craft. Unfortunately, the closest we ever got to any co-operation between the brick industry and the education sector came in the form of a prize given by the Castle Firebrick Co. to the best bricklaying students in the building trades department at Kelsterton College of Technology during the 1960s and 70s. The mining industry, on the other hand, was well catered for, with the Wrexham Technical College offering courses in mining science, colliery surveying, engineering, and shot-firing. Even the quarry industry could put its new workers into day release courses to qualify for a "Sand, Gravel and Quarrying Operatives Certificate".

So, apart from an absence of focused training

schemes, together with little or no attempt at co-operating in exchanging ideas and technologies, what other factor had contributed to the eventual disappearance of our district's brickworks? The answer in many cases was lack of investment; a problem which was also endemic within the coal and manufacturing industries. It's true to say that the hardships following the Second World War caused the brick industry irreparable damage, but the seeds of destruction had been sown well before the 1940s. Similarly, the lack of investment within the brickworks had been shadowed by a similar fate within the coal sector. With the onset in 1931 of the world economic depression, one of Germany's leading coalowners visited Britain to investigate our methods of production and discuss price regulations, but he was greatly shocked by the state of British mining, being forced to remark

"There is nothing doing. Britain has nothing to offer us. Most of your coalowners are a hundred years behind the times. Heaven knows how long it is since they put money into the business. They are casually inefficient, with an imperfect knowledge of the modern technique of coal mining, and an outlook devoid of imagination".

This slothful reluctance to invest in new technologies was a problem which had long been common throughout British industry. The Chester Chronicle in 1899 decried the situation by explaining that America was mining coal and minerals cheaper, and advancing in engineering faster than in Britain, simply because of America's willingness to invest in and experiment with ever more modern machinery. Even the railway industry fell foul of this general trend; a situation which has continued to this day with tragic circumstances. Despite Britain having invented the railway locomotive and creating an industrial revolution based on its promise and possibilities, the Baldwin Loco Works of Philadelphia were in 1899 constructing 30 locos for our Midland Railway and 20 for the Great Northern Railway, faster and cheaper than we could ourselves. Four locomotives for the British War Department had also been built and put onto ships a mere 30 days after they had received the order for them. Consequently, by the

end of the 19th century American industry had left ours lagging far behind.

A long continued reliance on age old techniques meant that by the time our local clay industry needed to become more competitive, it found itself lumbered with antiquated machinery, no alternative product lines, and too little capital left to make any difference. Probably the most notable exception to this trend was the Castle Firebrick Co, which with the financial backing of its wealthy parent company, British Steel, had found itself able to invest in the most effective modern plant. But with the collapse of the steel industry in the early 1970s Castle's holdings eventually found themselves sacrificed on the altar of "rationalisation".

The last company to survive in Flintshire was Hancocks Lane End Works, which had benefited from the modernisations it received from being one of Castle's holdings and was lucky enough to find a buyer after Castle folded. It's rather unique speckled brick helped it to maintain its position in the marketplace, but competition from cheaper products eventually forced its closure in 2003.

As for Denbighshire, the companies there had never foreseen the move away from the heavy marl brick which their clays produced, and having never experimented with the possibilities of trying to make lighter bricks, the district now makes none at all. The very last bricks ever made in Denbighshire remained unchanged from the very same types which it produced back in the Victorian age. Only Dennis Ruabon is left as a manufacturer of quarry tiles; a product ideally suited to the heavy Ruabon clays.

* * *

Chester Chronicle 4th October, 1947 – Is it not high time that something should be done to fence these abandoned clay pits and coal pits. In the Buckley area alone there are about six abandoned clay pits and forty coal pits; some of them abandoned sixty or more years ago – there in all their ugliness and waste. And it is not only this area alone, although this is the worst. The whole brick and coal area of Flintshire is dotted with these abandoned works.

So what has happened to the many sites which once proliferated around Flintshire and Denbighshire. During the last decade of the 20th century I witnessed the strident improvements undertaken to redevelop and landscape the old sites which remained, and for the most part only the ruins of some very few of the smaller country works still exist. Up until the 1990s there had been little done to eradicate the scars of the bygone industry. Even as late as in 1964 most of the large open area of the Buckley Common still resembled a bomb site, with acres of hillocks remaining from nearly two hundred years of small scale pottery, brick and colliery workings. When the radio journalist Brian Redhead visited Buckley in that year, he recorded that the area was

"open and scarred, as if someone had scraped out bowls of earth with enormous hands and wiped them clean on the grass".

Travelling the district today, it's very rarely that you might encounter any noticeable evidence of the one-time existence of the many brickworks and collieries once so common. The most you might find will be the overgrown colliery spoil heaps, although to the casual onlooker even most of these could today be mistaken for natural features; the tips of the Pentre Saeson, Elm and Pentrobin collieries being just such examples. There will no doubt come a time when pretty well every old clayhole will have been filled or landscaped, and simply nothing will be left to tell of the history which created them in the first place.

Given the effort and enthusiasm which originally created an industry which came so much to symbolise the importance of North East Wales, what we have left today is a sad legacy indeed. Although the warm texture of clay bricks is still happily favoured by modern architects and builders, the once many individual characteristics of the older, locally produced bricks have been replaced by a largely standardised product which you can find anywhere across the country. Today, large scale urban development is gradually destroying the character and individuality of districts which were originally fashioned by local builders, each of whom utilised their own distinctive architectural style and who had the choice of a variety of bricks and mouldings which modern builders could never find. Every town we now pass through is beginning to have the same "feel", and the unspoken, almost unconscious awareness of regionalisation is gradually disappearing from our districts.

Where there was once a Buckley built of dark red slop and glazed buff bricks… where once entire vistas of late Victorian Ruabon and Rhos were acres of glowing red terracotta… where once brick built countryside farmhouses and cottages were created from the unique and individual clays dug from the very ground upon which they were built – now, bit by bit, we find new buildings emerging, which in truth have no regional identity at all. As well designed as many of them are, modern houses stand orphaned from their true organic homes – refugees from brickworks far away. If ever it transpires that every part of Britain ends up looking like every other part of Britain, what will be left, other than nature itself, to inspire the aesthetic sensitivities which many of us feel towards our surroundings and our cultural homelands.

* * *

It has been said that "the past is another country", and as certainly as the ways and customs of foreign lands differ from our own, so the ways and working practices of our forefathers would be alien to us now. It is indeed the truth that there once existed a breed of clayworkers who were, even in their own times, spoken of in reverend tones by their younger peers as being men who "knew clay", and who could tell by the feel and the look of it as to how it should be worked. These were skilled craftsmen who would know how well a kiln was burning, not by looking at an indicator or a dial on an instrument panel, but by merely judging the colour and intensity of the flames. Such men had passed into history by the mid-20th century.

When you see a wall of old hand moulded brick are you aware of what went into its making. The whole fabric of our present day society has been built on the achievements and foundations laid by previous generations… on the toils and hardships, and sometimes the very mortal lives of an age of brickmakers and colliers, whose very lifestyles, if we today should have to relive them, would be regarded as intolerable.

Those men and boys who sweated at the kilns, who were injured in the clayholes and maimed by machinery, were the very men who helped to build those pathways of progress. Touch an old brick and you unwittingly touch the lives of the brickmen of old.